Gloria Barley.
£2.50
08/2+

...TION TO
MODERN M... ROSCOPY

THE WYKEHAM SCIENCE SERIES

General Editors:

    PROFESSOR SIR NEVILL MOTT, F.R.S.
    Emeritus Cavendish Professor of Physics
    University of Cambridge

    G. R. NOAKES
    Formerly Senior Physics Master
    Uppingham School

The aim of the Wykeham Science Series is to introduce the present state of the many fields of study within science to students approaching or starting their careers in University, Polytechnic, or College of Technology. Each book seeks to reinforce the link between school and higher education, and the main author, a distinguished worker or teacher in the field, is assisted by an experienced sixth form schoolmaster.

INTRODUCTION TO
MODERN MICROSCOPY

H. N. Southworth
University of Birmingham

**WYKEHAM PUBLICATIONS (LONDON) LTD**
(A MEMBER OF THE TAYLOR & FRANCIS GROUP)
LONDON AND WINCHESTER
1975

First published 1975 by Wykeham Publications (London) Ltd.

© 1975 H. N. Southworth. All rights reserved. No part of this publication may be reproduced, stored in a retrieval system, or transmitted, in any form or by any means, electronic, mechanical, photocopying, recording or otherwise, without the prior permission of the copyright owner.

Cover illustration—Proton blocking pattern from a single crystal of copper (*W. White.*)

ISBN 0 85109 470 8

Printed in Great Britain by Taylor & Francis Ltd.
10–14 Macklin Street, London, WC2B 5NF

Distribution:

UNITED KINGDOM, EUROPE, MIDDLE EAST AND AFRICA

Chapman & Hall Ltd. (a member of Associated Book Publishers Ltd.), North Way, Andover, Hampshire.

WESTERN HEMISPHERE

Springer-Verlag New York Inc., 175 Fifth Avenue, New York, New York 10010.

AUSTRALIA, NEW ZEALAND AND FAR EAST (EXCLUDING JAPAN)

Australia & New Zealand Book Co. Pty Ltd., P.O. Box 459, Brookvale, N.S.W. 2100.

ALL OTHER TERRITORIES

Taylor & Francis Ltd., 10–14 Macklin Street, London, WC2B 5NF.

PREFACE

ALTHOUGH its scientific development is comparatively recent, the art of microscopy originates in ancient times, a lens carved out of naturally occurring crystal from ancient Assyria having been discovered dating back to at least 700 B.C. Now a wide variety of microscopical techniques exists, using not only visible light but also electrons, X-rays and ions as the 'image-forming' radiation. These techniques are used extensively by biologists, chemists, mineralogists, geologists, metallurgists and materials scientists. Allied to these purely microscopical techniques, aimed at revealing the microstructure of the specimen, are further more indirect techniques for investigating the structure and composition of matter, such as X-ray and electron diffraction and spectroscopy.

That this book should attempt to cover almost the entire range of such techniques imposes certain restrictions on its method of treatment. Detailed discussion of practical methods and of advanced theories of image formation has been avoided in favour of providing a comprehensive understanding of the basic physical principles that underlie the operation of each instrument. Thus interest centres upon giving a simple idea of how each technique works, what kinds of information it is able to provide and what applications it can be put to.

Following a certain amount of revision of fundamental optical principles, the optical microscope is covered in considerable detail since this is probably the most commonly encountered of all the instruments described. Then the whole range of instruments for performing microscopy, diffraction and spectroscopy is explored, culminating in a discussion of some of the more recent advances and innovations in the field.

The level is such that the scientific sixth former should have little difficulty in understanding any of the physical principles involved, and a particular debt is owed to my collaborator, Mr. R. A. Hull, in achieving this. At the same time the range of topics covered should make it suitable as a University text, and indeed much of its content is based on a series of lectures given to first, second and third year students in Materials Science at Birmingham University. The discussion is, however, completely general, and the illustrations are selected from a wide variety of scientific disciplines. Acknowledgment to the many individuals and organizations who have contributed illustrations is made in the individual figure captions.

Birmingham
April 1974

H. N. SOUTHWORTH

CONTENTS

Preface			v
Chapter 1	IMAGE FORMATION		1
Chapter 2	OPTICAL MICROSCOPY		33
Chapter 3	ADVANCED TECHNIQUES IN OPTICAL MICROSCOPY		57
Chapter 4	ELECTRON MICROSCOPY		87
Chapter 5	X-RAY MICROSCOPY AND MICROANALYSIS		123
Chapter 6	EMISSION MICROSCOPY		147
Chapter 7	DIFFRACTION AND SPECTROSCOPY		169
Chapter 8	FUTURE MICROSCOPY		188
Further Reading			

CHAPTER 1
image formation

1.1. *Introduction*

THE basic function of any kind of microscope is to produce a *magnified image* of the object under investigation, the fine details of which the eye is now able to detect and study. Conventionally this magnification is produced by the focusing action of a lens on some form of radiation—light in the case of the optical microscope, electrons in the case of the electron microscope. Other principles of image formation exist, based on point projection and on the television scanning principle, but discussion of these will be reserved until later chapters.

For the moment we shall be concerned with the fundamental principles of image formation as they apply to all optical devices, from the human eye to the compound microscope. We can go quite a long way here using simple geometrical optics and ideal thin lenses. Later we shall need to consider the effect of lens aberrations, and to develop the concepts of wave optics, in order to explain the influence that processes such as interference and diffraction exert upon the mechanism of image formation. First we shall briefly discuss the various factors that determine the properties of an image.

1.2. *Image formation*
The thin lens

Let us begin by recalling the focusing action of an ideal 'thin' lens, fig. 1.1. An extended object OO' is located a distance u from

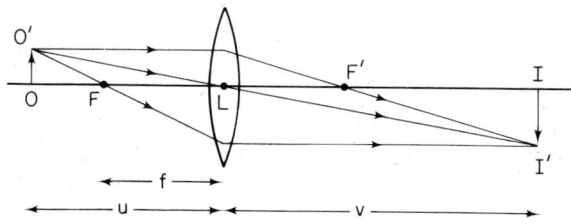

Fig. 1.1. Image formation by a lens.

a converging lens of focal length f. In order to locate the position of its image we can construct three principal rays from any point on it such as O′: one parallel to the axis of the lens which, after being refracted at the lens, passes through its far focus F′; one that passes through the near focus F and after refraction emerges parallel to the axis; one that passes through the optical centre of the lens L and is undeviated. These rays recombine at the point I′. The entire image II′ may be regarded as being built up point by point in this way, and is real and inverted with respect to the object. II′ is located at a distance v from the lens, where u, v and f may be related by the equation

$$1/u + 1/v = 1/f$$

using the 'real is positive' sign convention. The *power* of a lens in dioptres (D) is the reciprocal of the focal length in metres—a positive sign denoting a converging lens, a negative sign a diverging lens.

It is easily shown that the linear magnification of the image

$$m = \text{II}'/\text{OO}' = v/u = v/f - 1.$$

For the situation illustrated here m is greater than unity. Had the object been located at II′, however, its image would have been formed at OO′, and m would then have been less than unity.

If the object is located closer to the lens than F, i.e. $u < f$, then a virtual erect and magnified image is formed. This is the principle that is made use of in the simple microscope (page 4), and further discussion of this mode is deferred until then.

The human eye

Optically the eye is somewhat similar to a camera, incorporating as it does a lens system and a light sensitive area—the retina—on to which the incident light can be focused, fig. 1.2. The main focusing

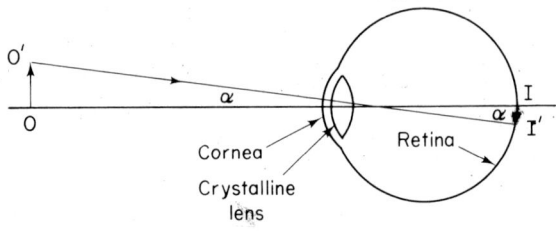

Fig. 1.2. Retinal image in the eye.

action is accomplished at the first face of the cornea, while the crystalline lens supplies an additional focusing action which, while smaller, is variable. The retina contains a large number of nerve endings of two types, rods and cones, which undergo change under the action of light, thereby conveying a sensory impression to the brain.

Although the eye is very far from being an ideal thin lens such as discussed in the previous section, it does act in essentially the same manner as the lens shown in fig. 1.1 with the exception that the image that is formed on the retina II′ is substantially demagnified with respect to the object OO′. In a camera variations in the distance of the object from the lens would normally be accommodated by varying the distance of the lens from the film. In the eye the lens-to-retina distance is effectively constant, and here variations in object distance are accommodated by varying the focal length (or power) of the eye by altering the curvature of the crystalline lens. There is a limit to the extent to which this may be done, and at the maximum power of the crystalline lens the smallest distance at which an object may be brought into focus is termed the least distance of distinct vision, or near point of the eye. This power of accommodation is gradually lost with increasing age, and the distance of the near point from the eye may rise from about 10 cm in a child to 50 cm in old age. It is conventional, however, to take its value to be 25 cm, corresponding to a power of about +4D.

Resolution

The ability of the eye to perceive fine detail is termed its *resolving power*, and the smallest separation between two points that it is able to detect is termed its *limit of resolution*. Several factors combine to control the eye's performance in this respect. First there is the fine structure of the retina. Since the length of the eye is effectively fixed, the smaller the angle α that the object subtends at the eye, fig. 1.2, the smaller will be its image on the retina. The most sensitive part of the retina, the *fovea centralis*, is composed entirely of cones whose separation is about 3 μm. If it is assumed that two object details will be differentiated only if the separation of their images spans at least two cones, then the minimum angle that they must subtend at the eye is 3 μm divided by the length of the eye (about 2 cm), that is 0·0003 rad or about 1′ of arc.

Clearly this angle may be increased by bringing the object closer to the eye. The limit is reached, however, once the object reaches the near point, and here an angle of 1′ of arc corresponds to the separation of two points in the object of just less than 0·1 mm. This then is the ultimate limit of resolution of the unaided human eye. We now need to replace the object with a magnified image of itself produced by a microscope.

Even if the structure of the retina were infinitely fine this would still not imply that infinitely fine detail could be resolved. This is because the eye, like all other lenses, is limited in its ability to reproduce faithfully all the details of the object in forming its image: below a certain level these are lost. This may be due to distortions produced in the image by various aberrations in the lens of the eye (page 9), or, more fundamentally, to limitations imposed by the wave nature of light itself (page 21). With its customary efficiency, evolution appears to have refined the structure of the retina only to the point at which it becomes comparable to these other limiting factors.

Similar considerations apply to all optical instruments. For example if the grain of the photographic emulsion used to record the image produced by a microscope is too coarse, then the finer image details will be lost. Usually this does not apply, however, since the image produced is sufficiently highly magnified. What does affect the resolving power of a microscope is the performance of its component lenses, and we shall be discussing this problem at considerable length.

Contrast

Even if the eye is capable of resolving an object, this does not mean to say that it will still be able to *see* it—consider the problem of trying to find a golf ball, either at night or in snow. In the first case the illumination is inadequate, while in the second case the object is insufficiently distinguished in appearance from its background.

These examples reflect limitations on image *contrast*, and apply equally well to images produced by a microscope, as discussed on pages 28–9. In practice there are a number of sophisticated optical techniques available which are able to overcome such limitations, and indeed to reveal features that the human eye never could detect.

Magnification, resolution and contrast, therefore, are the main properties by which we must judge the performance of a microscope, and these will be examined in greater detail in turn, during the remainder of this chapter.

1.3. *The simple microscope*

The earliest and simplest way of producing a magnified image is to use a single converging lens in the way illustrated in fig. 1.3. The object OO' is placed nearer to the lens than its first focus F, and the image formed II' is virtual, upright and magnified. The eye is placed close to the lens, and provided that this image lies at least as far from the eye as its near point it can then be focused onto the retina.

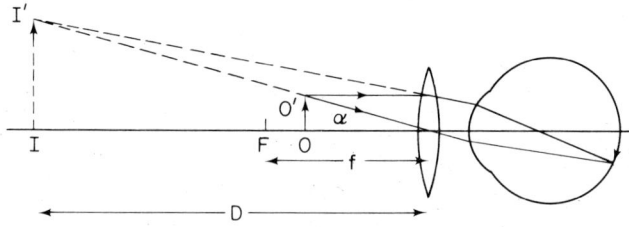

Fig. 1.3. Image formation at the near point of the eye by the simple microscope.

Some care is needed in defining the magnification that can be produced in this way. The linear magnification will be given as before by

$$m = v/f - 1.$$

If the image is located at the near point itself, then (assuming the eye to be very close to the lens) this becomes, putting $v = -D$,

$$m = -(D/f + 1)$$

where D is the least distance of distinct vision; here m is negative since it refers to a virtual image.

However it is often convenient to arrange for the image to be formed at infinity, since the eye is then unaccommodated, and hence under least strain. In this case the object must be placed at the first principal focus of the lens at F, whereupon u equals f and v becomes infinite. Hence m also becomes infinite. Clearly, though, this cannot represent the practical gain experienced by the microscopist. What we must remember is that the function of the microscope is to increase the angle that an object subtends at the eye, and hence it is strictly *angular* rather than linear magnification with which we should be concerned. Angular magnification in this context is defined as the ratio of the angle that the image subtends at the eye, to the angle that the object would subtend at the eye if it were placed at the near point. It is this that provides the effective *magnifying power* of the microscope.

In the case where v is finite and equal to D, then the angular magnification, M, is the same as m. When v is infinite, however, it can be seen from fig. 1.3 that the image II' must still subtend the same angle α at the lens (and hence effectively at the eye) as does the object OO'. Thus here

$$M = \text{OO}'/f \div \text{OO}'/(-D)$$
$$= -D/f.$$

This is slightly less than in the previous case. Thus a lens whose focal length is 2·5 cm has a magnifying power of ×11 when the image is formed at the near point, reducing to ×10 if it is formed at infinity.

Historically the use of a single lens to magnify probably dates back to several hundred years B.C., and it is still very much with us in the form of the hand lens of the botanist, the magnifying glass of the philatelist or the eye lens of the watchmaker. Probably the most successful application of this kind of microscope, however, was made by the Dutchman Antonio van Leeuwenhoek (1632–1723), one of whose microscopes is shown in fig. 1.4. Typically such a microscope consisted of a minute glass bead, sometimes as small as 0·5 mm in diameter, in front of a pointer on which the specimen was held. In this way van Leeuwenhoek was able to produce magnifications

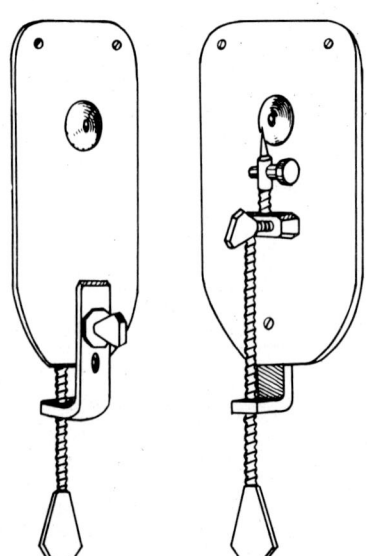

Fig. 1.4. Simple microscope used by van Leeuwenhoek.

exceeding ×300, which compares very favourably with the ×1000 magnification that typifies the modern compound microscope. Indeed, although the compound microscope itself existed just before van Leeuwenhoek's time, such was his skill that it was a further 200 years before his work could be matched using this technique.

1.4. *The compound microscope*

The actual invention of the compound microscope took place sometime between 1590 and 1609, and is generally attributed to the work of three spectacle makers working in Middleburg in Holland, Hans Janssen, his son Zacharias and Hans Lippershey; it was certainly in use by Galileo in 1609. The great pioneer of microscopy in this country was Robert Hooke, and a drawing made by Hooke of one of his own microscopes is shown in fig. 1.5.

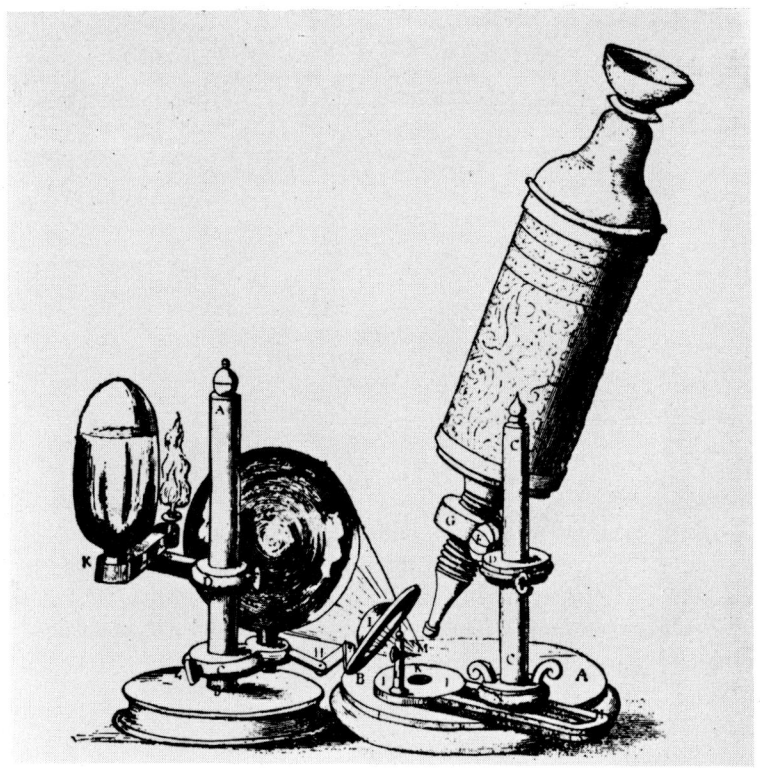

Fig. 1.5. Compound microscope used by Robert Hooke.

A schematic diagram of the compound microscope is shown in fig. 1.6. It comprises two converging lenses which are used quite differently. The lens nearest to the object is termed the objective lens L_O, and is used in an identical fashion to that illustrated in fig. 1.1. The object O is placed just outside its first principal focus and forms a magnified, real inverted image, I_1. The second lens L_E, which is the eyepiece, is positioned so that this first real image I_1 is slightly nearer to L_E than its own first principal focus. Hence L_E is being used in just the same way as the lens illustrated in fig. 1.3. A further magnified image is formed at I_2, which in this case is virtual (and still inverted). The best position in which to place the eye is where an image of the *objective lens* would be formed by the eyepiece, since all the light entering the microscope must pass through this region, which is known as the exit pupil of the microscope. Its location in fig. 1.6 is made clear by means of the dotted construction line from L_O.

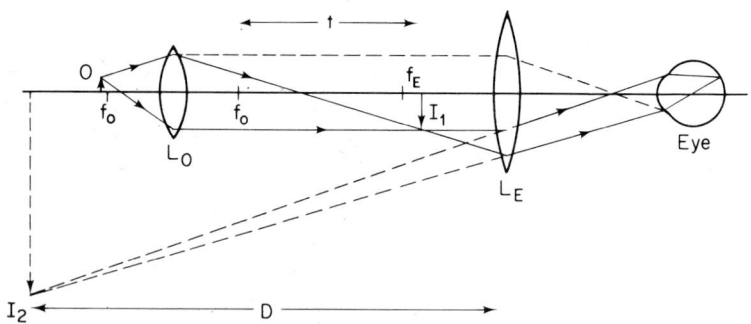

Fig. 1.6. Image formation in the compound microscope.

The compound microscope is thus a means of providing a simple microscope (the eyepiece) with an enlarged image to look at, rather than the object itself, so that a much higher magnifying power can be obtained. This magnifying power is simply the product of the linear magnification produced by L_O and the angular magnification produced by L_E, and hence is given by

$$M = -(v/f_O - 1)(D/f_E + 1)$$

where f_O and f_E are the focal lengths of the objective and eyepiece respectively, and v is the distance from the objective lens to I_1. The expression $(v/f_O - 1)$ is often replaced by (t/f_O), where the quantity t

is known as the optical tube length, and is the distance from the rear focal plane of the objective to I_1. For technical reasons most manufacturers have adopted a standard value for t. The magnification can be varied over a very wide range by changing the objective and eyepiece, and most modern compound microscopes have a range of between $\times 50$ and $\times 1000$.

1.5. *Lens aberrations*

Until now we have assumed our lenses to be ideal and hence, for example, to bring an incident beam of parallel white light to a single point focus. In practice there are a number of lens defects which combine to produce aberrations in the image. If these remained uncorrected they could severely limit the resolving power of the microscope as discussed on page 21.

First we shall consider spherical aberration. Unless it is infinitely thin, a biconvex lens whose faces have spherical curvature will focus a parallel beam of light as shown in fig. 1.7. Light passing through the outer zones of the lens is brought to a focus closer to the lens than is light passing through the lens nearer to its axis. The ideal point focus is replaced by a 'circle of confusion', whose radius r_s is indicated on the diagram. Conventionally this circle is defined in the Gauss image plane, that is the plane in which paraxial rays (those closest to the optical axis) are brought to a focus. In practice it does not correspond quite to the circle of *least* confusion, which is displaced slightly inwards towards the lens.

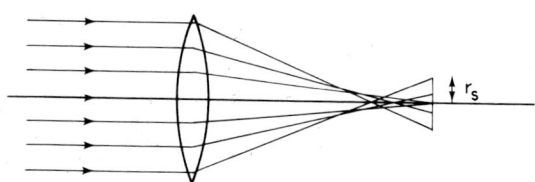

Fig. 1.7. Spherical aberration.

Since spherical lens surfaces produce this defect, the obvious solution appears to be to work out what the correct shape should be, and then to construct the lens accordingly. However it is so very much easier to grind, polish and test spherical (or flat) surfaces, that the construction of more complex shapes is rarely attempted. Thus it is simpler instead to try to reduce the magnitude of the aberration by suitable lens combinations, as described below.

The refractive index of glass varies with wavelength (an effect called dispersion) and so therefore does the focal length of a lens, fig. 1.8. This leads to chromatic aberration, and this again may be defined in terms of a circle of confusion. In principle chromatic aberration could be avoided by using light of one wavelength only but this would rarely be convenient in practice, and again its correction relies on suitable lens design.

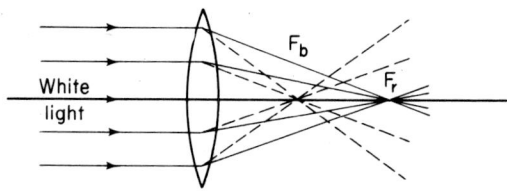

Fig. 1.8. Chromatic aberration. F_b and F_r are the foci for the blue and red components of white light.

We can approach the problem of reducing lens aberrations in two ways. The first is to use an aperture stop in order to limit the effective diameter of the lens, and fig. 1.9 (a) shows how this could be used to cut down spherical aberration. However this method may only be used to a very limited extent since it can lead to a reduction in image brightness, and is in any case unsuitable for an objective lens which requires the maximum aperture to obtain maximum resolution (page 27). The alternative is to combine together a number of separate lenses in order to produce the desired effect.

Thus one method of correcting for chromatic aberration is to use two lenses which are separated by a distance equal to half the sum of their focal lengths. Such a system will have the same focal length for all wavelengths, as illustrated in fig. 1.9 (b). Some degree of spherical aberration may be corrected for as well with this design, since the total deviation is distributed over four surfaces instead of just two. An alternative method of correcting for chromatic aberration uses lenses made out of two different kinds of glass. For example a converging lens made from crown glass may be combined with a diverging lens made from flint glass. The curvatures of their inner faces are made the same so that they may be cemented together, while those of their outer surfaces are chosen to minimize spherical aberration. The crown glass lens produces twice the *deviation* of the flint glass lens, but only the same *dispersion*. Thus the combined lens is still converging, but to a first approximation its dispersion is cancelled out. Figure 1.9 (c) shows a number of such achromatic doublets and triplets. Nowadays there is a wide range of 'crown' and 'flint' glasses from which to select in order to construct such compound lenses.

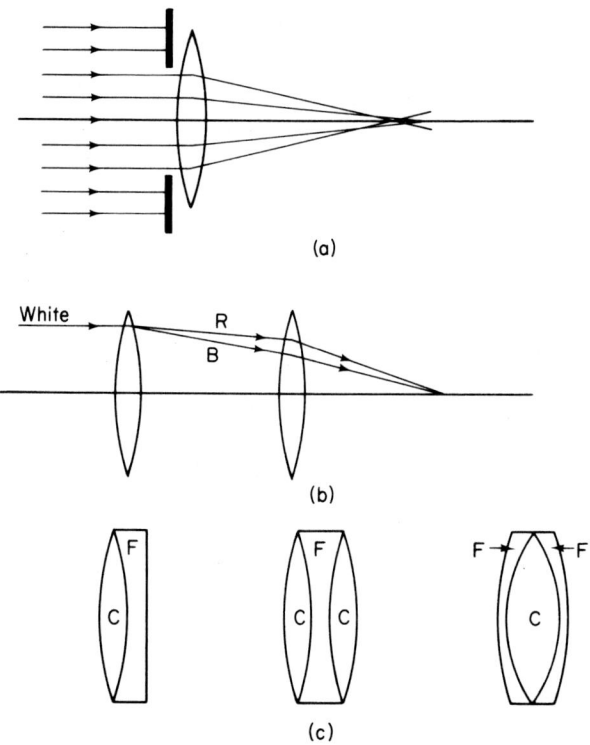

Fig. 1.9. Reduction of lens aberrations (a) use of a stop in order to cut down spherical aberration (b) combination of two lenses used to cut down both spherical and chromatic aberration (c) a number of achromatic lens combinations. C and F refer to crown and flint glass respectively.

To conclude this section it is of some interest to consider the aberrations of the eye. Since the density of the crystalline lens is greatest at its centre its focal length is less for axial rays than for peripheral rays, and hence its spherical aberration is in the opposite sense to that shown in fig. 1.7. The eye also suffers from chromatic aberration: we have to accommodate more to see red than blue at the same distance, and since the brain associates the amount of accommodation required with the nearness of an object, a red pattern appears to stand out in relief against a blue background. In normal circumstances, however, we are less troubled by the effect of chromatic aberration than would be expected, and it is possible that this defect is compensated for in some way either by the retina or by the brain. The eye, in common with other lenses, suffers from further defects such as astigmatism. These are fairly easy to overcome by correct spectacle design.

1.6. Wave optics

Light as a wave motion

So far the propagation of light has been discussed solely in terms of *geometrical optics*, light which is not being refracted or reflected being assumed to travel in straight lines or 'rays'. However if we are to understand the fundamental processes of image formation in the microscope, we must now turn to *physical optics*, considering light to be a form of wave motion.

If we regard the light as travelling in a direction x, then we can represent its motion as the propagation along x of a series of transverse oscillations in which the displacement y varies as shown by the

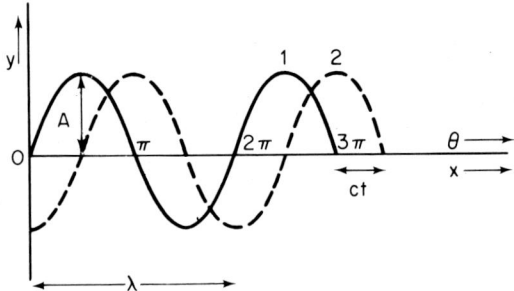

Fig. 1.10.   Representation of wave motion.

solid curve in fig. 1.10. These oscillations are assumed to be sinusoidal in form, whereupon we may write

$$y_1 = A \sin \theta$$

where A is a constant. If their wavelength is denoted λ, then it can be seen that as θ changes uniformly from 0 to 2π, x changes from 0 to λ, and hence that

$$\theta/2\pi = x/\lambda$$

and, rearranging,

$$y_1 = A \sin 2\pi x/\lambda.$$

This equation describes the displacement caused by the wave motion at any point x along its path. The constant A equals the maximum displacement or amplitude of the wave, its intensity being proportional to A^2.

Since the waves are travelling along the direction of propagation x with velocity c, a wave setting off a time t earlier would have reached the position shown by the dotted curve in fig. 1.10. The equation of this second wave is given by

$$y_2 = A \sin 2\pi/\lambda \, (x-ct).$$

This could now be written as

$$y_2 = A \sin (\theta - \phi)$$

where ϕ ($= 2\pi ct/\lambda$) is termed the difference in *phase* between the waves 1 and 2. In the diagram the dotted curve has been sketched such that $ct = \lambda/4$, so that here the phase difference ϕ equals $\pi/2$.

Frequently we are interested in two waves which originate at a single point (or at a single position at the wave front) and later are reunited after travelling by different routes. They may then arrive with a difference in phase if there is some difference in the optical

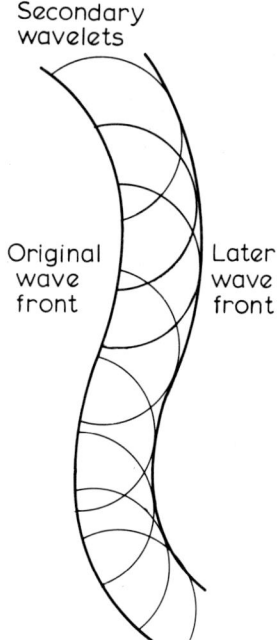

Fig. 1.11. Illustrating Huygens' principle.

paths traversed. It can be seen from the above that their phase difference may be expressed by

$$\text{phase difference} = 2\pi/\lambda \text{ (path difference)}.$$

A useful description of wave propagation is given by Huygens' principle. A wavefront can be defined for a series of waves that are being propagated through space as a surface at all points of which the oscillations are in phase. Huygens' principle considers that each point on the wavefront can be regarded as the centre of a secondary disturbance which gives rise to spherical wavelets. These spread out, and the new wavefront at any one time may be constructed by drawing the envelope to these wavelets, as shown in fig. 1.11. The normals to this wavefront, when it is unobstructed, are then the 'rays' of geometrical optics.

Interference

At any point where two or more waves are superposed they are said to *interfere*, and the resultant displacement at this point is in normal circumstances the vector sum of the instantaneous displacements produced by each individual wave. In order for a consistent effect to be observed the waves must all derive originally from the same coherent source of light; that is their phase difference must remain constant with time.

Let us consider what happens when two waves of equal wavelength and amplitude, but differing in phase by an angle ϕ, interfere at a point. If the two waves are represented by the equations

$$y_1 = A \sin \theta$$

and

$$y_2 = A \sin (\theta - \phi)$$

then their resultant is given by

$$y_1 + y_2 = A \sin \theta + A \sin (\theta - \phi)$$
$$= 2A \cos \phi/2 \sin (\theta - \phi/2).$$

This is the equation of a wave of amplitude $2A \cos \phi/2$, whose phase is $\phi/2$ behind that of the first wave (and $\phi/2$ ahead of that of the second). Figure 1.12 shows two special cases. In fig. 1.12 (*a*) the phase difference $\phi = 2\pi$. From the above equation it can be seen that the amplitude of the resultant wave will be equal to $2A$, and hence the two waves completely reinforce each other. This is known as 'constructive interference', and the general condition for

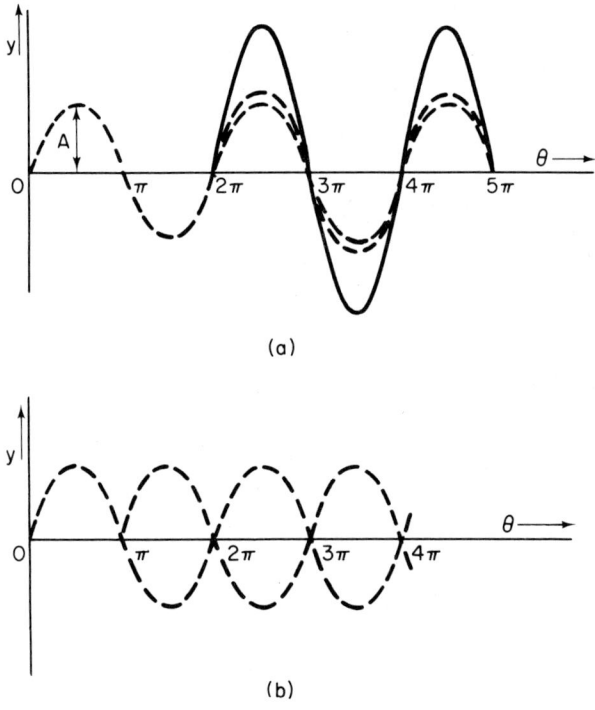

Fig. 1.12. Superposition of two waves (a) phase difference $\phi = 2\pi$; (b) phase difference $\phi = \pi$.

its occurrence is that there should be a phase difference of $2n\pi$ (or a path difference of $n\lambda$) between the two waves, where n is an integer or zero. In fig. 1.12 (b), on the other hand, $\phi = \pi$, $2A \cos \phi/2 = 0$, and hence the two waves cancel each other out exactly. This is known as 'destructive interference', and its general condition is that there should exist a phase difference of $(2n-1)\pi$, or a path difference of $(2n-1)\lambda/2$. If the phase difference lies in between these two extremes then the resultant amplitude lies between $2A$ and zero.

Diffraction

According to geometrical optics, if parallel light is incident upon a single slit, as shown in fig. 1.13, then it should form an illuminated area of the same size as the slit if it falls normally upon a nearby screen, with a sharp change in illumination at its edge. In practice a certain fraction of the light spreads into the region that should be in shadow, an effect that is accentuated if the slit is narrow. This observation is a result of *diffraction* and it occurs whenever a wavefront is restricted by an aperture or by some obstacle. The effect may be explained by means of Huygens' principle, whereby the entire aperture of the slit is considered as a source of secondary wavelets, which will then interfere with one another as they propagate towards the right of the figure. In certain directions, as shown, the wavelets will reinforce constructively to give brightness; in other directions they may exactly cancel out. The resulting maxima and minima are shown on the continuous intensity distribution across the screen plane to the extreme right of this figure.

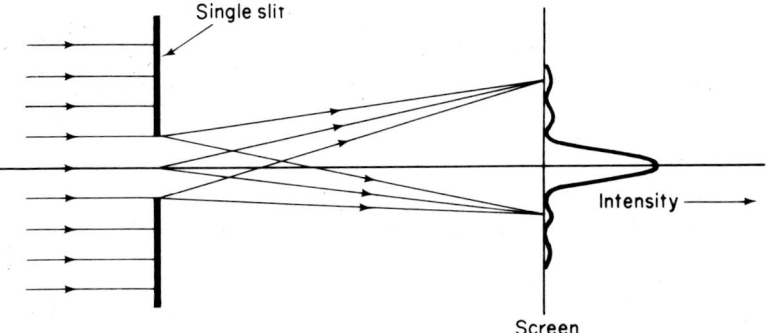

Fig. 1.13. Fresnel diffraction at a single slit.

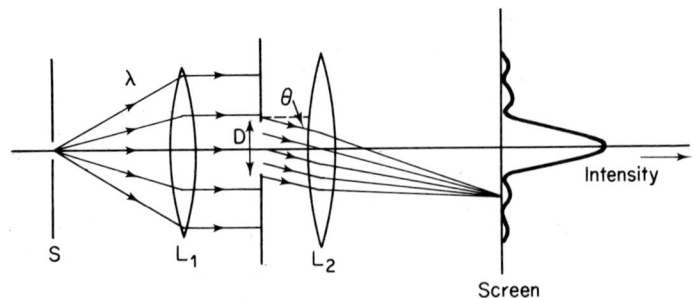

Fig. 1.14. Fraunhofer diffraction at a single slit.

Figure 1.13 is an example of Fresnel diffraction, in which rays coming from different directions unite at a single point, and together form what is effectively a fringed image of the slit. In microscopy we are more concerned with Fraunhofer diffraction, fig. 1.14. Again the slit is assumed to be illuminated by parallel light, formed by placing a slit source S at the focal plane of a collimating lens L_1. A second lens L_2 is placed in front of the slit, and using this arrangement all the rays which emerge from the slit in the *same* direction are brought to a focus at the same point, and together form what is effectively a fringed image of the source S. The intensity distribution on the screen is still somewhat similar to that in the Fresnel case and it can be shown that the condition for reinforcement is that

$$D \sin \theta = (n + \tfrac{1}{2})\lambda$$

where D is the width of the slit.

The diffraction grating

A property of the Fraunhofer diffraction pattern is that even if the slit is moved laterally parallel to itself in front of the second lens, the diffraction pattern remains in the same position, centred upon the axis of the lens (neglecting any effects due to lens aberrations). This is because all parts of the lens bring parallel rays to the same focus. Thus if we now consider a diffraction grating, that is a number of slits, each of the same width and whose spacing is d (fig. 1.15), then the distribution of light in the image plane owing to diffraction will be exactly the same as with the single slit, except brighter. However there is a further effect to consider, namely interference between the light emerging from each successive slit, which markedly affects this distribution.

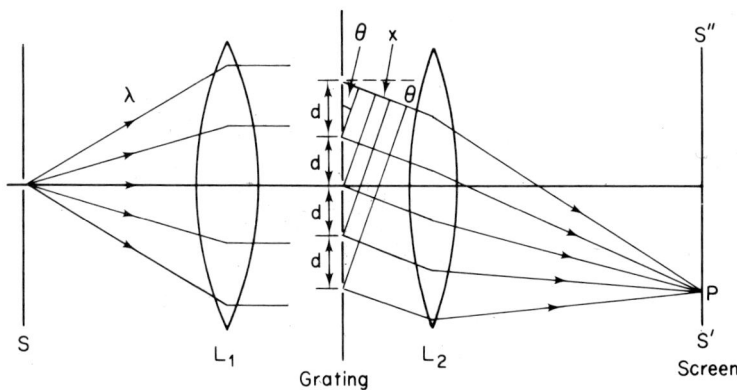

Fig. 1.15. The diffraction grating.

Consider for example a point P on the screen plane S'S". The wavelets diverging from the slits in the grating start out in phase, but travel along different paths to reach the point P. From fig. 1.15 it can be seen that the relative path differences are equal to some multiple of the distance x, where x is given by

$$x = d \sin \theta.$$

For perfect reinforcement to occur this must be equal to an integral number of wavelengths, and hence the condition for a bright interference fringe centred at P is given by

$$d \sin \theta = n\lambda$$

where n is an integer. This equation defines a series of bright

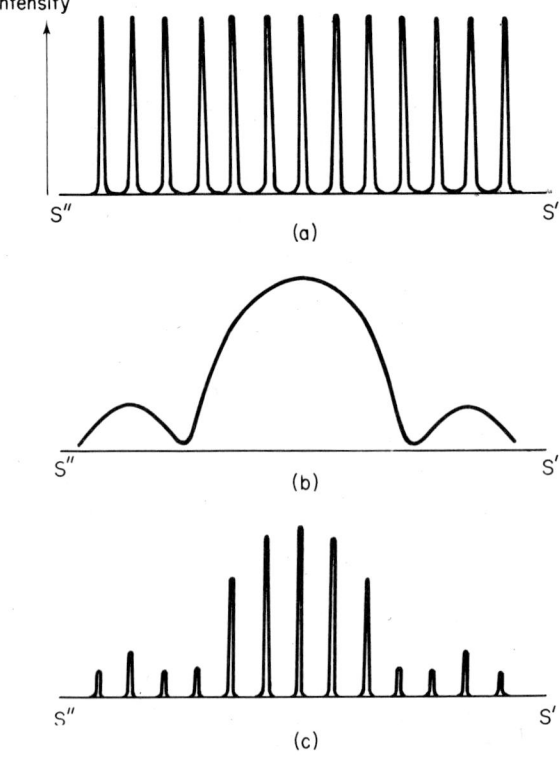

Fig. 1.16. Diffraction pattern from a grating showing the intensity distribution due to (a) interference between successive slits (b) diffraction at each slit (c) their combined effect.

maxima, for each value of n, with complete darkness in between.

Figure 1.16 (a) shows the intensity distribution that would be found in the image plane S'S" if we were to consider only the above interference effects between successive slits—a regular series of pronounced maxima and minima (in practice there would also be a number of subsidiary maxima and minima in between these, dependent upon the number of slits, but for simplicity these have been ignored). However the overall intensity that can be transmitted to any one point is still controlled by a diffraction curve such as that illustrated in fig. 1.14. This is shown in fig. 1.16 (b). Hence the resultant intensity distribution in S'S" actually follows the curve shown in fig. 1.16 (c).

Before we discuss how these ideas may be applied to the formation of images in the microscope, it will be useful to extend the discussion on diffraction to the three-dimensional case of a crystal lattice.

Bragg's law

In the case of the diffraction grating discussed in the previous section, the angle θ between the normal to the grating and the direction in which the various diffraction maxima are observed, only becomes appreciable when the spacing of the grating slits approaches the wavelength of light. Both electrons and X-rays, on the other hand, possess much smaller wavelengths than light, and it is not easy to construct an artificial grating to produce clear diffraction effects with them. However there is a vast range of natural 'diffraction gratings' for these radiations in the crystalline solids—materials such as metals, minerals and ceramics, in which the constituent atoms are arranged in a regular three-dimensional array. The atoms correspond to the diffracting elements of the grating, and their spacings are just of the magnitude required to give substantial values of θ. Hence, as we shall see in Chapters 4 and 7, electron and X-ray diffraction techniques are invaluable in providing information on the exact structure of such solids.

In a grating the diffracting elements, the slits, usually lie in a single plane. In a crystal they are the atoms, and form a three-dimensional network, making the analysis of the diffraction conditions that much more difficult. However, Bragg was able to simplify the problem in the following way.

Consider a single two-dimensional plane of atoms, fig. 1.17 (a). The incident wavefront is in phase across OA, and makes an angle θ with the plane. The atoms, such as O and O', scatter the incident

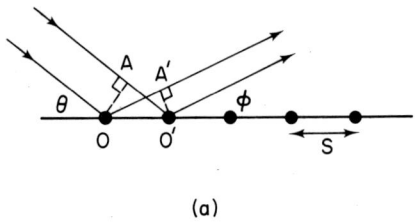

(a)

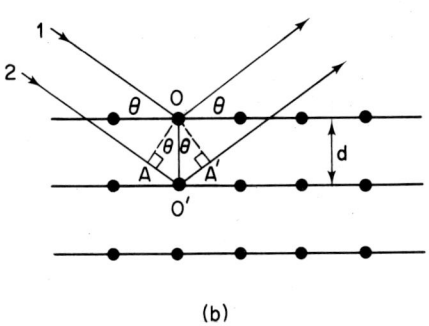

(b)

Fig. 1.17. Derivation of Bragg's law.

waves, and we wish to find the condition that the scattered waves are again in phase, i.e. the condition for which constructive interference occurs, and a strong diffracted beam is formed. Let the diffracted wavefront make an angle ϕ with the plane of atoms. One condition is that the path lengths of the two waves, AO′ and OA′, are equal. Hence, since AO′ = $s \cos \theta$ and OA′ = $s \cos \phi$, the angles θ and ϕ must be equal. Hence it is possible to consider the diffracted waves as being *reflected* from the plane of atoms.

If we now extend the analysis to three dimensions, fig. 1.17 (b), we must consider parallel planes of atoms a distance d apart. The diffracted waves are considered to be reflected from these atomic planes, and it is necessary to find the condition that waves 1 and 2 are scattered in phase. A general solution is that the path difference, AO′+O′A′ is equal to $n\lambda$, where n is an integer, and since AO′ = O′A′ = $d \sin \theta$, the condition becomes

$$2d \sin \theta = n\lambda$$

The above equation is known as Bragg's Law, and, since this analysis may be repeated between the next pair of parallel planes, it is fully able to describe the diffraction of X-rays or electrons by a crystalline solid in terms of reflection from successive parallel atomic planes. Different planar sections may be considered within the solid, and these will have their own particular values of the Bragg angle, θ.

1.7. *Resolution*

To the early microscopists it must have seemed that one need only design more and more powerful lens combinations in order to obtain higher and higher magnifying powers, until even the finest details of matter could be resolved. However it was eventually realized that, due to the various lens defects discussed on pages 9–12, there is a certain amount of spreading in the image. Thus the image of a point is actually a circle of finite size—the circle of confusion. The result is that if two point objects are too close together their images may overlap to such an extent that they cannot be differentiated.

During the latter part of the eighteenth century, therefore, a great deal of technical effort went into the design of lens combinations that minimized these defects. However it was then found that no matter how perfect the lens design became, after a certain point the microscope resolution could not be improved beyond about half a micrometre. The explanation for this was first realized in 1878 by Ernst Abbe, joint founder of the famous Zeiss optical works at Jena. He proposed that the restriction was more fundamental than merely imperfect lens design, and was connected with the wave nature of light and the phenomenon of diffraction.

In the next sections we shall see how Abbe's theory of the resolution limit is developed, and then an alternative, and complementary, approach will be described.

The Abbe theory of image formation

Abbe's treatment of image formation assumes the object to be a regular periodic structure such as a diffraction grating, fig. 1.18. This is identical to the situation discussed in fig. 1.15, and hence a Fraunhofer diffraction pattern will be formed in the rear focal plane of the objective lens, each point of which corresponds to constructive interference between rays leaving the grating from different points but at the same angle. Here, however, we are interested in the continuation of these rays on into the plane marked I_1. In this plane each point illuminated corresponds to constructive interference between rays leaving the grating *from the same point*, and hence is a direct *image* of the object grating. It is equivalent to the image I_1 in fig. 1.6, which may then be used by the eyepiece to form the final image.

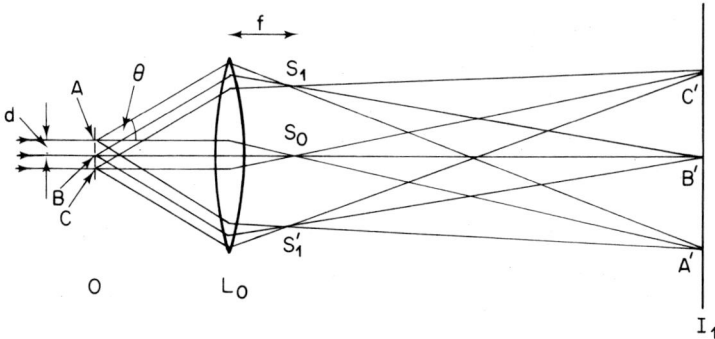

Fig. 1.18. The Abbe theory of resolution.

Since the objective aperture is of a limited size, not all of the diffracted beams can be collected, and therefore some information concerning the object will be lost. Abbe treated this problem by considering each point in the Fraunhofer diffraction pattern to act as a Huygenian secondary source. Thus if only the straight through, or zero order, beam is collected, the only secondary source present is S_0, and since there are no other wavelets to cause constructive interference with those from S_0, the image can contain no periodicity, and hence the grating structure is not resolved. If the objective lets through the zero order beam together with the two first order beams on either side, as shown in fig. 1.18, then the intensity in I_1 will be of the form shown in fig. 1.19. The dotted line shows the intensity distribution that would result if every diffraction order were present. However since the amount of light diffracted into the higher order beams rapidly becomes very small, neglect of these does not seriously affect the image, and the condition that interference

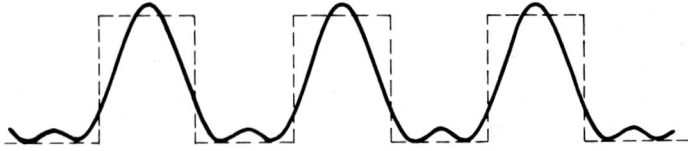

Fig. 1.19. Image of a grating when the N.A. of the objective lets through the zero order and the two first order beams only. The dotted line shows the appearance if all the orders are present.

between wavelets from S_0, S_1 and S_1', is able to take place allows the elements of the grating to be resolved.

The limiting condition that the two first order beams may just be collected by the objective may be obtained from page 18, namely

$$d \sin \theta = n\lambda$$

where d is the separation of the elements of the grating. Since the medium in the object space may not be air we should substitute λ/μ for λ, where μ is its refractive index,* and λ the wavelength in air. The limit of resolution, δ, is given by

$$\delta = d = \lambda/(\mu \sin \theta).$$

Abbe called $\mu \sin \theta$ the *numerical aperture*, N.A., of the lens (the angle 2θ is the angular aperture) so that this expression is normally represented by

$$\delta = \lambda/\text{N.A.}$$

If the elements of the grating are any closer than this then the divergence of the diffracted beams becomes greater and they will not be collected by the objective. However it is still possible to get interference if the direction of the incident illumination makes an oblique angle with the axis of the objective lens, such that the first order diffracted beam on one side of the axis is just collected at one edge of the lens, while the direct, zero order, beam just gets in at the other. Hence the absolute limit of resolution predicted using this approach is given by

$$\delta = 0 \cdot 5 \; \lambda/\text{N.A.}$$

The Abbe treatment assumes that the object is periodic, such as a grating. Although it is possible to think of objects which are like this (for example a diatom frustule, or, more importantly, the crystalline solids examined in the electron microscope, to which the theory may also be applied), most specimens are not. However it is possible to extend the analysis to consider the object to be made up of a complex array of non-periodic points, each of which will still diffract, and lead to interference in the image plane.

The Rayleigh criterion

The Fraunhofer diffraction pattern from a single slit was discussed on pages 16-17 and illustrated in fig. 1.14. A similar effect is obtained using a circular aperture, although now the fringes will be

---

* Conventionally we should use the symbol n for refractive index; however we shall use μ at this stage in order to avoid confusion with the integer n as used above.

circular, and the pattern is referred to as the Airy disc. Its appearance is illustrated in fig. 1.20.

Fig. 1.20. The Airy disc pattern.

This phenomenon is relevant to microscopy since the objective lens itself acts as a circular aperture. Hence even in the absence of lens aberrations, the image of a point object will not be a point, but an Airy disc pattern. Similarly for an extended object, the (magnified) image is surrounded by a similar series of diffraction fringes. Clearly the diffraction effect becomes important when the details of the image are of the same order of magnitude as the diffraction fringes, and hence this effect will set a limit to the fineness of object detail which may be resolved.

Figure 1.21 illustrates a number of possible situations. Ideally, in the absence of diffraction effects, the images of two point objects would exhibit the intensity distribution shown in fig. 1.21 (*a*); instead each image is an Airy disc, whose intensity distribution is shown in fig. 1.21 (*b*). In this latter figure there is no appreciable overlap of the two Airy disc patterns, and hence the two images are readily resolved. In fig. 1.21 (*c*) the Airy discs overlap appreciably, and the dotted line shows the resultant intensity of light in their vicinity: the individual maxima can no longer be resolved. Thus there must be some intermediate point, fig. 1.21 (*d*), where the resultant intensity shows a sufficient dip in the middle for the existence of two separate peaks to be detected, and hence for the two images just to be resolved.

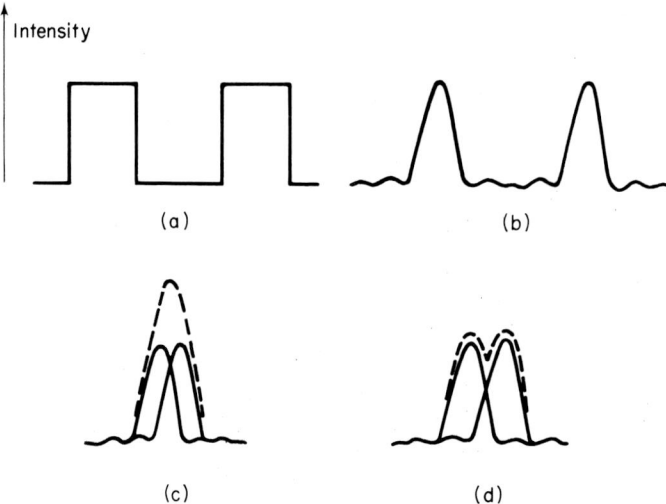

Fig. 1.21. Illustrating the Rayleigh criterion for resolution: (*a*) intensity distribution of two image points in the absence of diffraction (*b*) Airy disc patterns readily resolved (*c*) not resolved (*d*) just capable of being resolved.

The Rayleigh criterion states that this limiting point is reached when the central maximum of the Airy disc from one image coincides with the position of the first minimum in the Airy disc of the second image. At this point the intensity at the mid-point is 74 per cent of that of the maxima at either side. While this criterion is quite arbitrary, it agrees quite well with the practical limits of one's perception.

In the microscope, the radius of the Airy disc from a point object is determined by the angular aperture of the objective lens. Given that the latter is fixed, then the dimensions of the Airy discs will be such that two point objects will only be resolved, providing that their images are further apart than the situation illustrated in fig. 1.21 (*d*). It can be shown that this restricts the original separation of these two point objects, and hence the limit of resolution of the microscope, to

$$\delta = \frac{0 \cdot 61 \lambda}{\text{N.A.}}$$

Hence by considering the diffraction of light at the *objective lens*, we end up with very nearly the same value for the limit of resolution as if we consider the diffraction of light at the *object*, and both values depend in exactly the same way on the wavelength of the light and on the N.A. of the objective. For simplicity we shall keep to the Abbe expression.

Resolution and wavelength

In the above analyses the resolution limit of microscope has been defined in terms of the optical properties of the objective lens, since any detail that is missing here cannot be added at a later stage. If we take an approximate value for the N.A. as unity, then the optimum resolution comes about to be about one half the wavelength of the light used, and this is a fundamental limitation which cannot be overcome.

In order to make this dependence of resolution on wavelength quite clear, a simple analogy may be useful. Suppose a blind person is attempting to explore a room simply by feeling around with some sort of probe. Then the amount of detail that he can detect will depend on the fineness of this probe. For example, using a walking stick he could only detect the grosser objects, such as chairs and tables. To resolve finer detail, for example to discover whether the chair arms were carved or plain, he might need to resort to a finer instrument such as a pencil. Finally, with the help of a needle he might be able to make out the texture of the upholstery. The thickness of the probe which he uses is the analogue of the wavelength of the light used in the microscope.

It is evident from the expression for the resolution that the latter may actually be improved upon in three ways. Radiation of shorter wavelength may be employed, and this is discussed on pages 85–6;

some way may be found of increasing the refractive index, as in the oil immersion objective discussed on pages 41–3; and finally sin θ can be increased by increasing the angular aperture of the lens, although this is in conflict with the primary function of the objective which is to provide high magnification. The latter necessitates lenses of short focal length, and hence small diameter.

Resolution is the parameter by which the performance of any kind of microscope is eventually judged, and indeed many of the principles discussed in this section apply equally well to other kinds of microscope besides the optical variety. For example the principal advantage of the electron microscope is the considerably greater resolving power that it gives due to the much smaller wavelength associated with electrons. In addition, the resolution is involved in determining other parameters associated with image formation, such as depth of field and depth of focus as described below.

Depth of field and depth of focus

The depth of field and depth of focus of a microscope are two quantities which are simply related, but are often confused. The depth of field, D_1, is defined for object space and is the distance, measured away from the objective, over which different objects may be equally well in focus in the image. This is illustrated in fig. 1.22. A point object, O, forms an image focused at I. This will not be a point but an approximately spherical region whose radius is related to that of the circle of confusion (if substantial lens aberrations are present) or to that of the Airy disc (if the resolution limit is set by diffraction). If the images from points such as O' and O", a short distance either side of O, fall within this 'sphere' then they will appear to be as well in focus as is I.

Thus there will be a range, D_1, over which different parts of the object are effectively all in focus at the same time. It can be shown that D_1 is proportional to $1/(\text{N.A.})^2$, and for a high power objective it is of a similar order of magnitude to the diffraction limit, δ.

The term 'depth of focus' is often used instead of depth of field to describe D_1. However this usage is incorrect and the depth of focus, D_2, strictly refers to the equivalent distance in image space. It has little relevance when the final image is being viewed by the eye since the latter possesses its own power of accommodation. Where it is relevant is when the final image is being formed on a viewing screen, or is being photographed. Fundamentally it relates to the fact that provided the image screen is located within the radius of the 'sphere' centred on I (fig. 1.22) then the image will be equally well in focus.

The relationship between D_1 and D_2 may be derived as follows. If u and v are the object and image distances respectively, then as seen from page 2,

$$1/u + 1/v = 1/f.$$

Consider a small variation in u, du. Differentiating the above equation we get

$$-du/u^2 - dv/v^2 = 0.$$

Therefore

$$dv = -(v^2/u^2)du.$$

Let $du = D_1$, whereupon $dv = D_2$, and since $v/u = m$, the linear magnification, we find that

$$D_2 = -m^2 D_1.$$

The minus sign arises because an increase in u results in a decrease in v.

In passing it may be noted that the above analysis means that

$$dv/du = -m^2,$$

i.e. that the axial or longitudinal magnification of the microscope is equal to the square of the conventionally quoted transverse magnification. Thus the images of three-dimensional structures show large axial elongation.

1.8. Contrast

It is important to distinguish between the ability to detect the presence of an object—visibility—and the ability to determine its shape and dimensions—resolution. The limit of detection, or perception, appears to be set both by the overall intensity of light in the image (and hence a high N.A. aids perception as well as resolution), and by the contrast. The latter may be defined as

$$contrast = \frac{intensity\ of\ background - intensity\ of\ object}{intensity\ of\ background}$$

Rayleigh's criterion says that if there is a drop in intensity of about a quarter in between two peaks then they may be recognized as separate, but, for the peaks to be seen at all, their intensity must be significantly different from that of the background.

Thus high resolution on its own is not sufficient, and it may be the contrast conditions that eventually determine how much use may be made of the microscope's potential performance. To take an example, many biological specimens, viewed in transmitted light, contain structures whose dimensions place them well above the resolution limit, but whose transparency is so similar to that of the material in which they lie that they fail to give any detectable image contrast. This may be overcome by chemical staining, which renders selected regions of the specimen considerably more opaque. Alternatively a special kind of microscope may be used which is able to convert differences that exist in the phase of the light from various regions, but which are not detectable by the eye, into differences in intensity. This is discussed in Chapter 3.

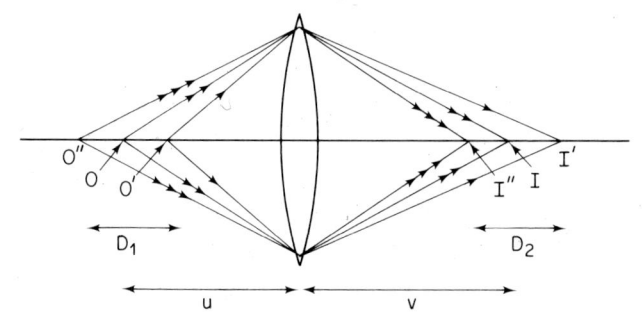

Fig. 1.22. Depth of field and depth of focus.

A further example of the importance of image contrast is the fact that under certain conditions it is actually possible to see objects which are much smaller than the limit of resolution. For example, if the object to be imaged is a small black disc against a white background, it may still be detected even though its radius may be as small as about $0 \cdot 04 \, \lambda/\text{N.A.}$ That this is considerably less than the resolution limit means only that its shape and size cannot be determined. This principle is made use of in the 'ultramicroscope', fig. 1.23. A strong beam of light is focused into a smoke cloud or liquid containing a fine suspension of tiny particles. The light then undergoes Tyndall scattering, which is a mixture of diffraction, refraction and reflection, and sufficient may be scattered sideways into the microscope for the particles to be detected as bright pin-points of light moving about under the field of view. After reading Chapter 3 it will become apparent that this is an elementary kind of *dark field* imaging technique. Many other ways of improving image contrast will be discussed in this chapter.

1.9. Microstructure

The main purpose of this book is to describe the fundamental physical principles underlying the operation of the various forms of microscopy, and therefore the illustrations have been selected with this aim in mind. Nevertheless a brief description of the type of information that is of interest in a microscopical study will assist both in understanding what is being revealed in the micrographs chosen, and also in appreciating the sort of information that each technique is able to provide.

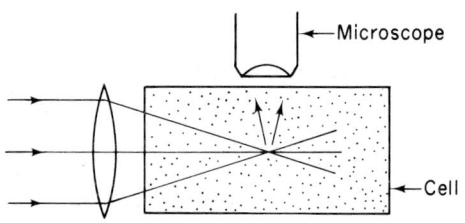

Fig. 1.23. The ultramicroscope.

Microstructure in metallurgy

Of the applications of microscopy in the physical sciences, those in metallurgy—termed metallography—form by far the largest category. In both metals and alloys the component atoms are arranged in a regular periodic fashion, similar to that shown in fig. 1.17. However their crystalline nature is not readily apparent to the naked eye since they are composed of a large number of differently oriented regions, known as grains, the interface between the grains being known as a grain boundary. Other deviations from the ideal atomic array are the vacancy, or single missing atom, and the dislocation, which is a linear disturbance in the correct stacking sequence of the successive atomic planes (c.f. fig. 4.6). These crystal defects are of vital importance in controlling the mechanical strengths of metals, and although their true description lies solely at the atomic level, special etching techniques can be used to render their presence visible under the optical microscope, as we shall see in the following chapter.

Alloying one metal with another metal initially takes place by the substitution of atoms of the second species for those of the first. At larger concentrations, separation into distinct phases may occur, usually in the form of particles of one phase—ranging in size from one nm to several μm—distributing themselves within a continuous matrix of the other. A knowledge of the size and distribution of such particles is necessary for the understanding of the properties of the material.

Usually this sort of microstructure is studied by observing the surface exposed when an arbitrary cross-section is taken through a suitable specimen. However there is a further class of metallurgical 'microstructure' that is of interest, namely the structure of the natural surface of the material, particularly where changes may arise due to mechanical deformation, reaction with the environment, such as oxidation and corrosion, or fracture. These topics form a different category since the specimen is being studied directly, rather than after the usual sequence of sectioning, polishing and etching that accompanies the examination of its internal microstructure.

Finally we may be interested in the geometry of the crystal structure itself, or in the precise composition, as opposed to morphology, of the various structures present. Neither of these questions may be answered directly by microscopy, but we shall also be discussing a number of diffraction and spectroscopy techniques which can be used to complete the picture of the material.

Microstructure in biology

The internal structure of metals is simplicity itself compared to the complex microstructures encountered in living matter. Although many biological substances do occur in crystalline form, their fundamental repeating unit, rather than being a single atom, as in the case of most metals, is usually a very complex arrangement of different atoms and molecules. These substances combine to make up the individual structures that go to form a single cell, which in turn is combined with many others, in a highly complex manner, to make up the total organism.

Considered as a whole, therefore, the understanding of such structures appears to be most formidable. However under the microscope only one level of complexity can be observed at any one time, and a reasonable overall picture may be synthesized from the results of investigations using a range of microstructural techniques. As a guide to the range of sizes in which we are interested, both in metallurgy and in biology, Table 1 depicts the magnifications required to make a wide range of details visible to the human eye.

Table 1. Size ranges of some objects of microstructural interest

1 mm	100 μm	10 μm	1 μm	100 nm	10 nm	1 nm	1 Å	Dimensions
		Surface features, steps etc.						Metallurgical features
	Grains							
			Second phase particles					
						Crystal defects		
							Atoms	
Protozoa								Biological features
		Blood cells						
			Bacteria					
				Animal viruses				
					Plant viruses			
					Macromolecules			
						Molecules		
×1	×10	×10²	×10³	×10⁴	×10⁵	×10⁶		Magnification required to make features visible to the eye

CHAPTER 2
optical microscopy

2.1. The compound microscope
Design

ALTHOUGH superficially they appear quite different, there are many fundamental similarities between the modern compound microscope which is illustrated in fig. 2.1, and that of Robert Hooke, fig. 1.5. In both cases the eyepiece and objective lenses are mounted on some sort of adjustable limb, while the position of the specimen may be controlled by means of a mechanical stage. In the modern microscope a revolving nosepiece carries a number of objective

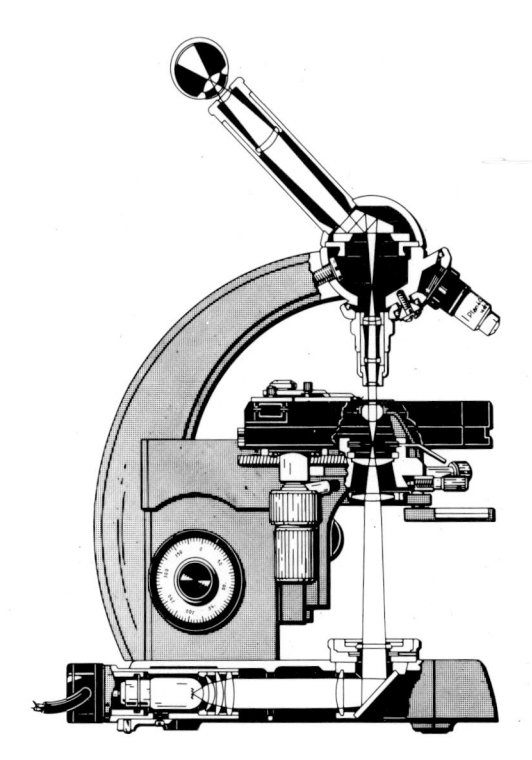

Fig. 2.1.   A modern compound microscope.   *Zeiss-Werkphoto.*

lenses, each with a different magnification, and all the lenses are of course lens combinations designed to correct for aberrations. A main difference between the two microscopes is their system of illumination. In Hooke's case this was an oil lamp focused on to the specimen via a brine-filled globe and a further convex lens. The modern microscope has a built-in substage condenser lens system illuminated by a powerful electric lamp, together with focusing and diaphragm controls. Figure 2.2 attempts to show the principle of image formation in this microscope in a rather more straightforward fashion, in order that the functions of the various optical components,

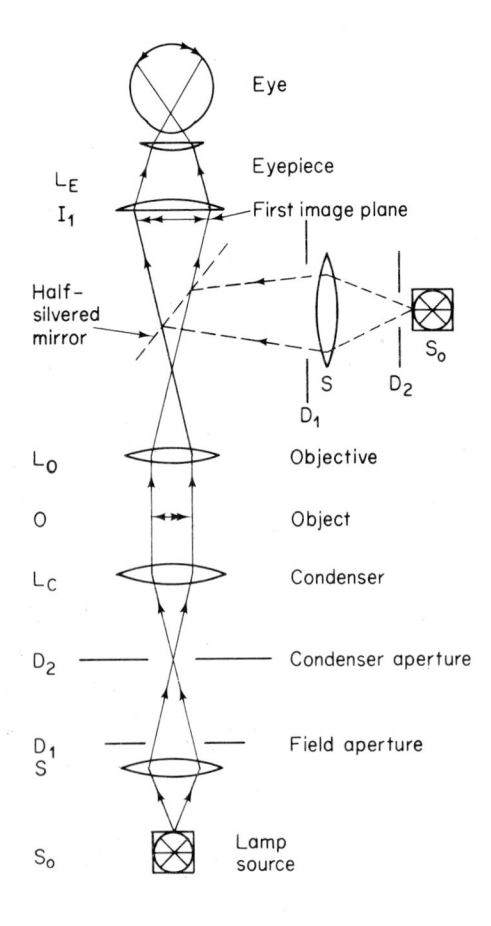

Fig. 2.2. Schematic diagram showing the optical layout of the compound microscope used both in transmission and in reflection (the latter shown with the dashed lines).

which are discussed in more detail in sections 2.2. to 2.4., may be more readily understood.

The metallurgical microscope

A further important distinction between figs. 1.5 and 2.1 is that Hooke's microscope was designed to examine specimens in reflected light rather than in transmitted light. This is of course imperative with metals and other opaque materials, while most biological substances may be examined in transmitted light. In the modern metallurgical reflection microscope the illumination enters the body tube between the eyepiece and objective lenses where it is reflected through a right angle (for example by a half-silvered mirror) to be focused on to the specimen surface by the objective lens, which thus has a second function as the final element in the condenser lens system. Figure 2.2. is intended to make clear the difference in layout between the transmission and reflection microscopes. The operation of the two is very similar, and most of the discussion which follows applies equally well to both.

Modern modifications

Minor variations to this basic design and the use of various attachments are discussed in the next chapter, but here we may mention some modern instruments which do differ fairly radically from the basic microscope of fig. 2.1.

In some cases a binocular design may be beneficial since the continuous use of one eye can be fatiguing. The image formed by the objective is doubled by a beam-splitting prism and presented to each eye through two further prisms and two eyepieces, the images seen by each eye being identical.

In normal vision, which is stereoscopic, each eye forms a slightly different image of an object, so that an impression of solidity and depth is given. Hence there is a further class of binocular microscope, known as a stereomicroscope, which has been developed to reproduce this effect. The most simple design consists of two separate objectives, body tubes and eyepieces, combined into one instrument. The magnification is usually limited to about × 100, one reason being that at higher magnifications the decreasing depth of field that is obtained automatically limits the three-dimensional effect. Some models have the facility to vary the magnification continuously by means of a zoom lens system, rather than by interchangeable objectives. More recently it has become possible to obtain a stereoscopic effect using a single objective, the two images being formed by light which is polarized in two different planes, each eyepiece transmitting only one of these. Applications of stereomicroscopy include the examination of fracture and corrosion surfaces of metals, dissection and delicate surgery, and the assembly of miniaturized engineering products.

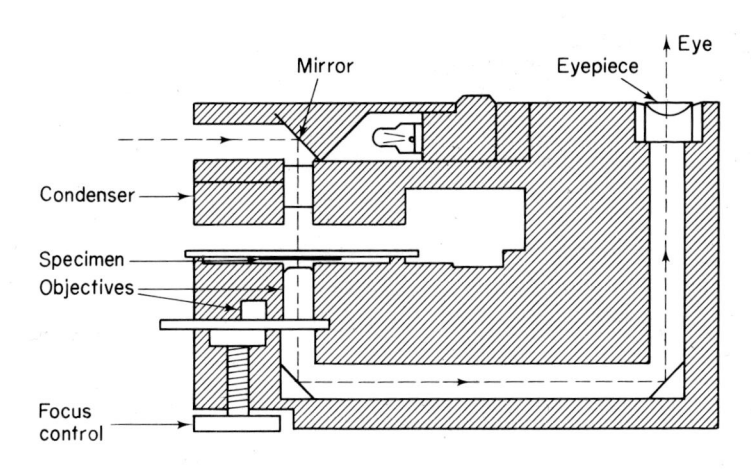

Fig. 2.3. The McArthur portable microscope.

It has long been an aim in microscope design to produce an easily portable microscope, although most attempts have resulted simply in a collapsible microscope, a compromise that has never really been successful. A fresh approach to the problem is found in the McArthur microscope (fig. 2.3), in which the eyepiece and the objective face the same way, the optical system being folded double. Since the body of the microscope is produced as a single unit it possesses sufficient rigidity to stand up to extremely severe handling.

2.2 *The illuminating system*

For low magnification work it is often sufficient to illuminate the specimen using an external lamp, or even the sun, the light being reflected into the objective by means of a mirror. However at the highest magnification, say × 1000, the object will be enlarged one million times in *area*, and hence will appear only one millionth as bright in the image. In order that the eye should be able to see this image clearly, very careful attention must be paid to the method of illuminating the specimen, and powerful filament or arc lamps are used, together with a condenser lens system well corrected for aberrations. Sometimes special filters are inserted, either to select the correct level of illumination for photography, or to produce monochromatic or polarized light for particular applications.

The objective lens is designed to give maximum resolution with a self-luminous object. This condition can effectively be achieved if an image of the light source is focused on to the plane of the specimen by the condenser, and if the incident cone of light is of sufficient angle just to fill the whole of the objective.

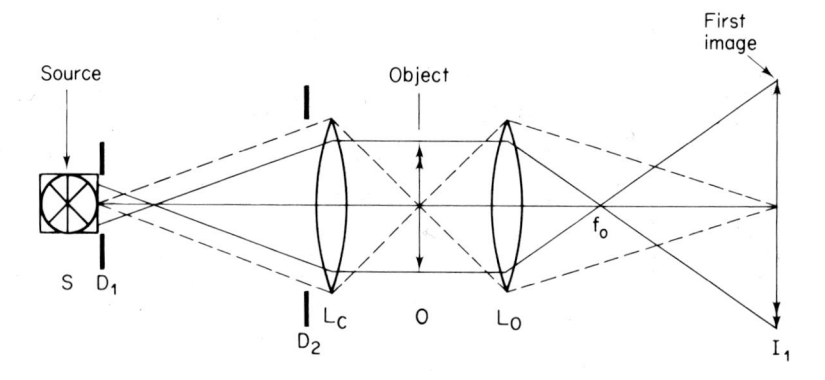

Fig. 2.4. Critical illumination.

There are two ways of doing this. The first method is known as 'critical illumination', fig. 2.4. Here an image of the lamp source S is focused directly onto the plane of the specimen at O by means of the condenser lens L_C. Two extreme ray paths have been drawn in order to make the process clear. The iris diaphragm D_1 is known as the field aperture, and its position is conjugate to that of the source (which it defines) and the object, and this in turn is conjugate to the first image I_1. D_1 is used to restrict the field of view which is seen on the object to the area which is of direct interest, thereby avoiding glare from other regions of the specimen. The second diaphragm D_2 is known as the condenser aperture, and it is this which controls the amount of light entering the objective. Normally it is adjusted until the back of the objective is just filled with light, thus utilizing its maximum aperture. If the illumination is too bright like this then D_2 may be stopped down, leading also to an increased depth of field, but poorer resolution. The method of critical illumination suffers from the disadvantage that the light source must be quite large and uniform, since any structure that it possesses, such as the coil of the filament, is superposed on to the final image of the specimen.

The second method is known as Köhler illumination, fig. 2.5. Here the effective light source, again designated S, is actually an additional lens which is illuminated from behind by the primary lamp source, now termed S_O. This secondary source S may be treated in exactly the same way as the primary source S in fig. 2.4: its image is focused directly on to the object plane, and the diaphragms D_1 and D_2 fulfil exactly the same functions as before.

Note that while S is conjugate with the object plane O and in turn with the first image plane I_1, S_O is conjugate with D_2 and with the rear focal plane of the objective (marked f_O at the focal point). The advantage of Köhler illumination is that a larger and more evenly illuminated source is effectively produced, and it is this method that is used in the more sophisticated research microscopes, and in

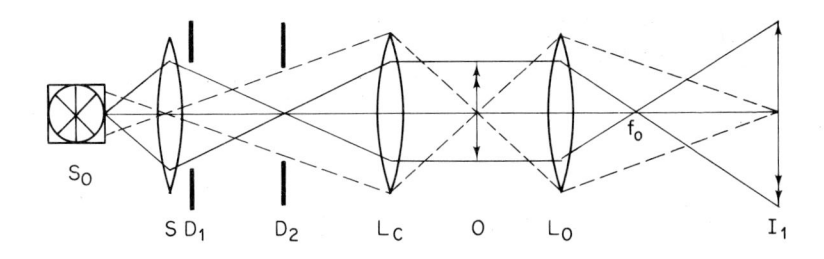

Fig. 2.5. Köhler illumination.

photomicroscopy. Köhler illumination is the method illustrated in fig. 2.2. In the case of the metallurgical microscope the position of the condenser aperture D_2 has to be somewhat different since here the objective lens serves also as the condenser lens itself.

2.3. *The objective*

As fig. 2.1 illustrates, most compound microscopes have a range of objectives, of varying magnifications, usually mounted on a revolving turret. These are normally designed to be *parfocal*, that is they may be interchanged without disturbing the focusing adjustment. Interchangeable eyepieces (page 45) are similarly designed, with collars of different lengths to locate their position correctly in the eyepiece tube. Typical values of objective magnification are × 10, × 40 and × 100.

It is the design of the objective lens that ultimately determines the quality of the microscope. The limit of resolution is set here since any detail that is not revealed at this stage cannot be added later by the eyepiece. Furthermore, since image detail that *is* revealed has been magnified by the time it reaches the eyepiece it should be resolved here with comparative ease despite the inferior performance of the eyepiece.

There are a number of different characteristics which define the performance of an objective. These are listed in Table 2 on page 56, and will be discussed below.

Numerical aperture and resolution

It was shown on page 23 that (assuming lens aberrations to be adequately corrected for) the limit of resolution of a lens δ is given by the expression

$$\delta = 0{\cdot}5\,\lambda/\text{N.A.}$$

where N.A., the numerical aperture of the lens, is equal to $n \sin \theta$, 2θ being the angle subtended at the object by the lens and n the refractive index of the medium in which the lens is situated*. In the compound microscope this expression must be applied to the objective lens. As we have just seen, the effective aperture of the objective is controlled by the cone of light supplied by the condenser lens, and in order to take account of the effect of the condenser on resolution we must replace the above equation by

$$\delta = \lambda/(\text{N.A.}_{(\text{cond.})} + \text{N.A.}_{(\text{obj.})})$$

For optimum resolution $\text{N.A.}_{(\text{cond.})} = \text{N.A.}_{(\text{obj.})}$ and this equation then reduces to the first one above, as it does of course for the metallurgical microscope, since the objective *is* then the condensing lens.

The higher the N.A. of the objective, the better is the resolution; so also is the image brightness, since the greater the cone angle 2θ, the greater is the amount of light which contributes to the image. The magnification produced by the objective rises as the focal length and hence the working distance decrease. The working distance is defined as the distance between the front face of the lens element closest to the specimen and the specimen itself. It must always be less than the focal length of the objective, and in the case of complex lens combinations it will be considerably less.

---

* Here we return to the conventional symbol n.

Thus higher magnification objectives will tend to have a higher N.A. (and hence, and fortunately, a better resolution), as is demonstrated by Table 2. The N.A. may of course be increased independently of the magnifying power simply by increasing the linear diameter of the objective (while keeping its focal length constant), but this would tend to be a prohibitively expensive procedure. A further method of increasing the N.A. would be to increase n rather than θ. This idea is the basic of the oil immersion objective discussed on pages 41–3.

Depth of field and curvature of field

While a high N.A. is in general beneficial, it does carry the drawback that the depth of field is decreased. This was discussed on page 27 and the dependence of the depth of field on $1/(N.A.)^2$ noted. This may also be seen from Table 2.

Curvature of field is another lens defect wherein the image is formed on a curved rather than a flat surface, and hence cannot all be in focus at the same time. In the past, attempts to overcome this were based on a general sacrifice in image sharpness, which was usually an unsatisfactory compromise. There are now objectives which are specially designed to increase the flatness of field, usually in conjunction with a matched eyepiece, although these are naturally rather more expensive.

Types of objective

The various kinds of objective that are available are classified according to their degree of correction for chromatic aberration, since this is usually the most severe of all the lens defects, although other aberrations are usually corrected at the same time.

(a) *Achromats*

These are the simplest and cheapest type of objective lens combination, and consist of one or more achromatic doublets (fig. 2.6 (*a*) and (*b*)). They are corrected for primary chromatic aberration—i.e. two colours, usually red and blue, are brought into focus in the same plane; the remaining colours are focused only approximately at this distance. Since spherical aberration is different for different wave lengths, this can be corrected for only one wavelength, corresponding to yellow/green. This performance is the minimum acceptable for reasonable microscopy, and achromats are widely used in student microscopes and those used for routine observations, where only moderate N.A. and resolution are required.

(b) *Apochromats*

These are corrected for chromatic aberration for three colours (red, green and blue) and for spherical aberration for two colours. Such a high degree of correction necessitates a large number of lens components, fig. 2.6 (c), and hence apochromats are very expensive. For this reason their main application comes in studies where high resolution is called for, and in colour photomicrography.

(c) *Fluorites (semi-apochromats)*

Materials other than glass may be used for making lenses and one of these is the naturally occurring mineral, fluorite (now available in synthetic form also). Objectives which use a substantial number of fluorite components are known as semi-apochromats, and usually come somewhere in between achromats and apochromats, both in performance and in cost. Thus they represent a useful compromise for fairly serious work, and in addition possess the ability to produce enhanced image contrast with certain kinds of material.

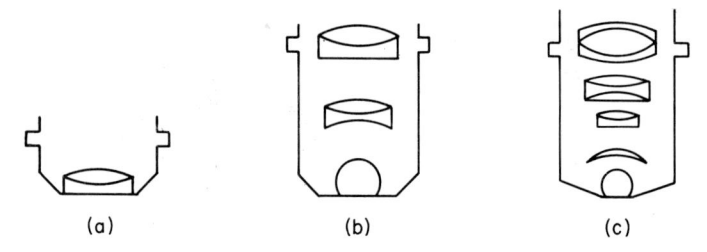

Fig. 2.6. Types of objective (a) low power achromat, (b) high power achromat, (c) high power apochromat (oil immersion).

The immersion objective

The apochromat shown in fig. 2.6 (c) is of the oil immersion type. The primary lens component is a hemisphere with the space between its flat face and the specimen filled with oil of the same refractive index.

The immersion oil fulfils two functions. Firstly it increases the N.A. of the lens ($n \sin \theta$), and hence leads to better resolution (page 27). For an air objective ($n = 1$) the maximum value of N.A. that can be obtained is 0·95. Using an oil of refractive index $n = 1·5$, the maximum value of the N.A. is about 1·4 (the value of θ is not quite the same), although values of 1·2 or 1·3 are more common.

In order to bring about an improvement in resolution, any medium for which n is greater than 1 could in principle be used. However a further benefit accrues when the medium is chosen so that its refractive index exactly equals that of the lens material. In this case the specimen may be so positioned that no spherical aberration is produced by the first lens. This is illustrated in fig. 2.7. The solid circle in fig. 2.7 (a) represents a glass sphere of radius r, and refractive index n. The dotted circles represent spheres of radii r/n and nr. These latter spheres are referred to as aplanatic surfaces. They have the property that *all* the rays emerging from a point such as O on the inner dotted sphere, after refraction at the surface of the real sphere give a virtual image at O'. This image is thus free from all spherical aberration.

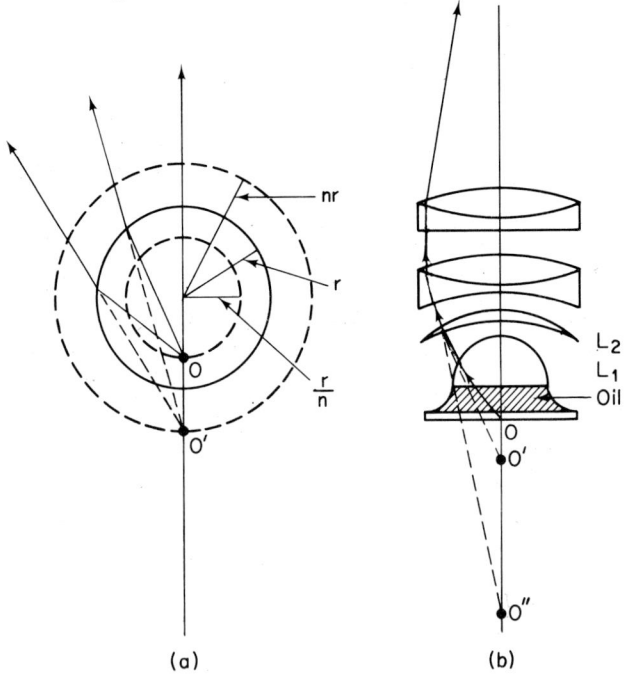

Fig. 2.7. (a) Aplanatic points, O and O', for refraction through the spherical surface of radius r, (b) Oil immersion lens using the aplanatic principle.

Figure 2.7 (b) shows how this principle is made use of in the oil immersion lens. The object, O, cannot be embedded in the glass of the first lens L_1 and so it is immersed in a film of oil below the first lens, which has the same refractive index as the lens. The object is situated at an aplanatic point and thus the lens forms a point image of it at the other aplanatic point O'. This is arranged to be at the centre of curvature of the lower face of a meniscus lens L_2 so that there is no refraction at this surface. It is also the aplanatic point for the upper surface of L_2, and so this lens again produces a point image, at O". In this way the lens produces considerable convergence without spherical aberration, although a substantial amount of chromatic aberration is introduced which must be corrected for by the subsequent lens elements. These also complete the process of convergence.

The long working distance objective

There are several occasions when the short working distance associated with high power objectives becomes a liability. For example in biological studies it may be desirable to be able to manipulate, and perhaps dissect, a specimen under high magnification. A working distance of 0·7 mm for a ×40 objective (Table 2) clearly does not give much scope. This limitation applies equally in metallurgy, where it may be necessary to study specimens at other than room temperature in order to investigate phase transformations,

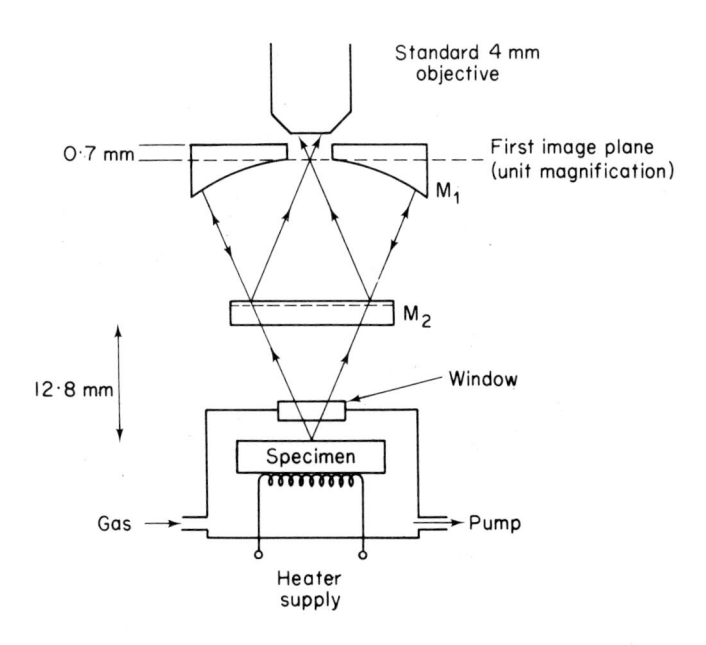

Fig. 2.8. Dyson's long working distance objective.

grain growth etc. If the specimen is to be heated to an elevated temperature then it must be protected from oxidation by means of a controlled atmosphere or vacuum environment. Hence the specimen is mounted within a small chamber and viewed through an optically worked silica window, again necessitating a fairly long working distance.

In order to overcome this difficulty, objectives containing special reflecting components have been designed. Figure 2.8 illustrates a method devised by Dyson which consists of a simple attachment which may be added to an ordinary microscope and is situated in between the objective lens and the specimen. The specimen is located near to the centre of curvature of the concave mirror, M_1, and since its image is then formed coincident with itself it is free from spherical aberration. M_2 is a half-silvered plate which is located midway between M_1 and the specimen, and reflects the light through a central hole in M_1 to form an image in the focal plane of the objective. In this way the distance between M_2 and the specimen—the working distance—may be increased from 0·7 mm up to nearly 13 mm, for a normal 4 mm objective.

Some spherical aberration will be introduced by the finite thickness both of M_2 and of the window of the hot stage which surrounds the specimen, but this may be corrected for by making the lower surface of M_2 slightly convex. A further drawback is that the half-silvered plate results in at least half of the illumination failing to reach the objective.

2.4. The eyepiece

Necessary magnification

It was shown on page 23 that two points in the object must have a minimum separation given by 0·5 λ/N.A. for them to be resolved by the objective lens. However for them subsequently to be resolved by the *eye*, their separation in the final image must be at least 0·1 mm (page 4). Thus there is a certain minimum magnification that the microscope must give in order to make full use of the resolving power of the objective.

This *necessary magnification*, M_n is given by

$$M_n = \frac{0·1}{0·5\,\lambda/\text{N.A.}}$$

where λ is in mm. For light of wavelength 550 nm (5·5 × 10^{-4} mm), near to that of the eye's maximum sensitivity, M_n comes out to be approximately 360 (N.A.). For a higher power oil immersion objective of N.A. = 1·4, M_n is, in round figures, ×500. This is working at the extreme limit of the eye and for more comfortable observation this figure may be doubled. Magnifications in excess of this lead to no gain in the information content of the image, and are referred to as *empty magnification*. The above derivation assumes that the exit pupil of the microscope eyepiece is no greater than the pupil of the eye; otherwise proportionately higher values of magnification are required.

Typical eyepiece magnifications are ×5, ×10, ×15 and ×20, and hence by combining a ×100 objective with a ×20 eyepiece a total magnification of ×2000 could in principle be obtained. Why then have a ×20 eyepiece when a ×10 eyepiece coupled with a ×100 objective can give all the useful magnification required? The answer is that if a given magnification is obtained using the maximum power objective together with a low power eyepiece then both the resulting field of view, and depth of field, will be unnecessarily restricted. Thus an objective should be selected whose N.A. is just adequate to give the desired resolution and the remainder of the magnification then made up using a sufficiently high-powered eyepiece.

Eyepiece design

Although the eyepiece functions essentially as a simple magnifying glass, in practice a compound eyepiece consisting of a couple of lenses is always used. This introduces several advantages. By careful control of focal lengths and lens separations both spherical and chromatic aberrations may be minimized (page 10). The field of view of the microscope may also be increased significantly, as shown in fig. 2.9. The effect of introducing the second lens L_F, known as the field lens, is to bend into the eyepiece rays from the objective which would otherwise have missed it. If placed as

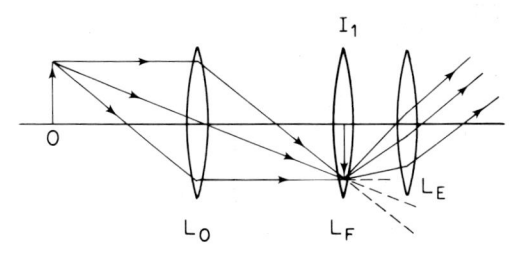

Fig. 2.9. Action of a field lens.

shown, in the plane of I_1, the field lens would have no effect on the magnification. In practice, however, its location is to one side or other of this plane, depending on the type of eyepiece used.

There are many variations on eyepiece design. The most frequently used is probably the Huygens or negative eyepiece, fig. 2.10 (a). The primary image I_1 is formed between the two lenses and a diaphragm placed in this plane serves both to provide a clean edge to the field of view and to support a transparent graticule in the image plane in order to permit measurements to be made on the image. A disadvantage of this design is that the field lens causes a slight reduction in the magnification of I_1, compared to that produced initially by the objective, and this must be allowed for when measurements are taken, unless the graticule is calibrated separately.

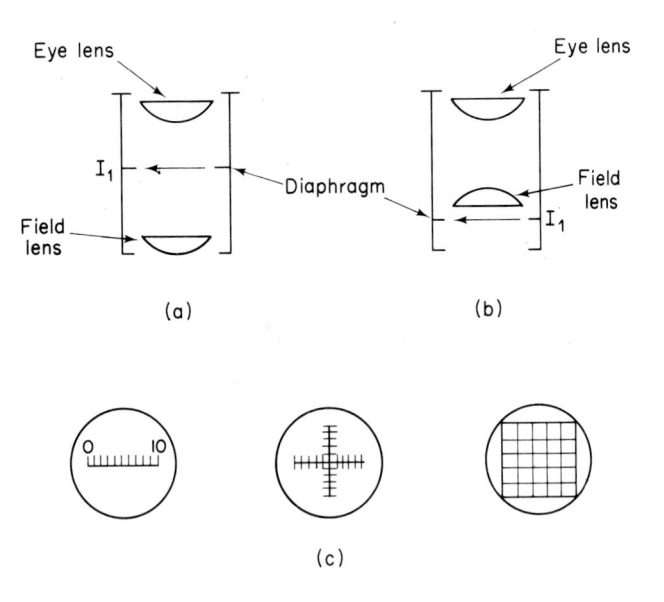

Fig. 2.10. (a) Huygens eyepiece (b) Ramsden eyepiece (c) graticules for use with such eyepieces.

The alternative is to use a Ramsden, or positive, eyepiece, fig. 2.10 (b). (It is this type which is illustrated in fig. 2.2.) In this case I_1 is formed before the field lens, although it is still just inside the focal plane of the eyepiece lens as it is with the Huygens type. This is the preferred type for measurements on the image since any change in magnification produced by the field lens acts equally on the graticule, and different graticules are easily interchanged. Examples of some of the types of graticule used are shown in fig. 2.10 (c). Often some form of movable vernier scale is incorporated with the lenses whereupon the whole becomes known as a micrometer eyepiece.

In addition to the types already mentioned there are compensating eyepieces (which may be either positive or negative) which are overcorrected for chromatic aberration in order to allow for lack of perfect correction in the objective, projection eyepieces, which form a real image which may then be photographed (below), and binocular eyepieces, which have already been discussed on page 35.

2.5. Photography and micrometry

Photography

Very often it is desirable to obtain a permanent record of the microstructure being studied. Although sketching by hand is still the method most likely to be encountered by the student, it has now largely been replaced by photography in most research and industrial work.

Apart from ensuring that an even and intense illumination is provided, the only alteration needed to the microscope design comes at the eyepiece. Since the eye is itself equivalent to a miniature camera, one method of photographing the image would be to locate a small camera, focused for infinity, in place of the eye. However the size of the image on the resulting negative would be extremely small, and only restricted enlargement would be possible, due to the graininess of the film.

The more usual method is to adjust the microscope so that a *real* final image is formed, which may then be focused either on to a screen for direct viewing, or on to a photographic emulsion. Reference to fig. 1.6 shows that, in its normal adjustment, the microscope forms a *virtual* final image since the eyepiece is so positioned that the primary image I_1 falls within its focal plane. If the eyepiece is displaced outwards by an amount sufficient to bring I_1 outside this plane, then a real and (with respect to the object) upright image will then be formed. The eyepiece is then being used in just the same way as the objective and as shown in fig. 1.1. Special projection eyepieces are manufactured with this aim in mind. Some designs incorporate a beam-splitting prism so that visual observation of the microstructure can take place during photography.

Micrometry

While the primary function of the microscope is to reveal the microstructure, a secondary concern is often to measure or to count the details revealed.

Two main techniques for measurement exist. The first type involves comparison of the object to be measured with some fixed scale such as a graticule located within the eyepiece. For accurate determinations the graticule must first be calibrated against a scale placed in the plane of the object. This method is rather difficult to apply if the object happens to be moving over the field of view, as might happen with some biological specimens.

A more recent method (imported from astronomy) that does not suffer from this limitation involves a technique known as 'image shearing'. A beam splitter is employed to produce two images of the object to be measured, and is adjusted until the two images move from perfect coincidence to the point where they just fail to overlap at all. The amount of adjustment required gives a measure of the size of the object. Again calibration against a known scale is desirable.

Various statistical treatments and sampling procedures have been developed in order to extract the appropriate data, such as grain or particle sizes, shapes and distribution, from the various types of microstructure, while the operation of an image-analysing computer, which does the job automatically, is described in Chapter 8.

2.6. *Specimen preparation*

The purpose of specimen preparation is to modify and mount the specimen in such a way that the microscope will reveal as much information as possible about its microstructure. The range of materials studied is immense, ranging from biological tissues and botanical specimens, through textiles and plastics, to ceramics, minerals and metals. The treatment of these various substances is well documented in specialist books on the subject. Thus here it will suffice briefly to mention the two most important categories, of biological and metallurgical specimens.

Biological specimens

Biological material, unless it is very thick, is usually sufficiently transparent to be examined in the transmission microscope. Thus it is normally studied in the form of a thin section cut using a microtome. In order to preserve the structure of very soft materials during sectioning they may be freeze-dried, or embedded in some material such as paraffin wax. Section thicknesses usually lie in the range 1–30 μm, although some materials may be cut as thin as 20 nm, using a sophisticated type of mechanical microtome.

The next major operation is usually staining. Many specimens are fairly uniformly transparent, so there is little recognizable contrast between different parts of the microstructure. Stains are chemical reagents which react selectively with different features to produce differences in colour or in light-absorbing power. An example of this is shown in fig. 2.11. Finally the specimen is mounted on a glass slide and protected by a cover glass. Refraction within the latter introduces a certain amount of chromatic and spherical aberration and high N.A. objectives (of the non-immersion variety) are corrected for this, providing that a cover glass of precisely the right thickness is employed. For N.A.s below about 0·5 this consideration is not critical.

Metallurgical specimens

Specimens such as metals, which must be studied using reflected

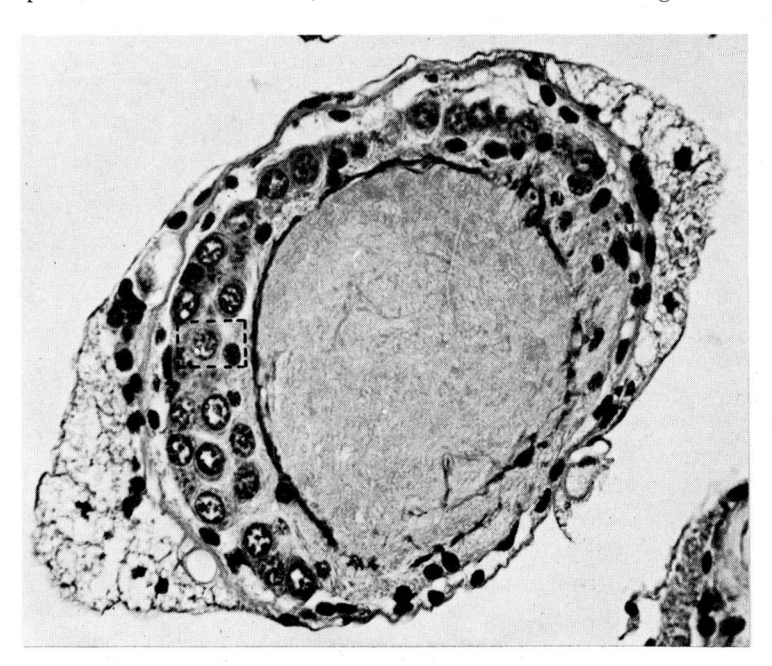

Fig. 2.11 (*a*). Stained transverse section through a ventricular ganglion from the desert locust ; optical micrograph, × 450.

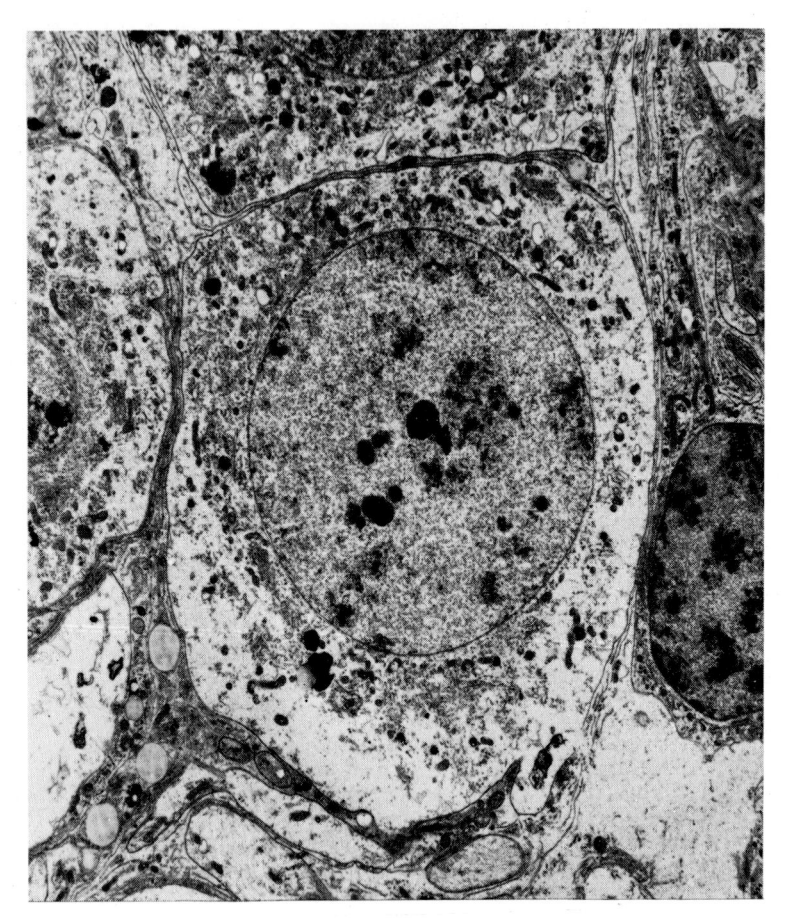

Fig. 2.11 (b). Electron micrograph of a region similar to that indicated in (a), ×2700. M. Anderson.

light, require an equally thorough preparation in order that their microstructure may be revealed. The first requirement, arising out of the limited depth of focus of the optical microscope, is that the specimen should be flat, in order that the entire field of view is in focus at the same time. More important, the surface must initially be highly polished and reflective. This is merely equivalent to saying that it must also be flat down to the sub-micrometre level, since high reflectivity arises out of the absence of surface steps and irregularities which could otherwise scatter the incident light. The reason for this condition is that image contrast depends on the intensity of the light reflected from the finally prepared metal surface, and must not be obscured by effects due to surface irregularities which are unrelated to the underlying microstructure.

A typical procedure is that a sample about 10 mm in cross section is cut off, filed smooth, and then mounted in a thermosetting resin for ease in subsequent handling. A perfectly smooth surface is produced by grinding down on a series of emery papers of increasing fineness, followed by polishing either electrolytically, or mechanically on a rotating disc covered by a slick of abrasive powder such as alumina. The polished surface thereby produced is generally featureless under the microscope (fig. 2.12 (a)) unless certain non-metallic constituents are present in the metal ; for example, graphite in cast iron shows up as dark areas.

Finally the specimen surface is subjected to selective chemical attack using an etching reagent. This has the effect of delineating the microstructural features at the surface of the specimen. For example, in a pure metal, or single phase alloy, the grain structure can be revealed. The grain boundaries are regions of higher energy than the grain interior (being departures from the ideal atomic structure) and hence tend to be attacked preferentially by the action of the etch, fig. 2.12 (b). The resulting grooves scatter the light sideways so that some of it fails to re-enter the objective, and hence the grain boundaries appear in the visual image as dark lines, figs. 2.12 (b), (d).

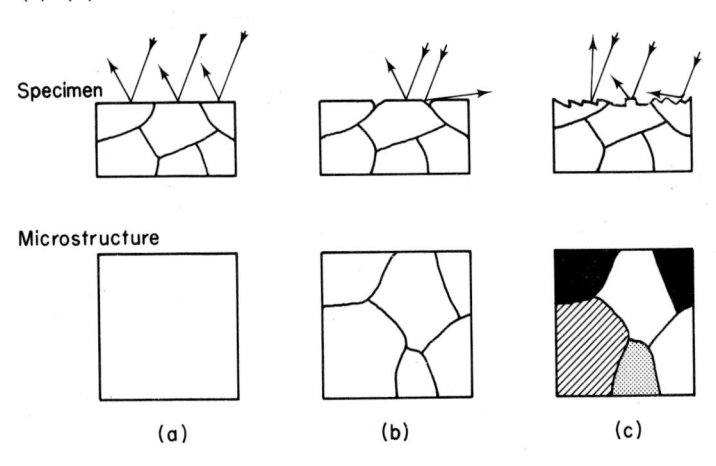

Fig. 2.12 (a), (b), (c). Effect of etching to reveal the grain structure of a metal. The upper sketches represent cross sections through the specimen; the lower ones the corresponding microstructures seen on their upper surface. (a) polished specimen showing no microstructure, (b) grain boundary etching, compare with (d), (c) grain etching, compare with (e).

(d)

(e)

Fig. 2.12 (d) micrograph of grain boundaries in iron, ×100, and (e) microstructure of α-brass showing grain contrast and annealing twins, ×100. *J. J. Knight.*

(a)

(b)

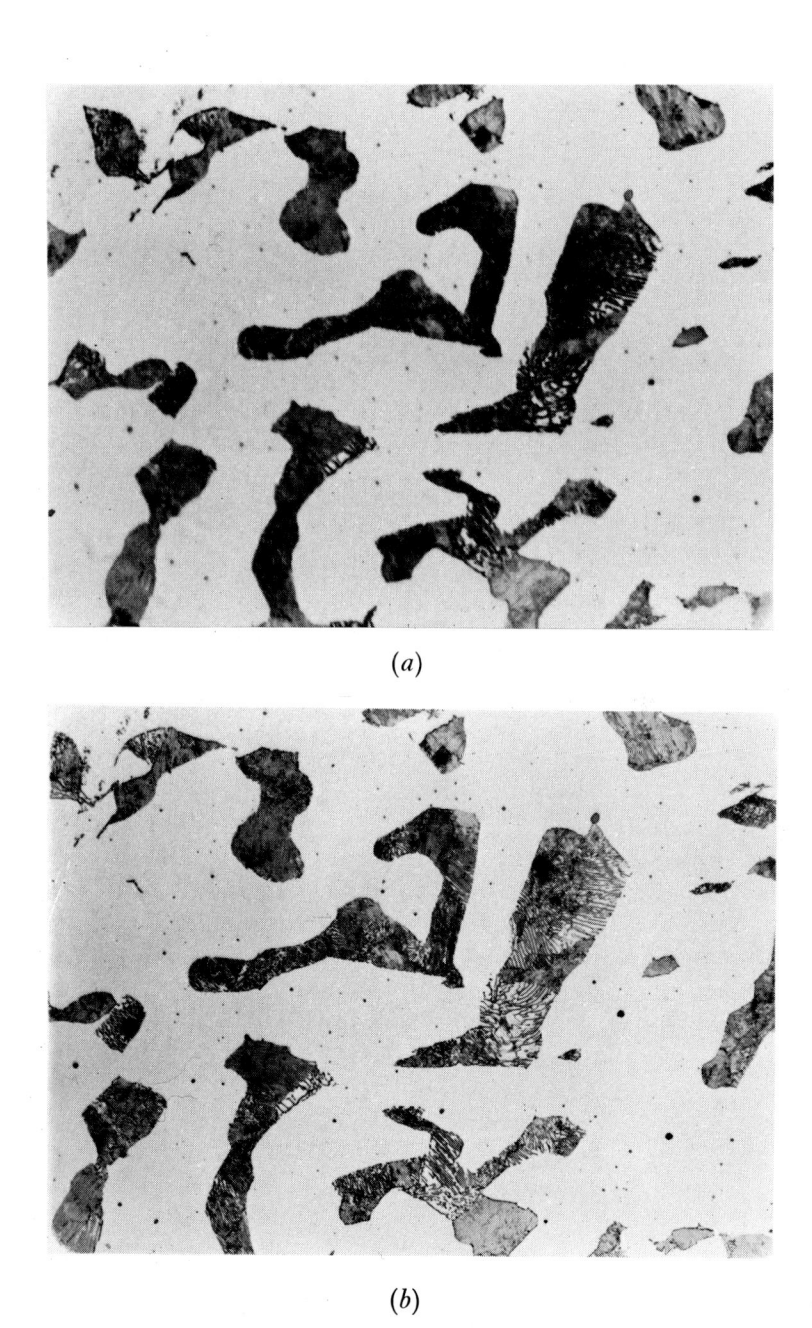

Fig. 2.13. Microstructure of a medium carbon steel showing regions of pearlite, ×360. (a) N.A. = 0·35, (b) N.A. = 0·65; note the improvement in resolution.

In some cases the grain surface is itself attacked in an irregular manner, the rate at which material is removed from the surface depending on the crystallographic orientation of the specimen, resulting in a faceted surface configuration similar to that shown in fig. 2.12 (c). Those grains that are so oriented that they do not reflect light back into the objective appear dark in the image, figs. 2.12 (c), (e). In the latter micrograph there are several instances of the parallel-sided regions known as annealing twins. These are regions of the grain possessing different, but specific, misorientations to the rest of the grain, giving abrupt alterations in contrast. In a very few materials the positions of dislocations may be detected by the characteristic pits produced by the etch at the point where the dislocation intersects the metal surface.

In alloys where more than one phase is present, differential attack or staining of the different phases is responsible for producing contrast between them. This is well illustrated in the case of a constitutent of steel known as pearlite which consists of alternate layers of ferrite (almost pure iron) and cementite (iron carbide). Using the etching reagent nital (a 2 per cent solution of nitric acid in ethanol), the ferrite is preferentially attacked and hence the cementite phase is left standing ' proud ' on the surface. This causes it to show up as dark lines, since the protruding plates scatter the incident light, fig. 2.13. Both ferrite and cementite occur separately, as well as in the pearlite form ; they are then difficult to distinguish using nital, since both are etched to the same straw-like colour. In this case it is necessary to etch with boiling sodium picrate, which stains the cementite a dark colour. In a similar way, using different etching procedures, it would be possible to bring out the grain boundaries in a similar way to fig. 2.12 (d).

In addition to such studies of the internal microstructure of the material in the form of an etched section, surface effects such as the slip bands produced by mechanical deformation can be observed directly by the surface relief produced. An example of this sort of contrast is shown later in connection with fig. 3.8.

2.7. *Using the microscope*
Resolution

Figures 2.13 (a) and (b) illustrate the control that numerical aperture exerts over resolution. In certain regions of fig. 2.13 (a) (N.A. = 0·35) it is impossible to resolve the spacing in between the cementite plates, whereas in fig. 2.13 (b) (N.A. = 0·65) it is quite easy. Ultimately the resolution limit of the optical microscope comes out to be just less than 200 nm for an objective of N.A. 1·4 using green light of wavelength 500 nm. Some improvement over this could be gained by using a blue or violet filter, since the wavelength is then reduced to about 400–450 nm. Disadvantages of this are that the eye is much less sensitive to radiation of this wavelength (although this may not be true of the photographic emulsion used), and that the objective lens is corrected for aberration primarily for green light. A further improvement can be obtained using ultraviolet radiation (of wavelength down to about 200 nm), but the practical difficulties are considerable (page 85).

Depth of field

When a high magnification objective is being used the depth of field is not very much greater than the resolution limit. While this is a slight disadvantage in metallography, since the specimen surface must be accurately level, it can be turned to advantage in biological studies. Since only a thin section of the specimen can be in sharp focus at any one time, successive layers can be imaged simply by varying the fine control of the microscope. The remainder of the specimen then causes only a general diffusion of the illuminating light, although if the specimen is too thick this will begin to obscure detail. A good working rule is that the specimen thickness should not exceed ten times the resolution sought.

A further extension of this 'optical sectioning' technique is the measurement of distances normal to the plane of the specimen. The objective is focused first onto the top and then onto the bottom of the feature whose depth is required, and this dimension is measured by the corresponding movement of the fine focus control, which is calibrated.

Interpretation

The correct interpretation of what is seen under the microscope is again mainly a matter of experience. To a large extent it depends on getting the correct illuminating and contrast conditions and, particularly in metallurgical specimens, in realizing that the structures are being viewed in section.

The recognition of image artefacts is an important aspect. In the case of metallurgical specimens these may be scratches, inadequately removed during the polishing procedure, small inclusions of the abrasive material, resulting from inadequate washing, or pitting and staining due to faulty etching. All of these can be mistaken for, or obscure, real features in the microstructure, and it is often a good idea to examine the specimen before etching in order to check for their presence.

Finally it might be useful to dispel a misconception that often follows the microscopical examination of living material, such as pond life. A most striking feature of such studies is the apparently frenzied activity of these tiny creatures. In fact this is a complete illusion brought about by the magnifying power of the microscope. For example, a small animal that is moving at, say, 1 mm in a second, will, under a magnification of ×1000, *appear* to be moving at a rate of one metre per second. It isn't, though !

Table 2. Typical objective lens characteristics (after Birchon)

Type	Magnification	Focal length in mm	Working distance in mm	N.A.	Resolution limit (in μm)*	Depth of field (in μm)*
Achromat	×10	16	6	0·28	1·0	10
	×20	8	1	0·50	0·55	3·5
	×40	4	0·7	0·65	0·42	1·5
Apochromat	×20	8	0·9	0·65	0·42	1·4
	×40	4	0·15	0·95	0·29	0·7
	×100 (oil immersion)	2·43	0·27	1·32	0·21	0·35
Fluorite	×100 (oil immersion)	1·8	0·14	1·30	0·21	0·37

* for light of wavelength 550 nm.

CHAPTER 3
advanced techniques in optical microscopy

3.1. *Image contrast*

Introduction

IT is now necessary to take a more rigorous look at the various means by which image contrast is produced. Figure 3.1 shows the several ways in which information can be carried by light. Figure 3.1 (*a*) shows two waves which are identical in all respects except that the *amplitude* of one is twice that of the other. The human eye might be able to differentiate between them if they were seen side by side on the basis of their different brightness (or intensity, which is proportional to the square of the amplitude). Several examples of

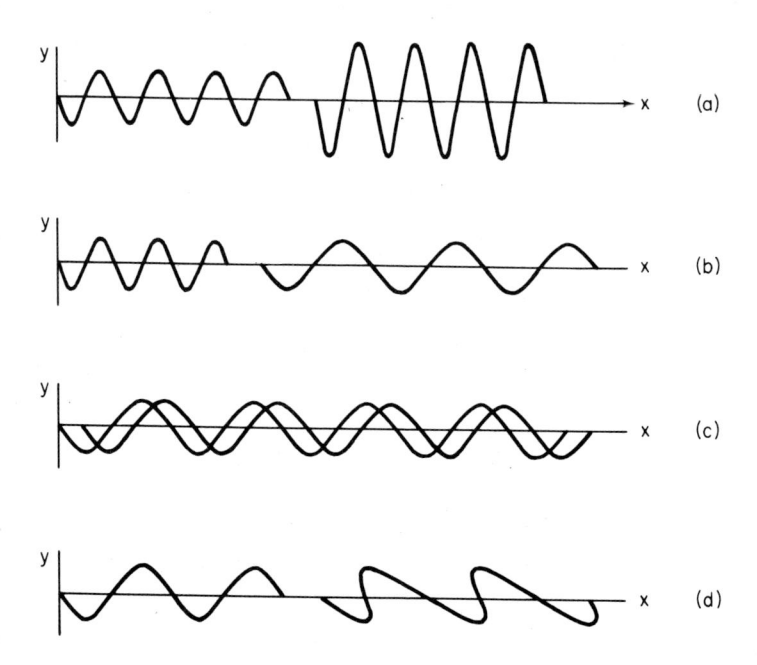

Fig. 3.1. The kinds of information carried by light waves (*a*) amplitude (*b*) wavelength (*c*) phase (*d*) plane of polarization. Differences in these can be used to provide image contrast.

this type of image contrast, which is termed amplitude contrast, have been encountered already.

In fig. 3.1 (b) the difference between the two waves is solely in their wavelength, λ. This again is registered by the eye (at least in most people) as a difference in colour.

The situation shown in fig. 3.1 (c) is new. This time the two waves have the same amplitude and wavelength, but differ in *phase* (c.f. page 13). Phase differences cannot be perceived by the eye and hence cannot lead directly to image contrast. This may be verified by considering two identical objects, one viewed directly, the other through a sheet of glass. Since light travels more slowly in glass than in air, the light passing through the glass would be retarded in phase by an amount depending on its thickness and refractive index. However the two objects would not differ in appearance.

Finally there may be a difference in the plane of polarization of the light, fig. 3.1 (d). Normally the transverse vibrations that characterize the light wave occur in all the possible directions normal to the direction of propagation of the wave. However, if these vibrations are confined to one particular plane, then the light is described as being *polarized*. Again, the human eye is unable to detect differences in polarization, although it appears that certain insects and animals can.

(a)

(b)

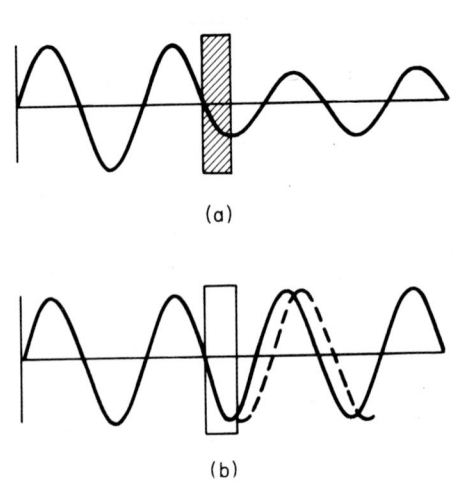

Fig. 3.2. Comparison of amplitude contrast and phase contrast. (a) Amplitude contrast, resulting from absorption of light; (b) phase contrast resulting from a difference in optical path length.

If *all* the light that is incident on the specimen leaves *unchanged*, enters the objective, and is finally collected in the image plane, then the field of view can contain no image contrast related to the specimen. It is only when the light forming different regions of the image differs in one of the ways outlined above, that any image detail can possibly be produced. The various kinds of image contrast that occur are discussed below.

Amplitude contrast

Amplitude contrast, leading to difference in image brightness, is the most commonly encountered form of contrast. Most of the ways in which it can arise have already been discussed and may be summarized below. They may be divided into two distinct classes : (*a*) where a portion of the incident light is *deflected* to such an extent that it fails to enter the objective. This is the situation described in fig. 2.12, where some of the incident light is reflected away by surface steps. The analogous situation in transparent specimens would occur when an inclusion of material with refractive index very different from that of the material in which it lay, again substantially deflected the incident light ; (*b*) where a portion of the incident light is *absorbed* in the specimen. This situation is represented in fig. 3.2 (*a*). After being transmitted through an absorbing region, which might be part of a heavily stained biological cell, the amplitude of the incident light is reduced to a significant extent. In this way image contrast would be revealed to the eye. The analogous case in a metal would be, for example, a particle of graphite found in cast iron (referred to on page 51) and which would appear black even in the unetched specimen due to the preferential absorption of light. (Note, even a very highly polished metal surface does absorb a small amount of light although the majority is reflected.)

Very fine microstructural detail, such as small surface steps or tilts, or the boundaries of cell structure, will produce negligible ' reflection ' or ' refraction ' contrast. However such features will *diffract* light to a certain extent, the finer the detail the greater the divergence of the diffracted beams (page 23). In principle, if the light is diffracted sideways to a sufficient extent, it could miss the objective and hence could also give rise to amplitude contrast. Using the conventional ' bright field ' conditions of illumination, wherein the undeviated incident beam contributes directly to the final image, this effect is normally too small to be observed. However a number of the sophisticated techniques to be described in this chapter are designed directly to make these subtle diffraction effects visible to the eye, and hence to render such fine microstructural details detectable.

Colour contrast

Colour contrast can also arise in two distinct ways. The first is the familiar everyday occurrence whereby an object illuminated with white light only reflects or transmits light of certain wavelengths, the remainder being absorbed : hence it appears coloured. This property is encountered with objects which are chemically stained, or with those which possess self-colour such as certain non-metallic inclusions found in steel.

The second mode of colour contrast arises when the object absorbs light of one wavelength and then re-emits light of another (and usually longer) wavelength. This is known as *fluorescence*, and is discussed further on page 85.

Phase contrast

Figure 3.2 (*b*) shows a similarly illuminated object, but this time it is unstained. It is assumed that the material of which it is composed has a refractive index different from that of its surroundings. Hence the light wave emerging from it will be shifted in phase relative to the incident light. However, if it is also assumed that, unstained, it is perfectly transparent, then the amplitudes of the two waves will still be the same, and hence the eye can detect no contrast. In

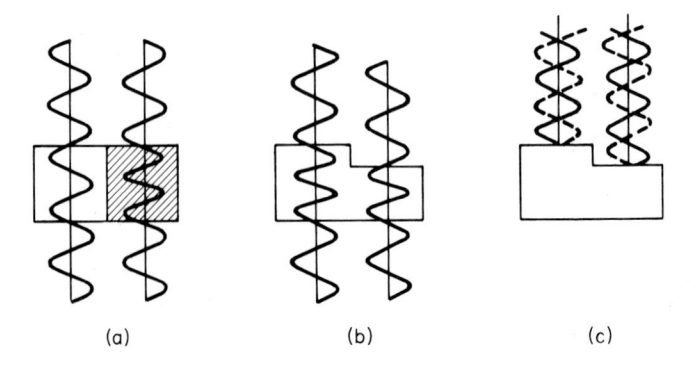

Fig. 3.3. Illustrating how phase differences may arise: (*a*) two materials of different refractive index (*b*) difference in thickness (*c*) (in reflected light microscopy) difference in surface level.

practice of course no material can be perfectly transparent ; similarly there will be some accompanying phase difference when light is differentially absorbed by different substances. However it is simpler to treat these as two quite separate cases.

Figure 3.3 shows the several ways in which phase differences can arise :

(a) as above where two materials possess different refractive indices,
(b) where the path length through the material varies,
(c) in the case of specimens studied in reflected light, where changes in surface height occur.

Comparison of amplitude contrast and phase contrast

It is instructive to consider the nature of the changes in amplitude or in phase, illustrated in fig. 3.2. In practice, the absorption of light (fig. 3.2 (a)) can be regarded as its being scattered or diffracted within the material in various directions other than that of the direct beam. This diffracted light is in fact exactly π (or $\lambda/2$) out of phase with the incident light. The effect of this is shown in fig. 3.4. The incident wave (1) has amplitude A_1. The diffracted light is represented by a single wave, D, and its total amplitude is A_D. These two waves then interfere to give a resultant (2) which can be seen to have a reduced amplitude A_2 which, numerically, equals $A_1 - A_D$.

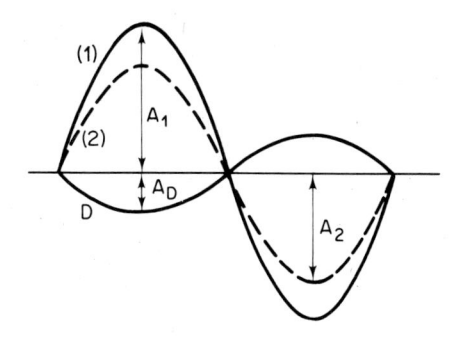

Fig. 3.4. Amplitude contrast: the resultant wave, (2), may be thought of as the sum of the original wave (1) and a diffracted wave, D, which is π out of phase.

Now let us consider the analogous situation when differences in phase are produced as in fig. 3.2 (b). Fig. 3.5 (a) again represents the incident wave (1) with amplitude A_1. After interaction with the specimen the resultant wave (2) is depicted with a small retardation in phase with respect to (1), but with the same amplitude. Again the difference may be attributed to some of the light being diffracted, and subtraction of (1) from (2) can be used to determine the location

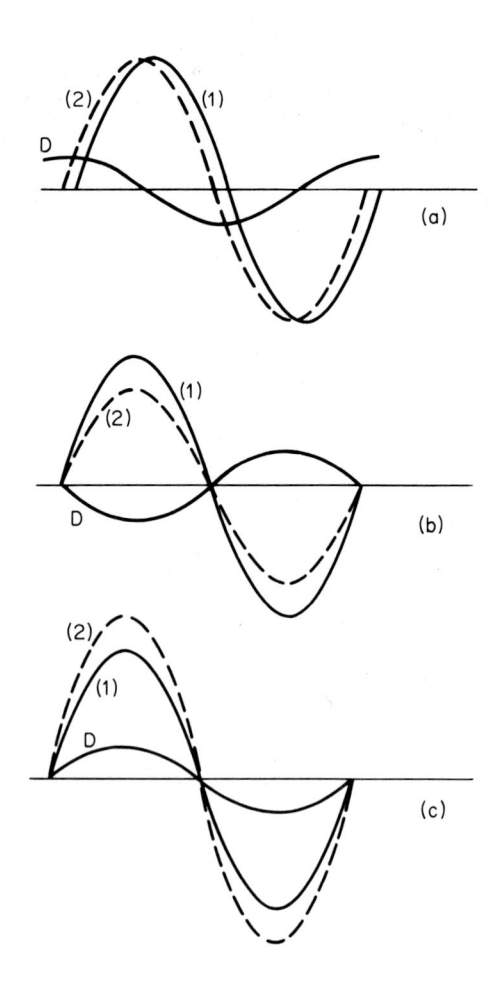

Fig. 3.5. Phase contrast: (*a*) this time D is only $\pi/2$ out of phase with (1), (*b*) the effect of retarding the phase of D by a further $\pi/2$, (*c*) the effect of advancing the phase of D by $\pi/2$. In both cases amplitude contrast is produced.

and amplitude of the diffracted wave, D. Following section 1.6, let us describe the waves (1) and (2) by the equations

$$y_1 = A_1 \sin \theta$$

and

$$y_2 = A_1 \sin (\theta + \phi)$$

where ϕ is the (small) phase difference between them. Then the diffracted wave D may be described by $y_3 = y_2 - y_1$, whereupon

$$y_3 = 2A_1 \sin \phi/2 \cos (\theta + \phi/2)$$

or, rewriting,

$$y_3 = 2A_1 \sin \phi/2 \sin (\pi/2 - \theta - \phi/2)$$

This represents a wave of amplitude $2A_1 \sin \phi/2$, and, providing ϕ is small, one whose phase differs from that of (1) or (2) by approximately $\pi/2$. Hence we can say that, to a first approximation, providing the phase difference between (1) and (2) is only small, the diffracted wave D is $\pi/2$ out of phase with (1). This is shown in fig. 3.5 (a).

In practice the waves (1) and D are separated at the specimen, take different routes through the optical system, and, when they are recombined in the image, interfere to produce (2). No amplitude contrast will be observed between (2) and a wave (1) which has passed unaltered through a different region of the specimen.

The above description refers to normal bright field illuminating conditions. In dark field microscopy (page 64) (1) is obstructed by blocking it off from the objective so that only D is allowed to form an image. This form of amplitude contrast produces bright features against a dark background, the idea being that these may be easier to detect than dark features against a bright background, as is obtained under bright field conditions. Note that if we were to obstruct D and only allow (1) through, then we could obtain no detailed imagery of the specimen (page 22).

In the phase contrast microscope, on the other hand, we merely alter the phase of the diffracted wave D, by $\pi/2$. If, as in fig. 3.5 (b), D is retarded in phase by a further $\pi/2$, the situation becomes identical to that shown in fig. 3.4. Now if the undeviated wave (1) and the phase retarded diffracted wave D are allowed to recombine in the image, they will interfere destructively so that the amplitude A_2 of their resultant is equal to $(A_1 - A_D)$, and hence the difference between (1) and (2) is now detectable by the eye. If instead D is advanced in phase by $\pi/2$ it will interfere constructively with (1) and the resultant amplitude $A_2 = (A_1 + A_D)$ will again differ significantly from A_1 as shown in fig. 3.5 (c). In this way a difference in phase is transformed into a difference in amplitude. The same effect will still be obtained to some extent even when the phase difference between (1) and (2) is not small, and D is not now initially $\pi/2$ out of phase with (1).

The limitation of amplitude contrast

Two particular instances may be cited where simple amplitude contrast fails to be adequate. The first concerns the important area of surface relief effects on metals, known as surface topography. Under normal bright field illumination, and at small numerical apertures (say, N.A. = 0·3) it is only possible to detect variations from a perfectly flat surface of 2–3°, while at larger numerical apertures such surface tilts need to be 5° or more to be rendered visible. Similarly, the minimum surface step height that can be detected is about 100 nm. A further limitation is that in any case neither the tilt angle nor the step height can actually be measured.

The second is in the biological sciences and is particularly important. Living organisms cannot very readily be studied since their inherent amplitude contrast is often very low, and staining involves killing them. This is where the phase contrast microscope has proved to be such an enormous advantage since it permits high contrast images to be obtained directly from non-stained material. However, before considering the principles involved in phase contrast and its associated techniques, we shall first consider the type of enhanced amplitude contrast that can be achieved using dark field illuminating conditions.

3.2. Dark field techniques

In these, and other techniques to be discussed later, the principle of operation is usually described in terms of the reflection microscope, partly because many of the more important applications of these techniques lie in the metallurgical field, and partly because there can be one or two additional features associated with this mode. By reference to fig. 2.2 it should be relatively simple to deduce the equivalent arrangement using transmitted light.

Oblique illumination

Figure 3.6 (a) represents, in a very schematic way, a metal surface illuminated under bright field conditions. The surface topography consists of a fairly broad surface tilt, together with a very small step, and it is possible, rather arbitrarily, to separate out two contrast effects. The tilt may give a small amount of amplitude contrast since some of the incident light reflected directly from its sloping surface misses the objective. The diffracted rays have not been considered since they will be very close to the main reflected ray. The surface step, on the other hand, is considered to be so fine that appreciable diffraction scattering will occur from it. In principle amplitude contrast will result if many of these diffracted rays pass outside the objective, although in practice it would probably not be detectable. The corresponding intensity distribution in the image is shown in the lower figure.

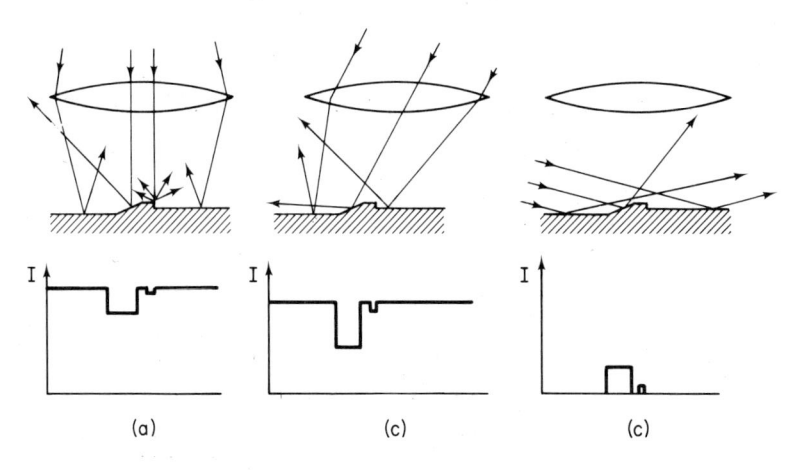

Fig. 3.6. Schematic illustration of (a) bright field, (b) oblique, and (c) dark field illumination. The corresponding intensity of light in the image plane is shown in each case.

Figure 3.6 (b) shows the effect of making the incident beam meet the surface obliquely, for example, by moving the condenser aperture off the optical axis, although several other more sophisticated methods exist. Now more of the reflected light will miss the objective, and the total level of illumination will be reduced. This effect will be proportionately greater for the surface tilt, and hence the contrast from this feature will be enhanced. The surface step may also give rise to enhanced contrast since a larger proportion of its diffracted rays will miss the objective. In effect, in these latter two cases, the surface features are thrown into shadow.

A disadvantage of this method is that the surface features must lie across the 'shadowing' direction, as drawn here, or they will not be revealed. Furthermore the full N.A. of the objective is not being utilized so that the ultimate resolution is poorer. However at its best the technique can be very nearly as sensitive as phase contrast for revealing fine surface detail.

Dark field illumination

Under true dark field conditions, the illumination is so arranged that the whole of the direct beam is reflected outside the objective, fig. 3.6 (c). Thus only light which has been deviated by reflection from surface tilts, or by diffraction, will form the image. The image contrast is thus the reverse (in the sense of exchanging light for dark) of that obtained under bright field conditions.

This technique is of particular value with transparent biological specimens where, for example, regions which contain abrupt changes in refractive index (such as fine threads, flagellae and folds in membranes) appear luminous and are readily detected, although they are invisible under bright field illumination. A familiar example of such a change in visibility on reversing the contrast is a spider's web. Viewed against a light background, such as a window, it may be invisible, but when illuminated with light from the window and viewed against a dark background it is readily detected. The ultramicroscope described on page 29, is another example of a technique relying on this method of dark field contrast to render tiny objects visible.

Opaque stop microscopy

A more versatile method of producing dark field illumination is the opaque stop technique, in which the condenser aperture is replaced by a special kind of diaphragm which consists of an opaque disc into which an annular (ring-shaped) opening has been made. The entire optical arrangement is very similar to that used in phase contrast microscopy, which is illustrated later in fig. 3.9. The effect that this has may be deduced from fig. 2.5. Here the condenser aperture, D_2, is normally used to regulate the width of the cone of light which illuminates the specimen. An annular diaphragm placed at this point allows a ring, rather than a disc, of light to be transmitted. In the plane of the specimen, at O, this has become a disc, but an image of the condenser aperture is subsequently re-formed in the rear focal plane of the objective lens. Hence all light reflected normally from the specimen surface (or transmitted directly through the specimen) must pass through this annulus, and if a second stop is placed in this position, this time consisting of an *opaque* annulus, it will intercept the whole of this light, and the eye will see nothing.

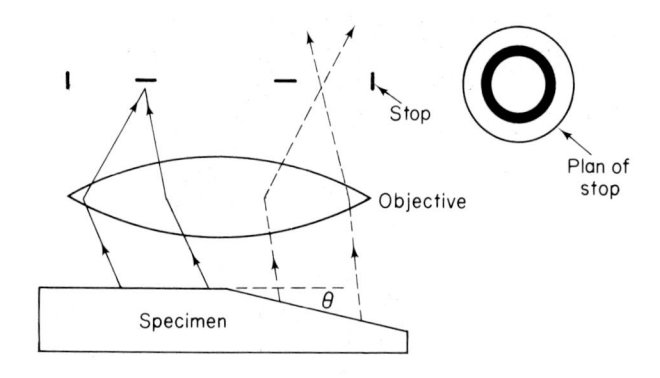

Fig. 3.7. Principle of opaque stop microscopy.

Figure 3.7 illustrates this situation and shows what happens if the specimen surface is not a horizontal flat, but contains a tilted region making an angle θ with the horizontal. Rays reflected from this region will form an image of the annulus which is displaced to one side. These will not now be intercepted by the stop and hence can proceed to form an image. Similar arguments apply to light which is diffracted to either side of the direct beam, or, in the case of specimens studied in transmitted light, undergoes refraction. However there is one modification that must be made to this simple picture in the case of the reflection microscope. In this case it is technically undesirable to locate a stop in the rear focal plane of the objective, since here it would also cut down the incident illumination too much. Hence an auxiliary lens is used to provide yet a further point which is conjugate to the condenser aperture, and it is here that the opaque stop is placed (c.f. fig. 3.9). Figure 3.8 shows a crystal of zinc which has been cleaved to expose a surface containing a number of fine steps and striations. Figure 3.8 (*a*) was taken under normal bright field conditions, while fig. 3.8 (*b*) was taken using the opaque stop technique.

The technique is extremely sensitive to small changes in surface slope, ranging from better than 1° at high magnification to about 1′

(a)

(b)

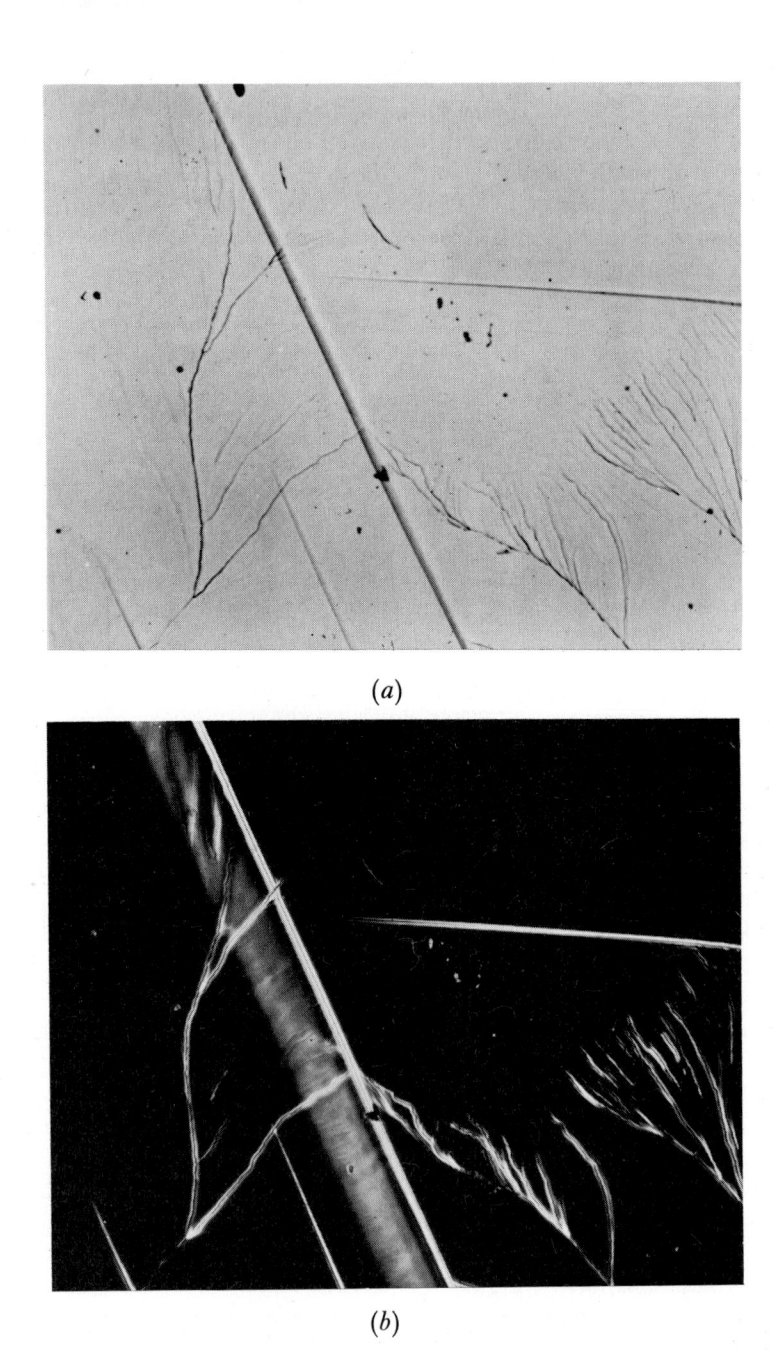

Fig. 3.8. Cleavage surface of a zinc crystal, ×100. (a) bright field illumination, (b) using opaque stop, (c) positive phase contrast, (d) negative phase contrast. B. W. Mott.

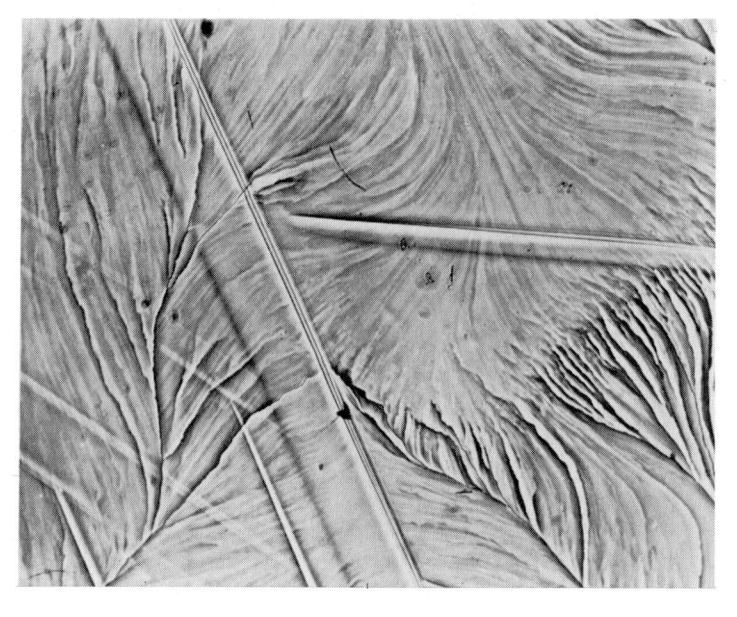

(c)

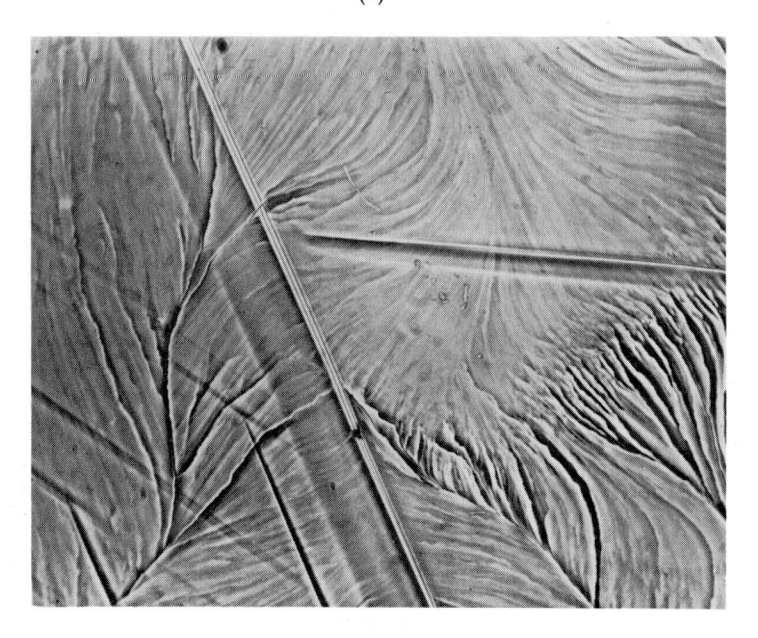

(d)

Fig. 3.8 (continued).

at low magnification, and actual measurements of the tilt angle may be made if the technique known as *schlieren illumination* is used. In this the opaque stop is displaced laterally from the image of the condenser aperture, so that the intensity of the direct beam is merely reduced to the same intensity as the diffracted beam and not completely eliminated. The amount that the stop must be moved in going from the ideal dark field condition to schlieren illumination is a measure of the tilt angle, and the arrangement may be calibrated using a perfectly flat specimen mounted on a tilting stage.

3.3 *Phase contrast microscopy*

Here we are concerned with object details which are too fine to give rise to appreciable reflection or refraction amplitude contrast, but which do give rise to diffraction, hence modifying the phase of the light incident upon them. The circumstances where this occurs were discussed on pages 60–61 and it was shown that in order to turn the phase difference into detectable amplitude contrast, the phase of the diffracted light must be advanced or retarded by $\pi/2$ relative to the undeviated beam. The opportunity to do this comes about since the diffracted beams leave the object detail in directions different from the direct beam, and, although they are all reunited in the final image, they follow a different path through the optical system of the microscope.

The principle behind the phase contrast microscope was developed in 1934 by the Dutch physicist Frits Zernike. Although Zernike was to receive the 1953 Nobel prize for physics for his invention, he found great difficulty at first in convincing manufacturers of its value (one even went so far as to say that if the method had been any good then they would have discovered it for themselves), and the technique was not in general use until about 1942.

The optical layout of the phase contrast microscope is similar to that used in the opaque stop technique : again compare with fig. 2.5. An annular diaphragm is located at the condenser aperture D_2 and its image is formed in the rear focal plane of the objective, fig. 3.9 (*a*), following the interaction of the light with the specimen. A device known as a phase plate, which differs from an opaque stop in that all regions of it are transparent to light, is located at this point. It is constructed so that there is still an annular region, exactly matching that of the image of the condenser aperture, whose optical thickness differs by $\lambda/4$ from that of the remainder of the phase plate. Light reflected directly from the specimen surface passes through this annular region, while light diffracted at the specimen is deviated away from the direct beam and most of it is transmitted through other regions of the phase plate. In this way a phase difference of $\pi/2$ is introduced between the direct and diffracted light. Once again in the case of reflected light an auxiliary lens is used to provide a further point conjugate to the condenser aperture, where the phase plate is actually located.

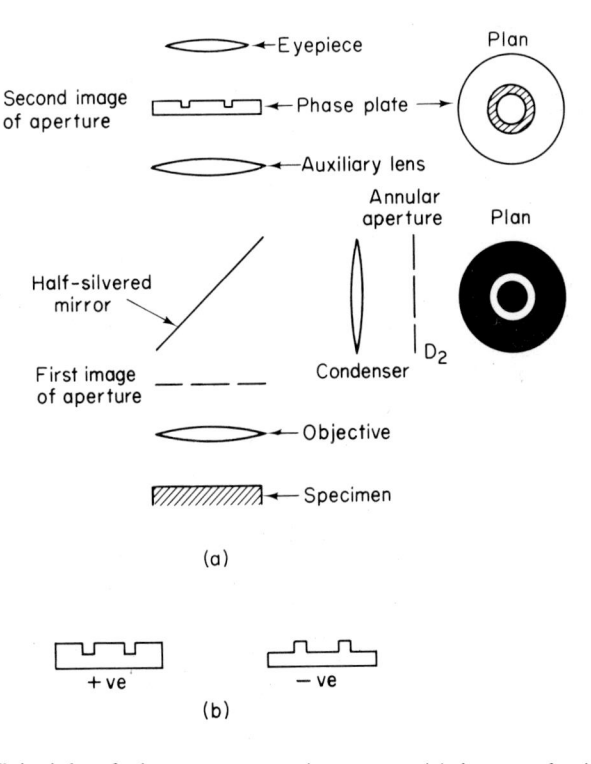

Fig. 3.9. Principle of phase contrast microscopy: (a) layout of microscope, (b) construction of phase plates.

Two kinds of phase plate may be used, and their detailed construction is shown in fig. 3.9 (b). On the left is shown a *positive* phase plate, containing an annular groove. The direct light (1) passing through this annulus is retarded in phase by a certain amount, while the diffracted light D passing through the remainder is retarded in phase by an amount $\pi/2$ greater. This corresponds to the situation shown in fig. 3.5 (b) ; destructive interference occurs between waves (1) and D from the same region of the specimen, and hence small depressions on the specimen surface appear darker than the background. Conversely, elevations appear brighter. Using the *negative* phase plate shown on the right of fig. 3.9 (*b*), the diffracted beam is advanced in phase by $\pi/2$ relative to the direct beam ; the situation shown in fig. 3.5 (*c*) applies, and the contrast is reversed. Typically the amplitude of (1) is ten times that of D. Hence it is customary to coat the annular region of the phase plate with an absorbing material, such as antimony, in order to cut down the amplitude of (1) to about the same order of magnitude as that of D. In this way the difference between $(A_1 \pm A_D)$ and A_1 may be considerably increased, leading to greater contrast.

The main application of phase contrast microscopy in metallurgy is in the study of specimens which have been lightly deformed, an example being the observation of the very fine slip traces formed during creep. In addition a number of alloys are difficult to etch to the degree needed to give good amplitude contrast, whereas a very light etch, or even the small amount of surface relief left after polishing (due to the different hardnesses of the various phases) will be sufficient to give rise to good phase contrast. Figures 3.8 (*c*) and (*d*) show the same specimen that was used to illustrate the opaque stop technique, viewed successively under positive and negative phase contrast.

The most important use of phase contrast microscopy, however, has occurred in the biological sciences, where it has become an essential technique for most serious work. Figure 3.10 compares the appearance of cell structures seen under bright field illumination and positive phase contrast. Here areas of greater refractive index appear darker than the surrounds. Since structures need not be stained, and hence killed, it is possible to study, and film, such dynamic events as cell division, and the action of drugs and other chemical and physical agents. It is also possible to measure the refractive index of substances by comparing their image contrast with that obtained from a series of mounting media of varying values of refractive index.

In metallurgical applications the sensitivity of the technique is such that the presence of surface steps 5 nm high may be detected. However once the difference in surface level exceeds $\lambda/4$ (about 150 nm) it is no longer possible to deduce from the image contrast whether the feature corresponds to an elevation or a depression. This may, however, be turned to some advantage since the magnitude of a surface feature can be judged by seeing whether or not it reverses contrast on interchanging a positive for a negative phase plate.

(a)

(b)

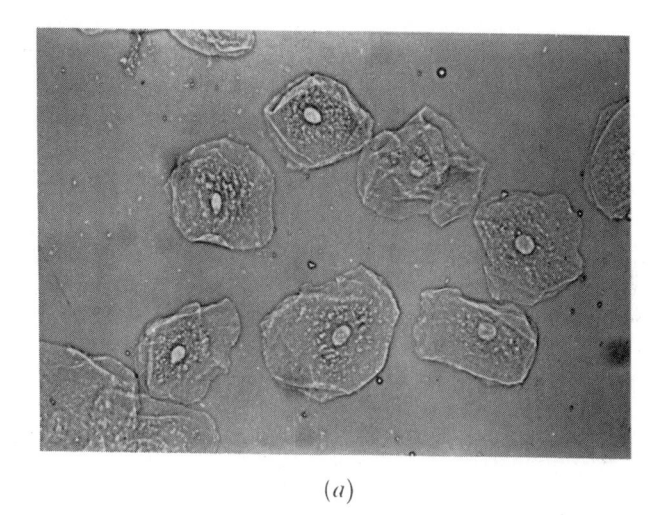

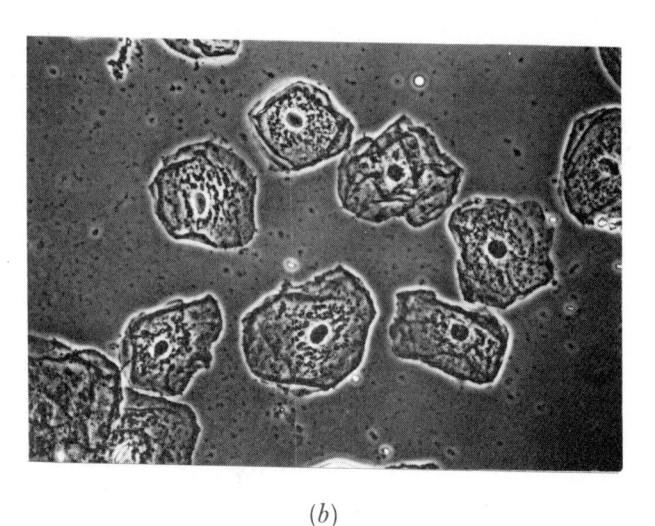

Fig. 3.10. Epithelial cells from the mucous membranes of the human mouth, ×220. (a) bright field, (b) positive phase contrast, (c) interference contrast. *Zeiss-Werkphoto*.

Unlike the opaque stop technique, phase contrast does not permit accurate measurements of surface features to be made, and the technique is more sensitive to surface steps than to tilts.

One point that should be stressed is that there is no contradiction involved in being able to detect features only a few nm in magnitude,

(c)

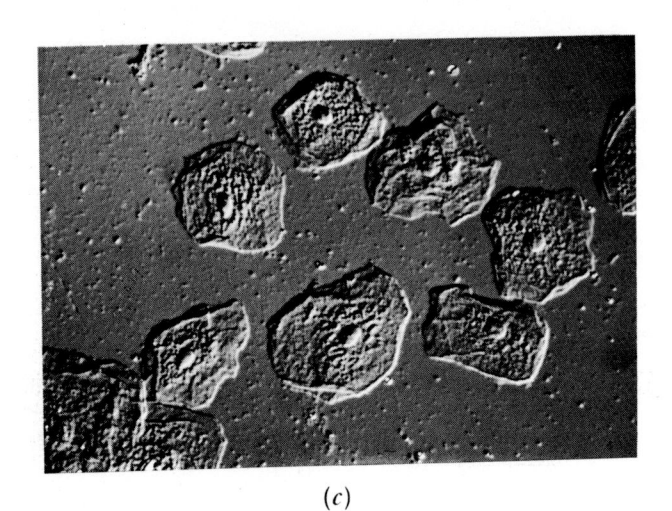

Fig. 3.10 (continued).

when the limit of resolution of the microscope is only about 200 nm. One is merely *revealing the presence* of such features; if two of them are present they must still be separated by a distance greater than the limit of resolution in order for them both to be detected.

The amount by which the phase of D may be altered is fixed in the phase contrast microscope, although it will be recalled that the original difference in phase between (1) and D is only equal to $\pi/2$ providing the overall difference in phase between (1) and (2) is very small. In practice this will not necessarily be the case of course. However, variable phase control can now be achieved using the more recently developed *interference contrast* microscopes, described in the following section, and these are gradually becoming preferred to phase contrast ones because of their greater versatility, and despite their greater complexity and price.

3.4 *Interference contrast*

The fundamental differences between phase contrast and interference contrast may be represented schematically in fig. 3.11. In the phase contrast microscope the incident light is split by fine detail in the object into a direct and a diffracted beam. The phase of the diffracted beam is then artificially changed by $\pi/2$, and the two beams then recombine in the image plane, where their interference gives rise to amplitude contrast relative to the background. In the case of interference contrast, on the other hand, the incident light

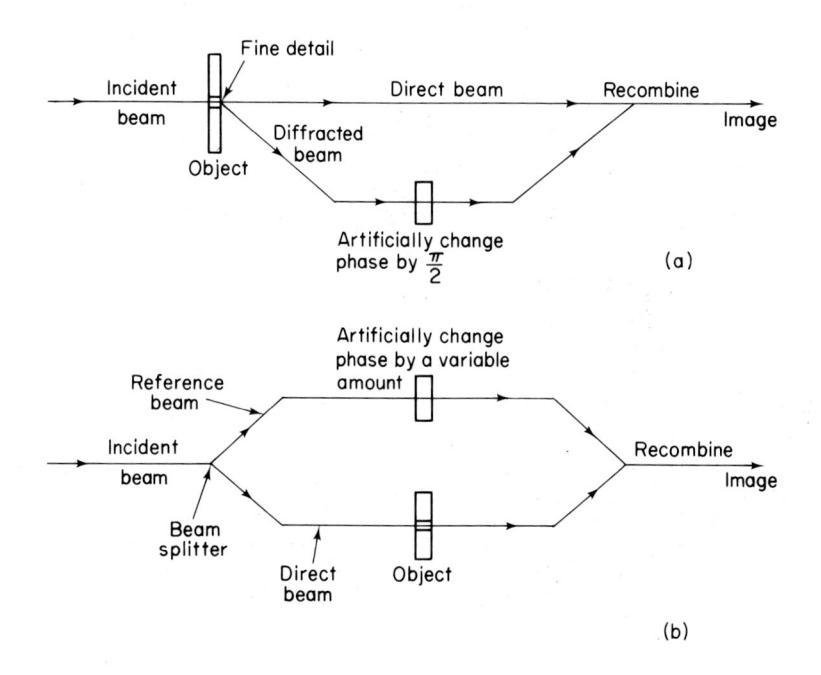

```
                    Fine detail
     Incident                    Direct beam      Recombine
     beam                                                        Image
                          Diffracted
                            beam
            Object

                          Artificially change
                          phase by π/2              (a)


                       Artificially change
                       phase by a variable
      Reference        amount
      beam
      Incident                                       Recombine
      beam                                                        Image

      Beam
      splitter
                        Direct    Object
                        beam
                                                        (b)
```

Fig. 3.11. Illustrating the difference in principle between (a) phase contrast, and (b) interference contrast.

is split into a direct beam and a reference beam before it can interact with the specimen. The phase of the reference beam is then altered by a variable amount before it is allowed to recombine with both the direct and diffracted beams produced at the specimen, and hence interfere to form an amplitude contrast image. This system allows the phase of the reference beam to be adjusted to whatever extent is required in order to produce the optimum contrast.

Several examples of what can be done using interference contrast are shown in fig. 3.12. Figure 3.12 (a) shows what happens if the phase of the reference beam R is retarded by π relative to (1). Regions of the specimen containing no microstructural detail give rise to the undeviated beam (1) and this gives perfect destructive interference when combined with R in the image plane : $(1) + R = 0$. On the other hand, regions of the specimen which diffract light significantly give rise to a beam (2), just as before, where $(2) = (1) + D$. Hence when R is recombined with (2) in the final image, the resultant is given by $(2) + R = (1) + D + R = D$. This situation is directly analogous to dark field contrast.

Alternatively we could produce the situation shown in fig. 3.12 (b). Here the difference in phase between (1) and (2) is not necessarily small, and D differs in phase from (1) by an amount not equal to $\pi/2$, say θ. This time we control the phase of R such that when it interferes with the undeviated beam (1), the resultant, S, differs in phase from (1) by this same angle θ. Thus $(1)+R = S$. Now when R interferes with the beam (2) we get $(2)+R = (1)+D+R = S+R$. Hence the intensity of the light forming the image of the diffracting detail is proportional to $(A_S+A_R)^2$, while that of the background is proportional to $(A_S)^2$. This situation is directly analogous to positive phase contrast. In a similar way contrast analogous to negative phase contrast, and to oblique illumination may also be produced, merely by selecting the appropriate phase change in R. As with phase contrast, a monochromatic light source is normally used, although if white light is used instead some quite brilliant colour contrast effects may be produced.

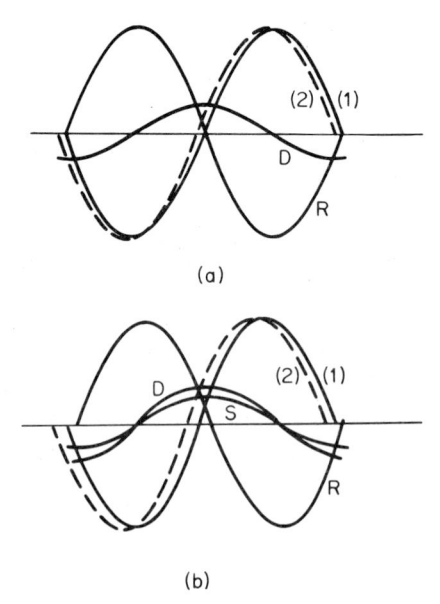

Fig. 3.12. Interference contrast: (a) contrast similar to dark field contrast, (b) contrast similar to phase contrast.

Quite striking 'relief' effects may also be produced using this technique, and comparison of figs. 3.10 (b) and (c) shows the same specimen imaged with phase contrast and interference contrast; the image is much sharper in the latter case, and the bright halo that usually surrounds features revealed using phase contrast is no longer present. Besides its much greater versatility, interference contrast is much more sensitive than phase contrast to gradual changes in microstructure (and hence, for example, reveals surface tilts as well as abrupt steps), and can be used to give equally good contrast with the coarser features as well. Phase contrast is less sensitive in this respect since the divergence of the diffracted beams from coarse features is much less than from fine, and hence they are much less likely to avoid the annular phase-changing region of the phase plate.

A large number of highly sophisticated techniques have been developed for producing interference contrast, some involving the use of polarized light. However the fundamental principles may be illustrated for the metallurgical case using the relatively simple two-beam interferometer shown in fig. 3.13. Light from a monochromatic source is divided by a beam splitter into two equal beams at right angles to each other. One beam passes through the objective to be reflected from the specimen surface in the normal way. The other beam is focused through an identical objective on to a metallized optical flat. The beam reflected from the reference surface is reunited by the beam splitter with that from the specimen, and they are then able to interfere with each other. The relative phase of the reference beam may be adjusted by controlling the distance of the optical flat from the beam splitter.

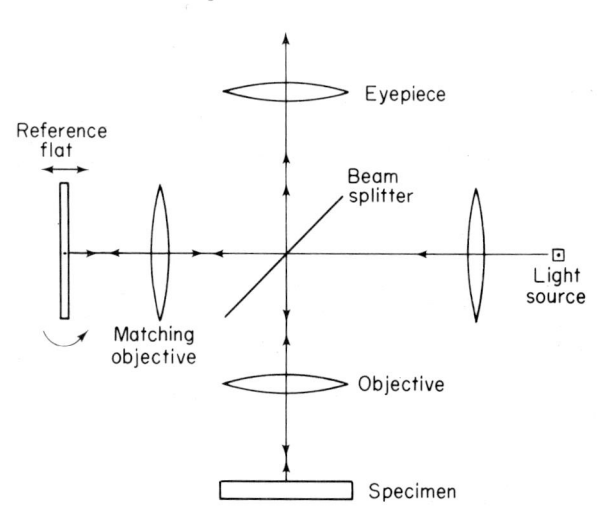

Fig. 3.13. Simple two-beam interference microscope. The reference flat may be tilted for its use in interferometry.

3.5. *Interferometry*

With the limited exception of the opaque stop technique, the above dark field and interference techniques are suitable only for revealing the presence of fine detail : quantitative measurements are not possible. As its name suggests, interferometry is concerned with such measurements, and it may be accomplished using the two-beam interferometer (fig. 3.13) in the following way.

When this instrument is being used in the interference contrast mode, the reference flat is oriented exactly at right angles to the optical axis. Hence path differences leading to interference occur solely due to differences in the surface level of the specimen. In typical applications the change is less than a single wavelength. If instead the reference flat is tilted through a small angle, then, even with a perfectly flat specimen surface, there will be a continuously increasing path difference between light reflected from the surface and from the corresponding area of the reference flat. As the path difference passes through $\lambda/2$, λ, $3\lambda/2$, 2λ and so on, a series of alternately dark and light interference fringes will be formed across the image. With a perfectly flat specimen they will be straight, parallel and evenly spaced. If the specimen was spherical they would be a series of concentric circles, rather like Newton's rings. Hence the fringes form what is effectively a contour map of the specimen surface with respect to a reference flat tilted towards it a constant angle. In principle, normal image details should be present within the bright fringes. However no attempt is made to observe these, and the fringes are treated solely as a measuring device.

If the specimen surface contains an abrupt change of height, such as a surface step, fig. 3.14 (*a*), the interference fringes will exhibit a discontinuity as shown in fig. 3.14 (*b*). Since the normal separation of the fringes corresponds to a difference in height between specimen and reference flat of $\lambda/2$, the magnitude of the step may be calculated by measuring the fraction of the fringe separation by which the fringes are displaced across the step. If, as in fig. 3.14 (*b*), this is about seven tenths of the fringe separation, then the step height is given by $0 \cdot 7\lambda/2$. Using this technique it is possible to measure down to about one tenth of a fringe spacing, and thus, using light of wavelength 500 nm for example, to detect variations in height of 25 nm. Figure 3.14 (*c*) shows a specimen of copper which has been lightly deformed, resulting in the production of surface slip steps.

The above result is somewhat ambiguous in that it is not possible to be certain that the fringes have been displaced by a simple fraction of their separation, or by several multiples of their separation, plus

(a) (b)

(c)

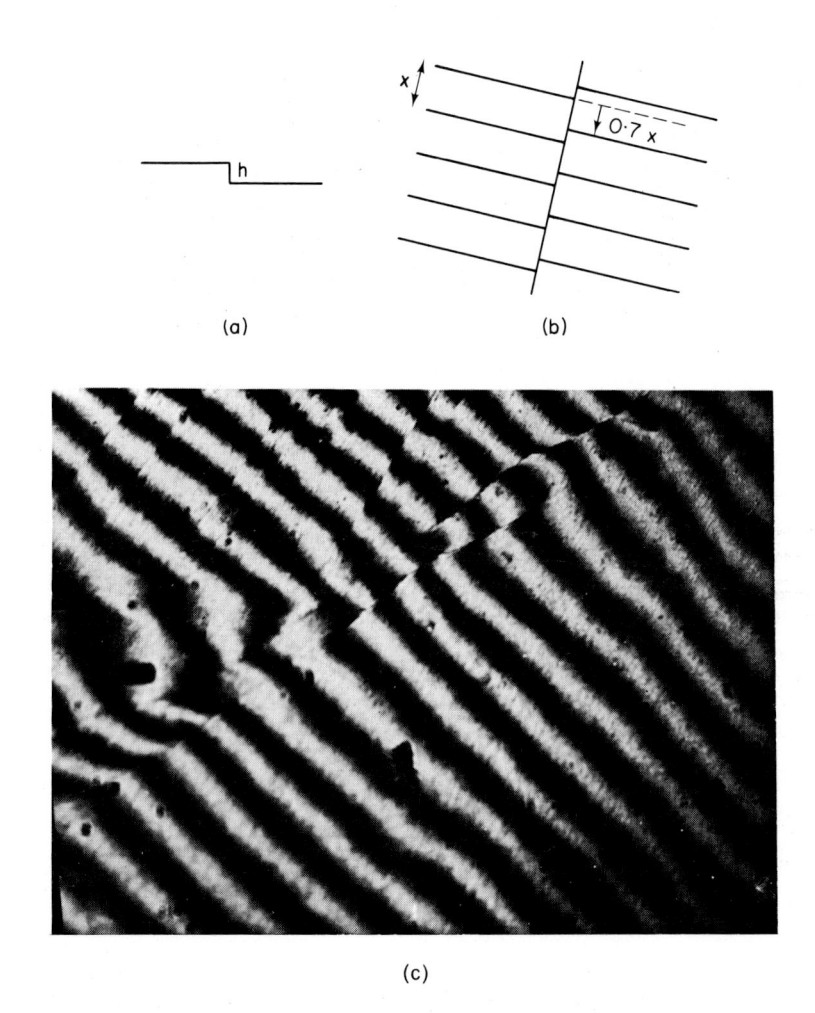

Fig. 3.14. Interferometry; surface step: (a) appearance of specimen surface (b) appearance of image (c) surface slip steps on a deformed copper specimen.

the fraction. Nor is it possible to determine which side of the step is elevated with respect to the other. However parallel observations using phase contrast or interference contrast may often be able to resolve the problem, and considerably more information may be obtained by observing how the fringe displacements vary when light of different wavelengths is used.

In the case of surface tilts the analysis is rather more direct, fig. 3.15. Across the tilt, as the slope of the specimen surface increases, the rate at which the path difference between the direct and reference beams alters, is also increased. Hence the fringes must become closer together, and, since they will remain continuous across the tilt, they must change direction as shown. In order to determine the tilt angle we must first determine the width of the tilt, w, by direct measurement from the micrograph, knowing the magnification, followed by measurement of h from the fringe orientation. Then $\tan \theta = h/w$. In order to measure h we select any one of the fringes, say ABCD, and produce AB across the step to E. The step height is then given by the number of fringe separations between CD and E (here about 4·3) multiplied by $\lambda/2$ as before. Providing the step height is uniform, it could equally well be calculated by counting the number of fringes from B down the face of the step to E (again 4·3). However this is not possible if the step is too steep, and the fringes too closely spaced. Eventually, if the slope became 90°, the surface tilt would have become a surface step, and it would no longer be possible to identify ABCD, and hence to determine whether the fringe displacement was 4·3 times the fringe separation, or merely 0·3 times.

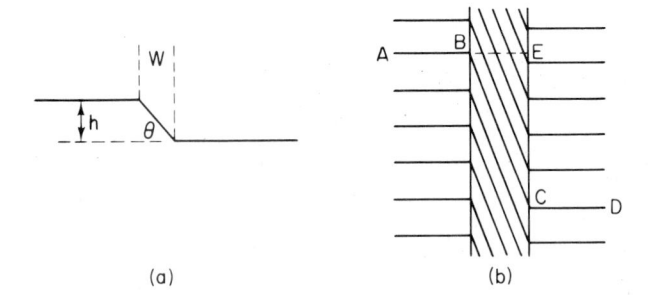

Fig. 3.15. Interferometry; surface tilt: (*a*) appearance of specimen surface, (*b*) appearance of image.

A considerable increase in sensitivity is possible using multiple-beam interferometry. This rather more complex technique involves a number of successive reflections between the specimen surface and a suitably located reference flat, such that up to a hundred beams may interfere to form the final fringe pattern. The net result is that the fringes are narrower and much more sharply defined, and with care it is possible to measure displacements down to about one two hundredth of the fringe separation, and hence both to detect and to measure height differences of only 1–2 nm.

3.6. Polarized light microscopy
Polarized light

Although it is convenient in a two-dimensional drawing to represent light waves as a vibration in a single plane, in practice with normal light the vibrations actually occur in all of the possible planes containing the axis of propagation, fig. 3.16 (a). This may be understood by considering that while the train of waves originating from a single atom in the light source may only be vibrating in a single plane, when the waves transmitted from all the millions of atoms are considered their orientations will be randomly distributed.

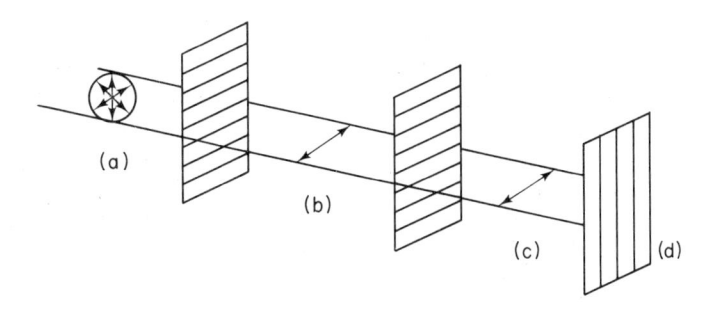

Fig. 3.16. Production of plane polarized light.

If such light is passed through a certain kind of material which acts as a polarizer (and whose nature is discussed below), only that light whose vibrations lie within a certain plane is allowed to pass, fig. 3.16 (b), and the emergent light is described as being 'plane polarized'. If this light is allowed to impinge on a second piece of polarizing material, whose polarizing plane is parallel to that of the first, the light will be transmitted without alteration (except for a small amount that will be absorbed since no material is perfectly transparent), fig. 3.16 (c). If, on the other hand, the second piece of polarizing material is rotated through 90°, fig. 3.16 (d), the light is totally absorbed and none is allowed to pass through. This is known as the 'crossed polars' position.

In the polarizing microscope, therefore, a sheet of polarizing material (usually the commercial product, Polaroid), which is known as the polarizer, is inserted into the illuminating system in much the same way as would be a colour filter. A second sheet of Polaroid, known as the analyser, is located somewhere within the eyepiece lens system, and is oriented such that its polarizing plane is at right angles to that of the polarizer. Now, providing the specimen does not have any effect on the plane of polarization of the light incident upon it, the resulting image will be totally dark. The technique is therefore a dark field one (c.f. page 64) and reveals regions of the microstructure which are optically active, i.e. on interaction with the incident light, alter its plane of polarization, so that complete extinction is no longer produced at the analyser. Such light, whose vibrations, while restricted, are not necessarily continued to a single plane, is called elliptically polarized light.

The polarization of light arises due to optical anisotropy. In an isotropic transparent material, the optical properties are the same in all directions, while in an anisotropic material the optical properties (together with other physical properties) are a function of direction, and result in polarized light. Materials that have crystal structures which exhibit cubic symmetry, together with amorphous materials (which have no crystal structure), are optically isotropic towards transmitted light. Materials possessing other crystal structures, and amorphous materials which are in a state of internal strain, are optically anisotropic. Thus, for example, the material Polaroid is made from sheets of long chain polymer molecules which have been aligned into a parallel orientation by mechanically stretching the sheet. Polarization may also be produced by reflection. This occurs even with isotropic materials, although in the case of solids with a very high value of refractive index (such as metals) its effect becomes significant only at glancing angles of incidence. With anisotropic materials the incident light will become polarized in a manner specifically related to the orientation of the crystal surface. Thus if the incident light is already plane polarized, as in the polarizing microscope, its interaction with optically anisotropic materials as above will result in its becoming elliptically polarized.

Applications

An important application of polarized light microscopy in metallurgy has been the study of anisotropic metals, such as zinc, magnesium and tin, and the technique has lately become particularly relevant with the increasing use of materials such as beryllium, zirconium, titanium and uranium, which are also anisotropic, and can sometimes prove difficult to etch satisfactorily. It is also particularly useful where it is undesirable to etch specimens in order to reveal the microstructure, for example when there are fine surface markings which one wants to preserve.

Under bright field illumination, unetched, such metals reveal little or no image contrast. Under polarized light, however, the grain structure is clearly revealed, as shown in fig. 3.17, since different grains possessing different orientations introduce different amounts of ellipticity into the incident light by reflection. Rotation of the specimen alters the orientation of the grains with respect to the incident light, and hence alters their contrast. This may be used to give useful information on the relative orientations of the grains, and can also be used to detect preferred orientation, since if there are groups of grains possessing a common orientation their brightness or colours will be similar.

Fig. 3.17. Micrograph of titanium taken using polarized light, × 80.

Metals with a cubic crystal structure are optically isotropic, and so their grains appear equally dark under crossed polars regardless of orientation. However in some cases specific chemical reagents may be used which will etch the surface to form characteristic pits or furrows in each grain. Thus an incident beam of light will meet these furrows at an oblique angle and undergo a significant amount of polarization (page 82), the extent varying between each grain, and hence revealing the grain structure. Alternatively, with metals such as aluminium, which can be oxidized electrolytically to form a relatively thick film, characteristic furrows are produced in the oxide film over each grain, producing a similar result.

A further application is the study of the non-metallic inclusions which are often found in steel. Under bright field illumination these may all appear fairly similar, while under polarized light they can exhibit different colours and hence may be identified. Finally there is the study of magnetic domain structures by means of the Kerr magneto-optic effect. The magnetic field of the specimen at its surface alters the polarization of the incident light, and hence gives contrast between surface domains of different orientation.

Applications outside the metallurgical field lie in the identification of mineral specimens and organic crystals from their optical properties when studied in transmitted light, together with the measurement of refractive indices in anisotropic liquids.

3.7. Ultraviolet and fluorescence microscopy

Since the resolving power of the microscope depends directly on the wavelength of the radiation used (page 26), it can be improved by using radiation of shorter wavelength than that of the visible spectrum, that is in the ultraviolet. Hence by using wavelengths in the region 400 to 200 nm, compared, say, to the 550 nm wavelength of green light, it is possible to halve the resolution limit down to about 100 nm. The difficulty is that normal optical glass will only transmit radiation of wavelength greater than about 300 nm, and hence for ultraviolet microscopy it becomes necessary to use lenses of quartz or a synthetic fluorite, which adds greatly to the expense. At one time this was felt to be worth while for the greater resolution gained, but the advent of the electron microscope has largely rendered straightforward ultraviolet microscopy unnecessary. A more important application nowadays is in fluorescence microscopy.

Fluorescence is the phenomenon exhibited by certain substances which, when illuminated with ultraviolet radiation (invisible to the eye), are able to convert it into longer wavelength radiation which can now be detected by the eye. (If visible radiation persists after removal of the exciting radiation, it is then known as phosphorescence.) Many natural materials, botanical and mineralogical ones in particular, are fluorescent, and display fluorescence in specific colours by which they can be identified.

A large number of other substances of zoological and medical interest do not exhibit this behaviour. However just as such substances may be allowed to react selectively with certain stains (page 49), they may also be induced to absorb certain fluorescent dyes—known as fluorochromes—in a selective manner, and hence to reveal their microstructure. This variation of the technique is of particular importance in medicine, and has recently been applied to the problem of identifying chromosome structures. In fluorescence microscopy it is quite acceptable to use the longer wavelength ultraviolet radiation, and glass lenses can still be employed.

CHAPTER 4
electron microscopy

4.1. *Introduction*

ALTHOUGH the existence of electrons as negatively charged particles was known in 1897, it was not until 1924, when de Broglie first proposed that they could also be regarded as waves of very short wavelength, that their potential value for microscopy became apparent. Once it was realized that the concentrating action of a magnetic field in focusing an electron beam was analogous to that of the lens used with visual light, the development of a rudimentary electron microscope soon followed. By 1933 Knoll and Ruska had produced an instrument capable of exceeding the resolving power of the best optical microscopes, and the first commercial instrument appeared three years later.

Today there are over fifty makes and models of electron microscope, including numerous variations on the basic microscope idea. The most familiar instrument is perhaps the conventional transmission electron microscope, which operates in a way very analogous to the transmission optical microscope in that the imaging radiation—here electrons—is passed through a thin specimen and is then focused in such a way as to produce a magnified image. Other types of microscope are designed to study the surface of opaque objects, either by reflecting the electrons from the specimen surface, just as in the metallurgical optical microscope, or by using a more complex system based on the television scanning principle (page 112).

Hence, although it is only 40 years since the first commercial instrument was produced, the electron microscope has probably added more to our knowledge of the microscopic world than has the optical microscope in its almost ten times longer existence. One reason is the electron microscope's far superior resolving power, but there is the additional feature that it is not restricted solely to providing microstructural information. It is also possible to obtain electron diffraction patterns from the same area of the specimen that is examined in the main microscopy mode, thus adding both structural and crystallographic information (page 101). Furthermore there are a number of techniques that permit a direct chemical analysis to be made of the composition of the specimen, some of which are discussed further in Chapter 8. In this chapter we shall concentrate on the fundamental principles of electron microscope design and operation.

The electron wavelength

The key to the advantage of the electron microscope over the optical microscope lies in the much shorter wavelength associated with the electron, and hence in the much greater resolving power that may be obtained. It is beyond the scope of this book to go into the particle/wave duality of the electron : let us accept that both descriptions are correct, their relative usefulness depending upon the particular physical situation being considered. They may be reconciled by means of the de Broglie relationship,

$$\lambda = h/m_e v$$

where λ is the wavelength, m_e the rest-mass of the electron, which can be used if its velocity v is not too great, and h is the Planck constant.

If, as in the electron microscope, the electrons, of charge e, are accelerated by a potential difference V, the kinetic energy which they acquire is
$$\tfrac{1}{2} m_e v^2 = Ve.$$
Hence
$$\lambda = h/(2m_e Ve)^{1/2}.$$

Inserting the appropriate values of the constants into the above equation, V being measured in volts, we find that to a good approximation,

$$\lambda = (1\cdot 5/V)^{1/2} \text{ nm}.$$

With higher accelerating voltages the velocity of the electrons becomes significant in comparison to the velocity of light, c, whereupon m_e must be replaced by $m_e(1-v^2/c^2)^{-1/2}$, and the expression becomes

$$\lambda = [1\cdot 5/V(1+10^{-6}V)]^{1/2}.$$

Values of λ for the accelerating voltages commonly used in electron microscopy are given in Table 3 on page 121.

For an accelerating voltage of say 100 kV, it can be seen that the electron wavelength is about 10^{-5} times that of visible light. If the imaging system of the electron microscope could be made as effective as that of the optical microscope (that is with a N.A. of up to 1·4) then the limit of resolution would in theory be of the order of

0·0013 nm, many times better than that required to resolve individual atoms.

Unfortunately the lens aberrations associated with the use of magnetic fields for focusing are so great that the practical value of the N.A. is kept down to a remarkably small 0·01, corresponding to a semi-angle aperture of only about 30′ (compared to the 70° or so of the optical microscope). Hence the practical resolution limit is of the order of 0·2 nm. Even so, this value is three orders of magnitude better than that of the optical microscope.

Even with the most sophisticated modern electron microscope actually achieving such resolutions requires considerable operating skill. However, just as with the optical microscope, the majority of the work is not carried out at the limit of performance of the instrument, and a more usual working resolution is 1–2 nm. In any case, so far as the imaging of individual atoms is concerned, it is their ability to give sufficient *contrast* to be distinguished one from another that constitutes a more serious limitation than the instrumental resolution.

4.2. The transmission electron microscope

General description

An electron microscope consists of an electron gun and an assembly of magnetic lenses, all enclosed in a column which must be evacuated to about 10^{-5} Torr to prevent the electrons colliding with gas molecules and hence being scattered out of their correct path. As shown by fig. 4.1 the optical arrangement of the electron microscope is in principle very similar to that of the transmission optical microscope, and indeed the rapid progress in electron microscopy owes much to the borrowing of ideas from the latter field. The main difference between these figures is that the final lens in the electron microscope is used to project a *real* image on to a viewing screen or photographic plate. However, as we have seen on page 47, the optical microscope can be used in exactly the same way by displacing L_E so that I_1 lies outside its focal length.

Since the resolving power of the electron microscope is so much greater than that of the optical microscope, much greater magnifications can usefully be obtained. This is accomplished by having more than one projector lens. Thus a magnification of $\times 200\,000$ might be divided between the objective and the two projector lenses as $\times 100$, $\times 20$ and $\times 100$, respectively. Considerable variations in magnification may be achieved simply by altering the current through

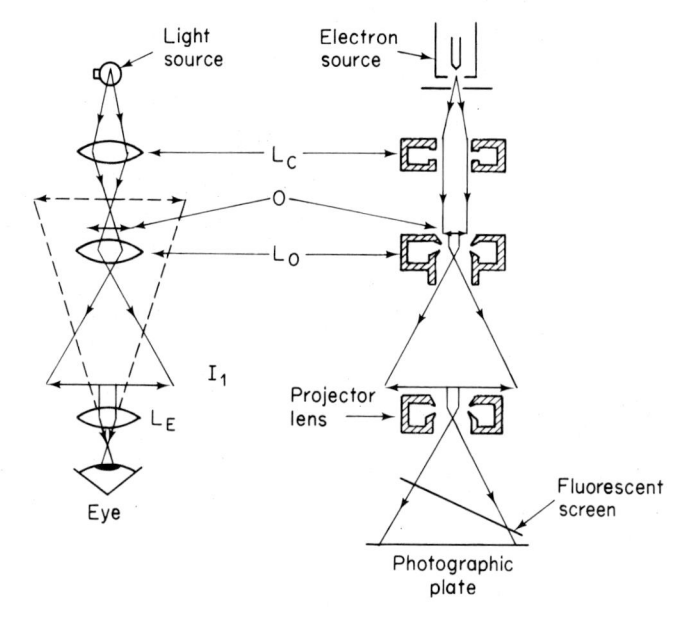

Fig. 4.1. Comparative layouts of the optical and electron microscopes.

the coils of the magnetic lenses—a facility denied to the optical microscopist who must exchange his lenses bodily. The actual construction of the electron microscope is quite different from that of the optical microscope (see fig. 4.2). The microscope column is about 2 m high and sits vertically above a desk-like console containing the controls for vacuum instrumentation, lens operation and specimen manipulation.

The electron optical system

The electron source is usually a pointed tungsten filament which emits a steady stream of electrons on being heated to a temperature of about 2500°C by the passage of a small current through it (page 147). The filament is kept at a high negative potential (-40 to -100 kV) and the electron beam is accelerated through a small hole in the earthed anode, before being focused on to the specimen by means of a system of condenser lenses. It is this accelerating potential that determines the wavelength of the electrons, as discussed on page 87.

Each of the various 'lenses' consists of a radial magnetic field which is generated by passing a small current through a coil made up of a few thousand turns of fine wire. The magnetic field produced is concentrated by a soft iron casing around the coil. When very high magnetic fields of maximum symmetry are required, further very accurately machined pieces of soft iron, called pole pieces, are placed in the centre of the coil. These concentrate the magnetic field into a gap only a few mm wide in between their faces.

Fig. 4.2. A modern electron microscope. *A.E.I. Scientific Apparatus Ltd.*

Apertures of different sizes may be inserted into the lens system in order to control the angular divergence of the beam. These apertures are typically discs of platinum or molybdenum a few millimetres in diameter containing a hole which is a few micrometres across. While the function of the condenser aperture is similar to that in the optical microscope in controlling the illumination of the specimen, the primary role of the objective aperture is to control the formation of image contrast, as discussed later in this chapter. Again the ultimate resolution is limited by the performance of the objective lens, since any detail which is lost here cannot be replaced later.

Attachments and mechanical stages

Specimens are introduced into the microscope chamber via a vacuum airlock so that it is unnecessary to pump out the entire system each time a new specimen is examined. The specimen stage allows full lateral movement in the horizontal plane so that the entire area of the specimen may be examined. Probably the most important attachment to the specimen stage is a tilting device. With this it is possible to bring the specimen into a particular orientation with respect to the electron beam and hence to obtain particular contrast effects. It may also be used for obtaining 'stereo pairs'. These are two photographs, taken at a slightly different angle to each other, which when viewed stereoscopically, give an impression of solidity to the image.

In the case of metallurgical specimens useful information may often be obtained by carrying out certain thermal or mechanical treatments while the specimen is under continuous observation, and special attachments may be fitted to accomplish these. In the case of biological specimens a cooling facility is particularly useful in minimizing changes in the structure of the specimen caused by heating due to the electron beam.

Specimen preparation

In order that the electron beam should be able to penetrate it, the specimen must be a thin section of thickness in the range 20–200 nm. This is fairly easily accomplished in the case of metals by electropolishing a thin disc or foil until it just perforates, whereupon the regions just adjacent to the perforation will be of the required thickness. Alternatively a thin metal film may be formed by vapour deposition on to a suitable substrate, which is then removed.

Sectioning of biological specimens is performed in a similar way to those used in optical microscopy, i.e. using a microtome, although the sections must be an order of magnitude or so finer. The difficulty lies in the fact that it is necessary to exclude all water from the specimen to avoid contamination of the vacuum system with water vapour, and once all the various fixation and embedding procedures have been gone through it is by no means certain that the final microstructure truly represents that which was present originally.

4.3. Resolution

Lens aberrations

Like their optical counterparts, magnetic lenses are subject to chromatic and spherical aberration and astigmatism. Thus chromatic aberration arises when electrons of different wavelength are refracted to different extents. Variations in wavelength are caused by fluctuations in the accelerating voltage, and it is necessary that the latter should be stabilized to at least one part in a hundred thousand. It may be noted than an additional spread in the energy (and thus wavelength) of the transmitted electrons may arise directly due to energy losses within the specimen itself. This may be turned to advantage in supplying information about the local chemical composition in the specimen (see Chapter 8). Generally, though, chromatic aberration is much less important than spherical aberration.

Spherical aberration arises because it is inherent in the design of magnetic lenses that the outer zones focus more strongly than the inner zones. Since magnetic lenses are always converging, this defect cannot be overcome by combining two opposing lenses, as might be done in optical microscopy. The radius r_s of the disc of confusion in the image plane, due to spherical aberration, is given by

$$r_s = MC_S\alpha^3$$

where M is the magnification produced by the lens, C_S the spherical aberration constant and α the semi-angle of the lens. This imposes a limit on the fineness of detail that may be resolved in the *object* plane equivalent to $C_S\alpha^3$. For a given value of λ, the only way to reduce spherical aberration is to decrease α by means of a suitable aperture, as described in the following section.

A further important lens defect is astigmatism, which is due to asymmetry of the magnetic field about the lens axis. Ideally the holes in the pole pieces of the objective lens would be perfect circles.

However deviations of only a few millionths of a centimetre can produce appreciable astigmatism, and it is beyond the capability of modern manufacturing techniques to achieve better than this. Fortunately this defect can be corrected for by means of a device known as a stigmator. This superimposes a weak additional magnetic field across the gap in the pole pieces, which may be varied in both strength and direction to correct for the asymmetry.

The resolving power

In the case of the optical microscope it is possible to ignore the effect of spherical aberration in determining its limit of resolution, since the Abbe diffraction limit is the larger quantity. However in the case of the electron microscope the reverse is true. Accordingly we can increase the resolving power of the electron microscope by decreasing the angular aperture of the objective lens, owing to the dependence of the size of the disc of confusion on the third power of this function. At the same time, decreasing the objective aperture leads to an increase in the calculated Abbe diffraction limit, so that eventually these two become equal. At this point

$$C_S \alpha^3 = 0\cdot5 \, \lambda/n \sin \alpha$$

and this condition determines the optimum size of the objective aperture. Since α is very small we can approximate $\sin \alpha$ to α, and so

$$\alpha = 0\cdot85 \, (\lambda/C_S)^{1/4}$$

since for electrons *in vacuo* n is one. For a microscope operating at 100 kV, $\lambda = 0\cdot0037$ nm, $C_S = 0\cdot5$ mm and hence α equals 10^{-2} rad or about 30′. This gives a resolution limit of about 0·4 nm. Customarily the resolving power of a microscope is tested by finding out the closest spacing of successive atomic planes which may be detected, using the microscope in rather a different mode to that normally encountered (page 100).

Before such a calculated resolving power may actually be achieved, however, there are a number of experimental features to be controlled. Firstly, during photography, the specimen must not move relative to the microscope by more than the resolution distance required, and this means that very high mechanical stability is needed in the microscope. Furthermore all the apertures must be kept scrupulously clean since the presence of dirt or carbonaceous material introduced by the oil of the vacuum pumps will cause them to become charged, and hence deflect the electron beams, leading to quite serious astigmatism.

Depth of field and focus

One advantage of the very small apertures that are necessary with the electron microscope are the comparatively large depth of field and focus that may still be obtained despite the very great reduction in δ. The depth of field, D_1, is approximately given by the expression $2\delta/\alpha$. With $\delta = 1$ nm, say, and $\alpha = 10^{-2}$ rad, D_1 comes out to be $0\cdot 2$ μm. This is roughly comparable with the depth of field obtained using the optical microscope at its optimum resolution. It is also comparable with the specimen thickness itself, so that the whole of the specimen will be in equally good focus at the same time.

As with the optical microscope, the depth of focus, D_2 is equal to $D_1 M^2$, where M is the magnification. Since for a total magnification of say 100 000 times this makes D_2 equal to 2 km, this estimate must perhaps not be taken too literally. However, for all practical purposes the depth of focus may be taken as well exceeding the dimensions of the microscope, and hence it is possible to have the image equally well in focus when viewed on a screen held several centimetres above the photographic plate (c.f. fig. 4.1) as it is on the plate itself.

4.4. Contrast

Interaction of electron beams with matter

In order to understand how image contrast is obtained in the electron microscope it is necessary to consider the various ways in which an electron beam interacts with a solid. In practice there are many more interactions than are made use of in the conventional transmission electron microscope. However it will be convenient to consider them all at this point since each one is involved in one or other of the techniques discussed later in this chapter or in subsequent chapters. These processes are illustrated schematically in fig. 4.3.

Firstly, if the specimen is sufficiently thin, a portion of the incident electron beam will be transmitted through it without any change either in its energy or direction. This is known as the direct beam. Secondly, since the electrons are charged particles, they may interact with the electric fields within the atoms making up the specimen. The fields are of two kinds, and arise due to the presence both of the positively charged nucleus of each atom, and of the negatively charged electrons which surround it.

The effect of the positively charged nucleus is to deflect or scatter the electrons from their path, but without altering their energy. This is known as elastic scattering. If the atoms are arranged in a periodic fashion, as in a crystalline solid, then this scattering occurs in a regular and repeated fashion throughout the crystal, and the scattered electrons emerge making specific angles with respect to the incident beam. This process is referred to as coherent elastic scattering, or, more simply, just as electron diffraction, since when it is considered in terms of the wave nature of the electrons it can be seen to correspond to the constructive interference of the electron waves in these directions. In this way it is largely analogous to optical or X-ray diffraction, and may be treated similarly. If the solid is non-crystalline or amorphous, such as a polymer, then, while such scattering is still elastic, the scattering centres are no longer arranged periodically and the direction of the resulting electrons does not bear a constant relationship to that of the incident beam. Such electrons are referred to as being incoherently elastically scattered.

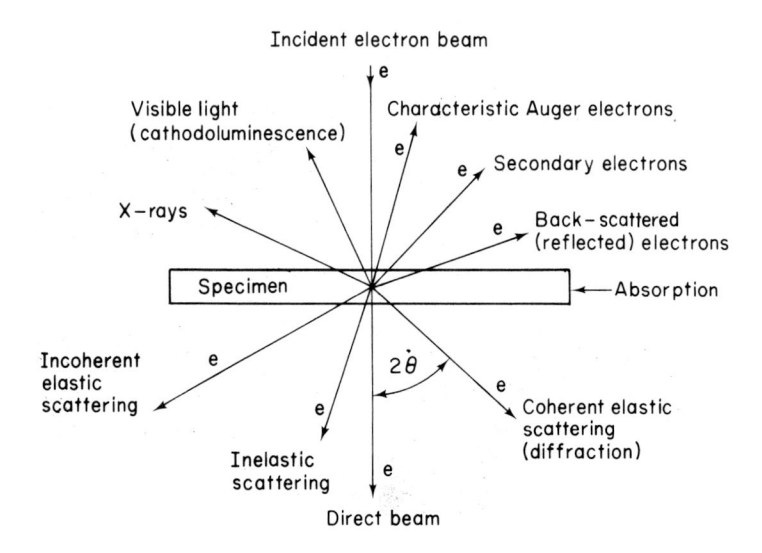

Fig. 4.3. The interaction of an electron beam with matter.

The second type of scattering is due to electron–electron repulsion between the incident electrons and those which surround the positive nucleus. In this case the scattered beam is deflected by varying amounts, and in addition suffers a change in energy. This is known as inelastic scattering and these electrons contribute to the general undifferentiated background radiation. These are the electrons referred to on page 92, which may introduce some chromatic aberration, and can also be used in analysis.

In the transmission electron microscope image contrast depends primarily on the relationship between the direct beam and the diffracted beams.

Similar kinds of scattering occur from the side of the specimen which faces the incident beam. For convenience, in fig. 4.3, these electrons have been represented by a single arrow and are referred to as back-scattered or reflected electrons.

Some of the electrons will be absorbed within the specimen itself, and will never reappear. Their energy together with that lost by the inelastically scattered electrons may be manifested in several different ways. Firstly it may appear as heat, which may have a variety of undesirable effects on the actual structure of the specimen, but which will not be considered further here. More importantly, the energy given up by the incoming electrons may be sufficient to dislodge electrons from their orbits around the atoms making up the solid, and hence to produce ionization. This process may in turn lead to the emission of further radiation, and it will be convenient to summarize here the forms that the latter may take, more complete descriptions being given later in various sections.

Firstly there is electron emission. This is made up of secondary electrons and Auger electrons. The former are electrons which were present within the solid and which are given sufficient energy to be ejected, typically with energies in the range 0–50 eV. These are used for image formation in both the scanning electron microscope and the electron probe microanalyser. Auger electrons, on the other hand, are emitted with quite specific energies, the values of which depend solely on the kinds of atom from which they are emitted. Hence these electrons may be used to give a chemical analysis of the solid, as discussed in Chapter 7.

Alternatively the ionization event may be followed by the emission of X-ray photons. Some of these will possess energies which are characteristic of each of the different chemical species which make up the sample, and hence may again be used for chemical analysis, or alternatively may be used directly in image formation (page 140). An analogous process is the production of lower energy (longer wavelength) photons which correspond to visible light. This phenomenon is known as cathodoluminescence, and may again be used both in image formation and in identification.

If the specimen is sufficiently thin then this newly generated radiation may equally well be transmitted through the specimen as re-emitted from the back surface. However this is not shown to occur in fig. 4.3, since the diagram has been drawn so as to distinguish the radiation which is actually used in transmission electron microscopy of thin specimens, shown emerging below the specimen, from that which is used in the various other techniques. These are generally used in back-reflection and hence here the radiation is shown being re-emitted upwards, back towards the incident beam.

Summarizing, the radiation leaving the specimen may be used in three ways:
(a) for image formation, such as the direct and scattered electrons, X-rays and visible light;
(b) for crystallographic analysis, via diffraction either of the incident electrons or of the X-rays generated within the specimen;
(c) for chemical analysis, by spectroscopic determination of the characteristic Auger electrons and X-rays that are emitted.

Contrast from metal specimens

In fig. 4.3 the angle that the diffracted electrons make with the direct beam is shown as 2θ, and its value may be calculated by means of the Bragg equation. In practice there are of course a number of these diffracted beams, each with its own value of θ, resulting from the various sets of suitably oriented atomic planes. However in metals even the first order diffracted beam from the most widely spaced atomic planes has a value of 2θ greater than that of α, the semi-angle of the objective lens. Thus normally all the diffracted beams are stopped by the objective aperture and only the direct beam contributes to the image, as shown in fig. 4.4 (a). This is known as bright field imaging. The intensity of the direct beam may be given by $(I-D)$, where I is the intensity of the incident beam and D the total intensity of all the diffracted beams (again for simplicity the diffracted radiation has been represented here by a single beam, and other electron interactions have been neglected).

Any alteration in the orientation of the specimen changes the ratio of the directly transmitted to diffracted electrons, and hence the value of $(I-D)$, leading to a different degree of brightness, or intensity, across the image. This would happen, for example, across a grain boundary. In addition, dislocations appear in bright field images as dark lines as shown in figs. 4.5 (*a*) and (*b*). This is because the crystal structure is strained or distorted around the dislocation as is demonstrated in fig. 4.6. If we consider electron diffraction to occur due to the electrons being *reflected* from suitably oriented atomic planes (page 20), then we can see how an enhanced degree of diffraction can occur from around the site of the dislocation, due to these distortions, leading to the formation of dark contrast in the image. Careful consideration of how the dislocation contrast varies with the orientation of the specimen enables the precise geometry of the dislocation to be determined, as discussed on page 107. In alloys, second phase particles may give rise to image contrast either due to differences in their scattering power, structure or orientation with respect to the matrix, or because their presence strains the matrix giving rise to contrast in an analogous way to dislocations.

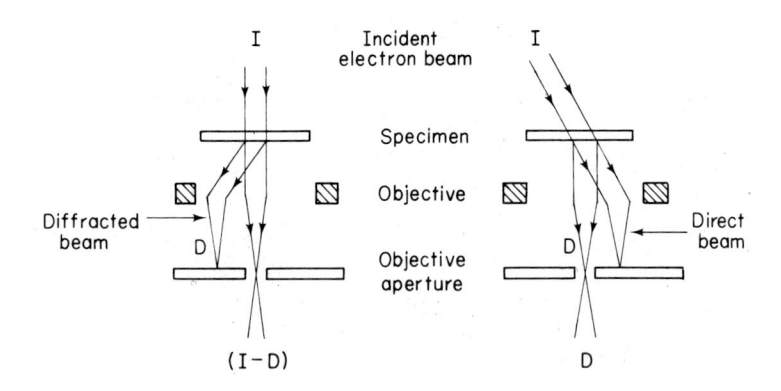

Fig. 4.4. Illustrating diffraction contrast for (*a*) bright field, and (*b*) dark field illumination.

As an alternative to bright field imaging, the direct beam may be obstructed and one of the diffracted beams allowed to form the image. This is known as dark field imaging, and is illustrated in fig. 4.4 (*b*). Although dark field imaging may be obtained by displacing the objective aperture as shown here, this leads to poorer resolution since the rays are now off-axis. As an alternative either the electron gun may be tilted or the beam deflected so as to strike the specimen at an angle. Since it is now the diffracted electrons that are used for imaging, the contrast will be the reverse of that seen under bright field

(a)

(b)

Fig. 4.5. Electron micrographs showing dislocations in niobium. Bright field micrographs taken under two beam conditions with different diffraction spots operating, ×25 000. M. H. Loretto.

conditions, and in particular, dislocations would appear as bright lines against a dark background. The technique is particularly useful when imaging second phase particles since the aperture may be placed so as to receive electrons diffracted from the particles alone, whereupon the latter will appear bright against the dark background from the matrix. If these particles are especially small they may be quite difficult to detect under bright field conditions.

Direct resolution of the crystal structure

The type of contrast discussed in the previous section is known as *diffraction contrast*, and while it is capable of revealing the presence of many microstructural features, it cannot reveal the periodic crystal structure itself. This follows directly from Abbe's theory of image formation which was discussed in our first chapter, where it was deduced that a periodic structure could only be imaged as such providing that at least one diffracted beam was present to interfere with the direct beam. This is not the case in either bright field or dark field imaging.

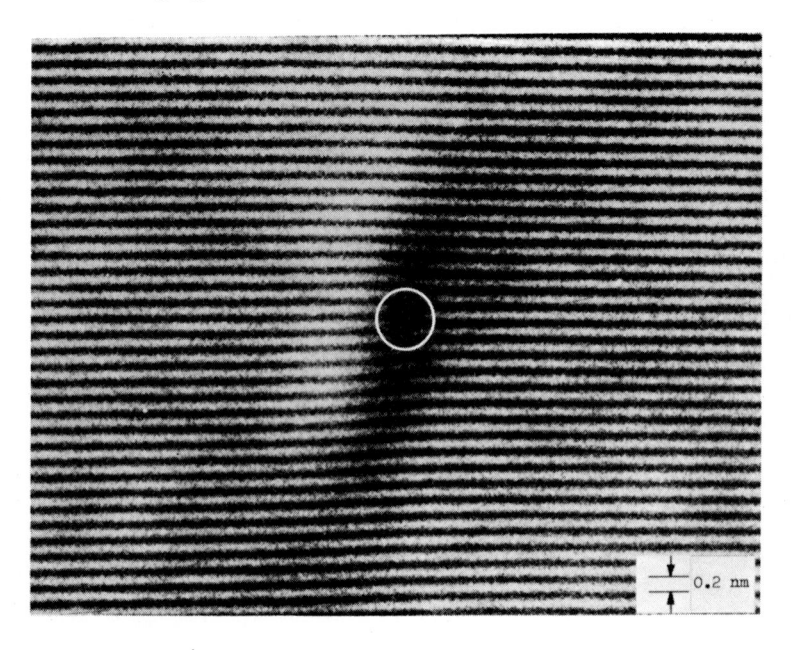

Fig. 4.6. Direct resolution of the crystal planes in an aluminium–copper alloy. A dislocation can be seen terminating within the circled area. *V. A. Phillips.*

However, by opening up the objective aperture to let through one or more diffracted beams in addition to the direct beam, planes of atoms lying parallel to the incident electron beam may be imaged, providing their spacing is greater than the resolution limit of the microscope. Figure 4.6 shows the kind of image that is obtained. A useful application of this direct imaging technique is as a resolution test for the microscope by finding the minimum crystal structure spacing that can be resolved. Since the microscope is being tested under less than optimum conditions (the objective aperture being open wider than it would be for normal image formation), it is only within the last few years that it has been possible to resolve the very closely spaced planes of metallic crystals as shown in fig. 4.6. This micrograph is also interesting in that it reveals, in a much more 'direct' form than in fig. 4.5 (*a*) or (*b*), the effect that the presence of a dislocation has on the relative positions of the atomic planes.

Contrast from biological specimens

Just as in optical microscopy, a major difficulty with biological specimens is the inherent lack of contrast between the various structures. Image contrast derives from differences in electron scattering, and living organisms are made up almost entirely of very light elements, such as carbon, hydrogen and oxygen, which are relatively ineffective at scattering electrons.

In order to overcome this, selective 'staining' techniques are employed, again just as in the optical microscope. Heavy metal salts are used which are incorporated to different extents in different parts of the cells and tissues. The presence of these heavy elements leads to greater electron scattering and hence to contrast between the different structures.

4.5. Crystallographic analysis
Electron diffraction

We have seen that the electron microscope is capable of revealing *microstructural* information at very high resolution. What makes this technique so very powerful, however, is the complementary ability to extract *crystallographic* information, at least from crystalline materials.

The principal technique used is electron diffraction, and as we have seen this may be treated using the Bragg equation

$$2d \sin \theta = n\lambda$$

This equation enables one to relate d, the interplanar spacing of the reflecting planes concerned (from which may be obtained details of the crystal structure) to θ, the angle that the incident electron beam must make with these planes, and which may be measured from the positions of the various spots making up the diffraction pattern. It might appear unlikely that in general very many sets of reflecting planes will be so oriented as to satisfy the above equation, since λ, the electron wavelength, and the value of θ for any given specimen orientation, are both fixed. This is certainly the case with X-ray diffraction. However, it turns out that for the case of electron diffraction through a specimen that is thin in the direction of propagation of the electrons, the Bragg condition need not be obeyed precisely. This means that θ can range by a few degrees to either side of its ideal value, and hence that a number of planes which are just away from the true Bragg condition may still diffract. For this reason the diffraction pattern is able to contain a sufficient number of points for accurate information to be extracted.

Selected area diffraction

The procedure whereby an electron diffraction pattern is formed in the transmission electron microscope is shown in fig. 4.7. Just as in fig. 4.4, only one set of diffracted beams is shown, in addition to the direct beam. Under normal imaging conditions these diffracted beams are stopped by the objective aperture, and hence on changing to the diffraction mode, the first thing to do is to remove this aperture. Now it is possible to form a diffraction pattern in the rear focal plane of the objective lens. This consists of a series of points, each one of which is formed by rays which leave the specimen in the same *direction*. This is very similar to the formation of an optical Fraunhofer diffraction pattern by a grating, as discussed on page 17 and fig. 1.15.

Eventually we want to be able to form a magnified image of this diffraction pattern, but first we must consider what is probably the most important aspect of this technique, namely that we can restrict the region from which we take the diffraction pattern to quite a small area on the specimen—1–4μm in diameter—rather than from the entire area illuminated by the electron beam. In order to achieve this an aperture termed the selector aperture is inserted into the first image plane, fig. 4.7. Thus, for example, the *image*, c', of a point c, on the specimen is obscured by the aperture, ensuring at the same time that the diffracted beams coming from the point c are also blocked automatically. Hence while the diffraction pattern formed in the rear focal plane of the objective carries information from every point on the specimen which is illuminated, only those beams arising in the selected small area are allowed to pass further through the optics to form the final image of the diffraction pattern. This latter step is accomplished by reducing the strength of the intermediate lens until it is focused onto the rear focal plane of the objective lens (i.e. the diffraction pattern) the image of which is then further magnified and projected on to the screen.

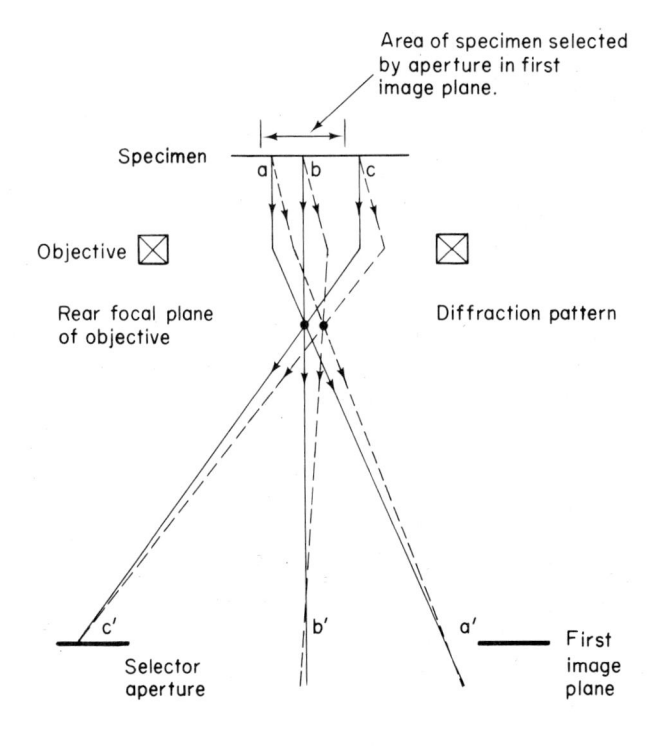

Fig. 4.7. Selected area electron diffraction.

Figure 4.8 compares the relative ray paths taken through the electron optics in both imaging and diffraction modes. It can be seen that in the direct imaging mode all the rays originating from a single point on the specimen are reunited in a single point in the image. In the diffraction mode, on the other hand, all the rays originating in the same parallel direction from all points on the specimen (within the area selected) are united in a single point on the fluorescent screen.

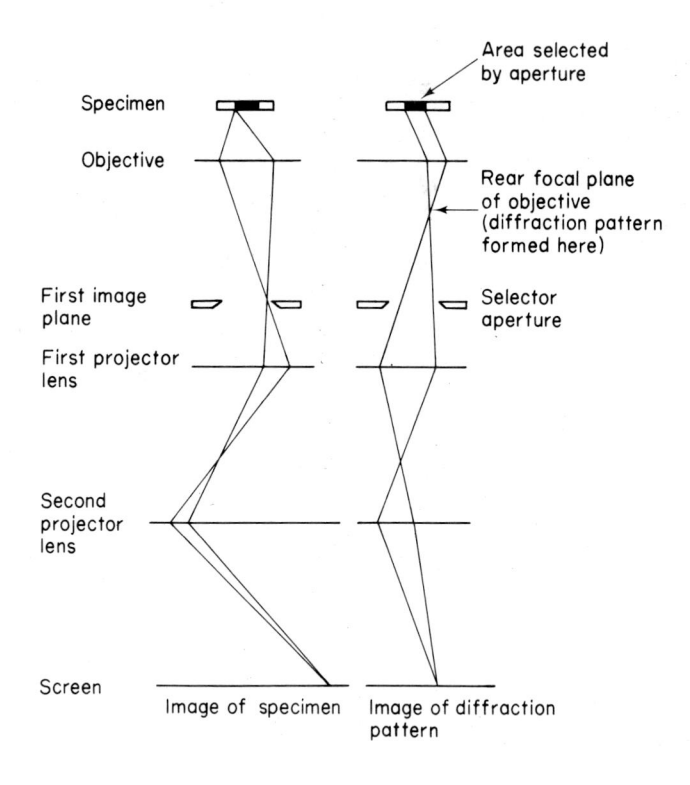

Fig. 4.8. Ray paths through the electron microscope (a) for microscopy, and (b) for diffraction.

An example of how selected area diffraction may be applied is shown in fig. 4.9. Figure 4.9 (a) shows an area of a titanium specimen containing six or seven different grains (together with a large number of dislocations). After removing the objective aperture and refocusing the intermediate lens, the diffraction pattern from the entire field of view is as illustrated in fig. 4.9 (b). With the selector aperture in the position indicated in fig. 4.9 (a), entirely within a single grain, the diffraction pattern is as shown in fig. 4.9 (c). Effectively the diffraction pattern in fig. 4.9 (b) consists of a number of such patterns all superimposed, the various diffraction spots beginning to form rings, rather as in the X-ray texture diffraction pattern illustrated in fig. 7.5. By making measurements on such diffraction patterns it is possible to determine the relative orientations of each of the grains. In other applications the selector aperture might be used to pick out small precipitate particles which could then be identified and their orientation relationship with the matrix established.

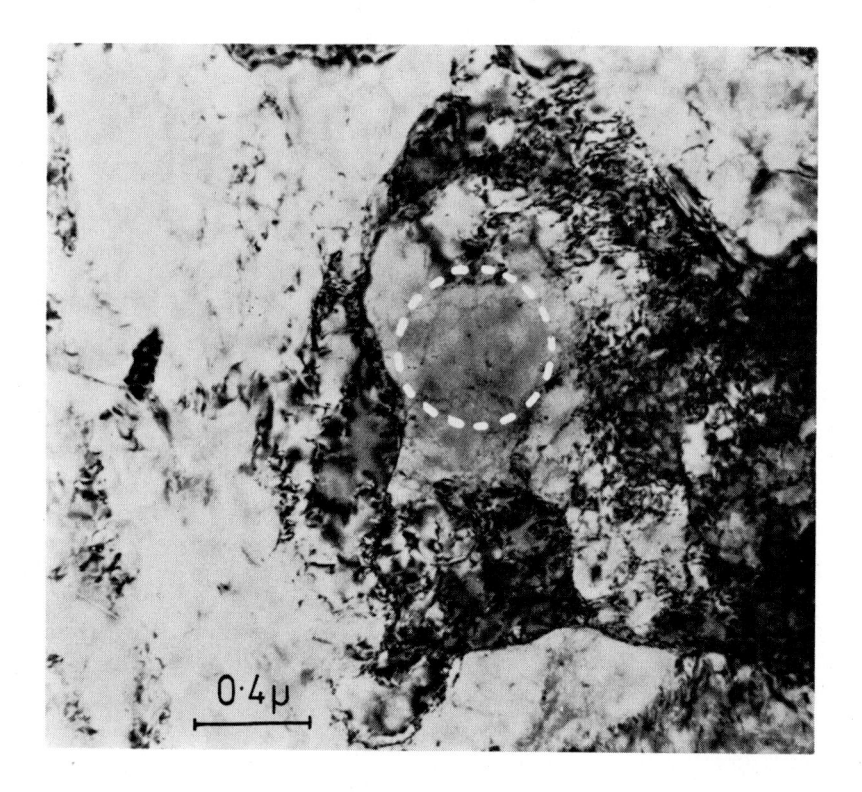

Fig. 4.9. The application of selected area diffraction: (a) area of the specimen being studied showing the position of the selector aperture (b) diffraction pattern from the entire field of view (c) diffraction pattern from the selected area. *M. H. Loretto.*

Two beam conditions

Crystallographic information may also be obtained directly from observing how the image contrast changes as the orientation of the specimen with respect to the incident electron beam is altered by means of the tilting facility described on page 91.

It is first necessary to obtain what is known as 'two-beam' imaging conditions. It may be seen from fig. 4.9 (c) that in general a large

(b)

(c)

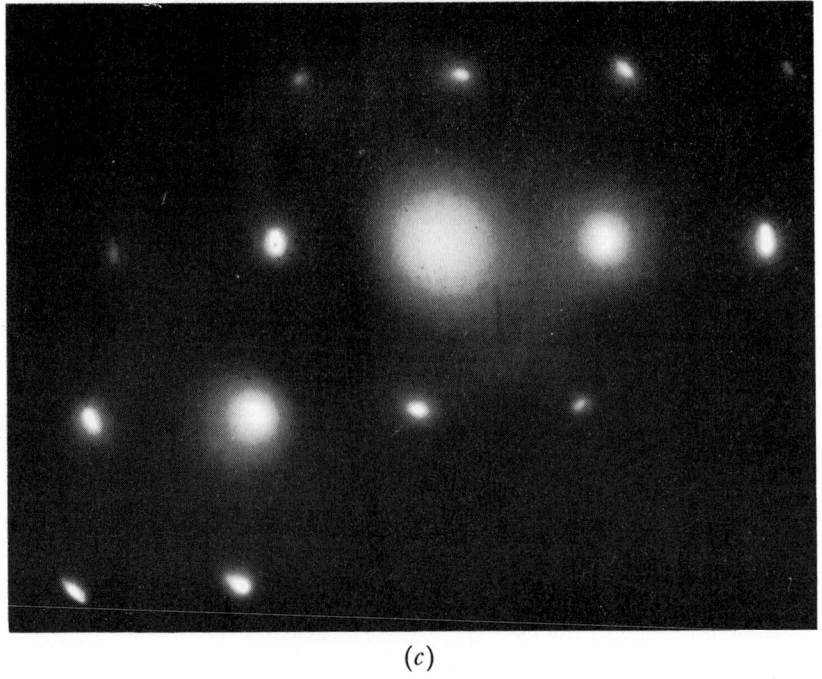

Fig. 4.9 (continued).

number of spots appear in the diffraction pattern from the specimen. However, by suitably tilting the specimen it is possible to reduce the diffraction pattern to two spots only, one due to the direct beam, and the other due to diffraction from one particular chosen set of atomic planes.

As an example, let us consider the contrast produced by a dislocation. We know that the dislocation gives rise to image contrast when the bending of the atomic planes around the dislocation gives rise to enhanced diffraction, and fig. 4.6 gives some idea of the distortions involved, together with the important fact that there is one set of planes, those *parallel* to the plane of the paper, which still remain parallel to one another (although the atoms within the planes are displaced) despite the presence of the dislocation. Hence if the particular diffraction spot which is selected corresponds to this one undistorted set of reflecting planes, then the dislocation will not be seen. In practice, therefore, one discovers for which diffraction spot a given dislocation image suddenly disappears, and from this one can deduce the crystallographic orientation of the dislocation with respect to these planes. This is illustrated in figs. 4.5 (*a*) and (*b*). Both are bright field images, taken under two-beam conditions, but with a different diffraction spot operating. Some dislocations remain

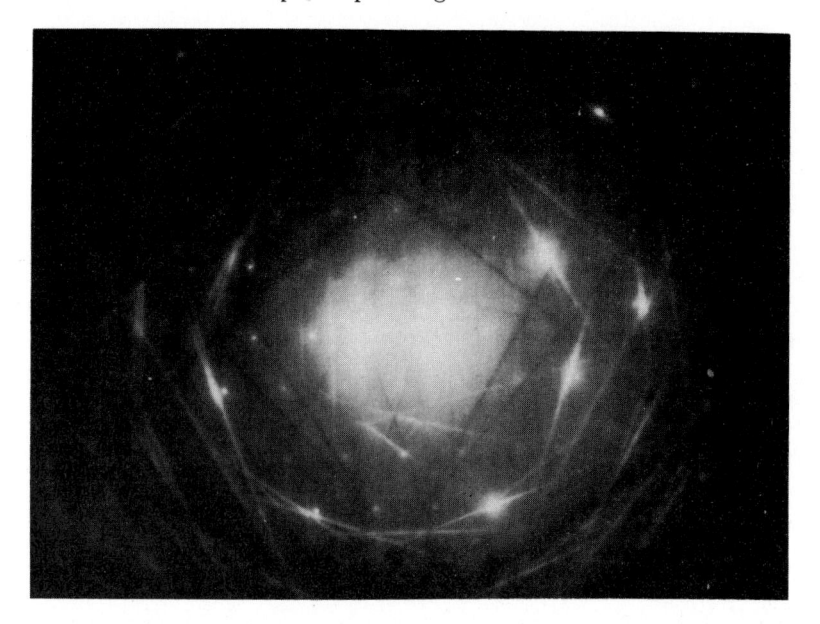

Fig. 4.10. Kikuchi lines in a diffraction pattern from silicon. *M. H. Loretto.*

visible in both ; others are visible in only one of them. Other crystal defects may be analysed in a similar way, as may small precipitate particles when they similarly distort the matrix in which they lie.

Kikuchi lines

Yet another source of crystallographic information is given by the dark and bright bands which are often seen crossing selected area diffraction patterns and which are known as Kikuchi lines, fig. 4.10. These originate from electrons which are first scattered *incoherently* within the specimen, and then undergo Bragg diffraction at various sets of reflecting planes. Thus again their position is related to the orientation of the specimen, and with their help it is possible to obtain rather more accurate crystallographic information than with using the normal diffraction pattern alone.

4.6. *Applications of transmission electron microscopy*
In metallurgy

It is probably true to say that electron microscopy, more than any other technique, has been responsible for changing metallurgy from the semi-empirical subject that it was only a few decades ago, into the highly developed science that it is now. Primarily one is interested in the mechanical strengths of metals and alloys, and the technological development of such materials has stemmed from discoveries made along two fronts. Firstly there is the direct study of crystal defects, and their complex interaction under the influence of mechanical stresses. Figure 4.5 is an example of this sort of study. Secondly there is the investigation of phase transformations—the nucleation and growth of small precipitates, and their interaction with crystal defects. Other studies have included the observation of radiation damage, the kinetics of grain boundary movement and the effects of controlled oxidation and corrosion.

In biology

An early application of the transmission electron microscope in biological studies was to the study of plant and animal viruses, only a few of which are sufficiently large to be visible in the optical microscope. The most exciting results, however, have come from studies of the internal structure of a wide variety of plant and animal cells, particularly with the revelation of unsuspected fine detail within the nucleus and cytoplasm themselves. Figure 2.11 (*b*) is an illustration of this, and should be compared with fig. 2.11 (*a*) which is an optical micrograph of a similar region taken at much lower magnification.

The difficulties of obtaining adequate image contrast in such studies has already been discussed, and a further disadvantage is of course that there is no guarantee that the structures observed in killed organisms are truly representative of those which exist in the living version. With the advent of the high voltage electron microscope (Chapter 8) it is hoped that in some cases this problem may be overcome since here it can be possible to examine living specimens.

4.7. *Electron microscopy of surfaces*
Introduction

In the transmission electron microscope we are concerned with the use of thin sections for studying the internal microstructure of materials, this being the same principle as that employed in the transmission optical microscope. As an alternative, where perhaps it is not convenient to prepare a thin section, the microstructure may be studied in the form of a surface section. This is the principle of the reflection, or metallurgical, optical microscope. In addition it may be of interest to examine the topography of surfaces which are not flat. Examples include the external shape of cells and other biological organisms, together with the relief effects introduced on to metal surfaces by fracture, corrosion or mechanical deformation (page 31). The disadvantage of the optical microscope for relief effects is its comparatively poor depth of field.

The resolution and the depth of field of the electron microscope are both very good, and several techniques have been devised to take advantage of these in the study of surfaces. Firstly, in some designs of electron microscope it is possible to orientate the specimen with respect to the beam so that electrons are reflected from its surface into the objective lens and then form an image in the normal way. However this technique has received comparatively little application and will not be discussed further here.

In the second method, used for studying rough surfaces, a *replica*, rather analogous to a plaster cast, is taken from the surface, which is made sufficiently thin to be studied in the normal way by transmission electron microscopy. A rather different method of image formation is employed in the third technique, the scanning electron microscope, and this instrument, developed only some ten years ago, has largely replaced both reflection and replica techniques owing to its greater versatility and convenience of operation.

Surface replicas

Some of the ways in which surface replicas may be taken are illustrated in fig. 4.11. The image contrast depends mainly on variations

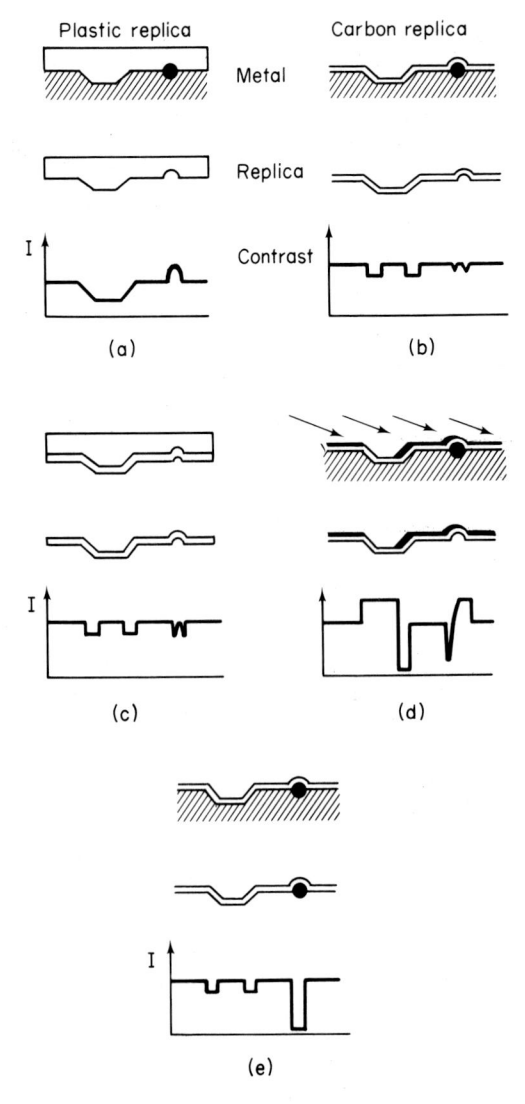

Fig. 4.11. Contrast formation using different replica techniques.

in the thickness of the replica, which themselves correspond to variations in the surface contour of the original specimen. This is because the material from which the replica is formed is generally amorphous, i.e. it possesses no periodic crystalline structure. Thus the electron scattering, whether elastic or inelastic, is non-coherent, and depends for its extent on the amount of material that the electron beam passes through. The electron intensity at the image I_t may be related to the local thickness of the replica t by the expression

$$I_t = I_0 e^{-At}$$

where I_0 is the original intensity of the beam and A is a constant which depends on the replica material. Since atoms of a higher atomic number possess a greater scattering power, the contrast may sometimes be increased by 'shadowing' the replica with a metal atom deposit, as described below.

The characteristics required of a replica are firstly that it should accurately reproduce the detail on the specimen surface and secondly that it should itself contain no structure down to the limit of resolution of the microscope. The various kinds of replica material in common use are as follows:

(a) Plastic replicas, such as Formvar and collodion. The plastic is dissolved in a suitable solvent and a drop of solution applied to the specimen surface and allowed to dry, so that the plastic can be stripped off again. The result is shown in fig. 4.11 (a) and it may be seen how the intensity in the image is directly related to the surface profile. The best resolution that may be obtained using this technique is about 10 nm.

(b) Carbon replicas, the carbon being evaporated on to the specimen surface *in vacuo*. In this way an extremely thin film may be formed which is able to follow the surface contours with sufficient accuracy to give a resolution of about 2 nm. The replica is then removed from the specimen surface by etching. The resulting image contrast is shown in fig. 4.11 (b). This differs somewhat from that obtained with the plastic replica since the differences in replica thickness occur at different points.

(c) Two-stage replicas. The disadvantage of the direct carbon replica technique is that the original specimen surface is destroyed, or at least altered, by the etching technique used to remove the carbon film. This may be avoided by first taking a plastic replica of the surface, and then taking a carbon replica of this, as shown in fig. 4.11 (c).

(d) Shadowed replicas. A considerable enhancement in contrast may be produced if a further amount of some heavy metal such as chromium or uranium is evaporated on to the surface of the carbon replica from a glancing angle. A varying thickness is obtained depending on whether the surface is tilted towards or away from the direction of deposition, as shown by fig. 4.11 (*d*). As well as enhancing contrast, this method allows a distinction to be made between depressions and elevations as may be seen from the contrast diagram.

(e) Carbon extraction replicas. The metal surface shown schematically in fig. 4.11 contains a precipitate particle. By following the procedure described above for the preparation of carbon replicas, but using an etchant which attacks the matrix while leaving the precipitate particle unaffected, it is possible to extract the particle embedded in the replica material, fig. 4.11 (*e*). Owing to the large difference in atomic number between the particle and the carbon matrix, particularly strong image contrast is given, and it is often possible to identify the particle by means of electron diffraction.

Summarizing, this method of taking surface replicas allows fairly simple surface structures to be imaged at a magnification and resolution which exceeds that obtainable in the optical microscope by an order of magnitude. However it will be appreciated that the replication process is not successful when the surface has a more complex topography, especially where some regions may be re-entrant. Nor is the technique suitable for studying the bulk microstructure in the form of a surface section. For the latter two instances we must turn to the scanning electron microscope.

Scanning electron microscopy

Although the layout of the scanning electron microscope is superficially rather similar to that of the conventional transmission electron microscope, its principle of operation is very different. In the transmission electron microscope, as in the optical microscope, the area of the specimen which is to be studied is illuminated with a static beam of radiation. After interacting with the specimen the radiation is focused by means of a lens system to form a magnified image. In the scanning electron microscope, on the other hand, the purpose of the lens system is merely to focus the electron beam down to an extremely fine spot, typically 10–20 nm in diameter. This fine spot is then scanned systematically across the specimen surface.

Electrons scattered from the surface are collected and the resulting signal, after amplification, is used to modulate the brightness of a cathode ray display tube which is being scanned synchronously with the incident beam, fig. 4.12. In this way a point-by-point image of the specimen surface is built up on the viewing screen, as shown by fig. 4.13. Thus no further focusing occurs after the electrons leave the specimen surface, and the magnification is simply the ratio of the size of the cathode ray tube (which is constant) to that of the area of the specimen over which the scan takes place. The latter is variable, and the magnification may be varied continuously between $\times 10$ and $\times 200\,000$, without any refocusing being necessary.

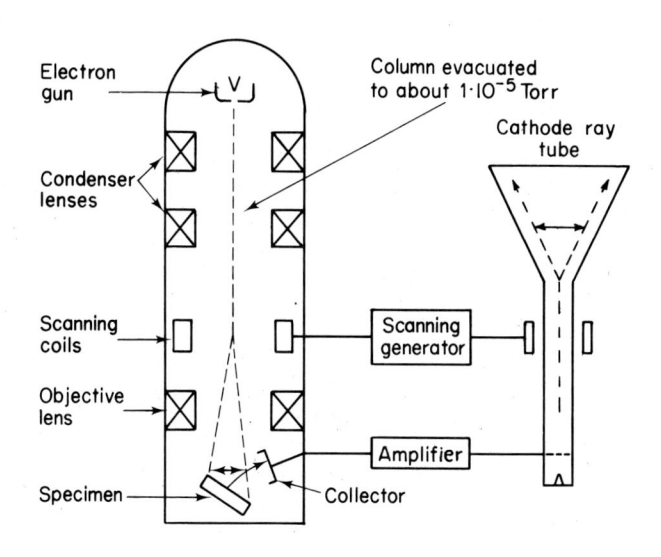

Fig. 4.12. Schematic diagram of the scanning electron microscope.

To use an analogy, if image formation in the transmission electron microscope is likened to that of a cinema projector, then that in the scanning electron microscope is similar to that of a television tube.

The resolution limit of the instrument is mainly defined by the size of the scan spot, and with conventional electron guns the signal intensity becomes too low to be really usable if the beam size is decreased below about 10 nm. However a new type of electron source has recently become available which removes this restriction, allowing beam sizes down to 0·1–0·2 nm to be used. Just as in the conventional electron microscope, the effective angular aperture of the electron beam is a very small fraction of a degree. This means that the depth of field is again very great, ranging from about half a centimetre at a magnification of around $\times 20$, down to about 1 μm at

At scan time t

Specimen Cathode ray tube

ℓ_1 ℓ_2

Radiation Signal

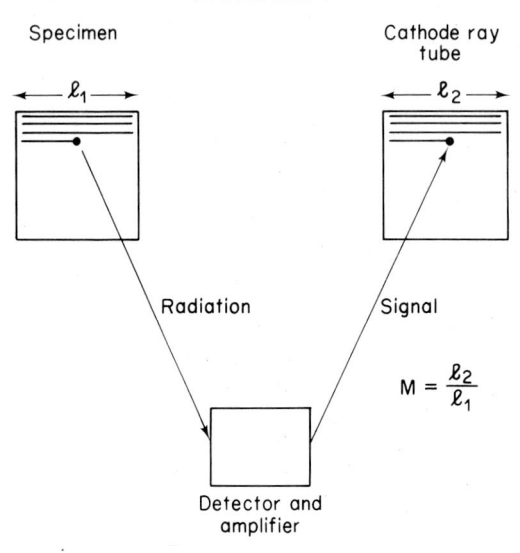

$$M = \frac{\ell_2}{\ell_1}$$

Detector and amplifier

Fig. 4.13. Schematic diagram showing how a point by point scanning image of the specimen is built up on the cathode ray tube screen.

× 10 000. This very considerable improvement in depth of field over that obtainable with the optical microscope is put to great effect in topographical studies as described below. It also facilitates the taking of stereoscopic pairs, which are obtained by tilting the specimen between two exposures, just as in the transmission electron microscope.

First, however, the different modes of image contrast that may be obtained will be discussed in connection with flat surface sections through the microstructure. These modes of contrast are illustrated in fig. 4.14, and they depend on the type of radiation selected for detection.

In the emissive mode, fig. 4.14 (*a*), which is the most commonly used, the collector is biased so as to attract the secondary electrons which are emitted from within the specimen, page 96. Since these are of quite low energy they are able to escape only if they originate from within a small distance—5 nm or so—of the specimen surface. Hence the image contrast is quite sensitive to any variations in surface flatness, and it also affected by composition to a certain extent.

In the reflective mode, fig. 4.14 (*b*), the collector is negatively biased so as to repel the low energy secondaries, leaving only the higher energy back-scattered primary electrons to be collected. These originate from much deeper within the specimen surface and the back-scattering yield (and hence the image contrast) is very strongly dependent on atomic species. Thus here it is possible to make some qualitative discrimination between various phases, in much the same way as different phases may be distinguished in the optical microscope.

In the specimen current, (or absorptive) mode, fig. 4.14 (c), an electrical lead is attached to the specimen and the current collected here acts as the signal. Clearly the more electrons that are back-scattered or secondary emitted from the specimen, the smaller will be the current generated in the specimen, and hence the contrast in this mode is the reverse of that in the previous two modes.

In the luminescent mode, fig. 4.14 (d) the electron collector system is replaced by a light guide and photomultiplier. In this way it is

(a)

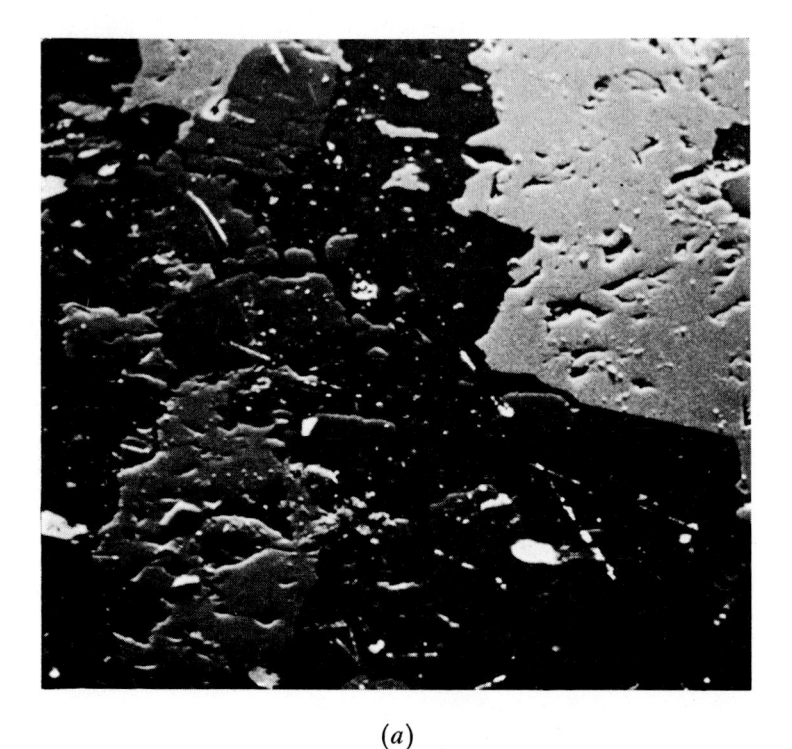

Fig. 4.14. Comparison scanning electron micrographs of a mineral section taken in the (a) emissive mode (b) reflective mode (c) absorptive mode (d) luminescent mode, × 220. *Cambridge Scientific Instruments Ltd.*

(b)

(c)

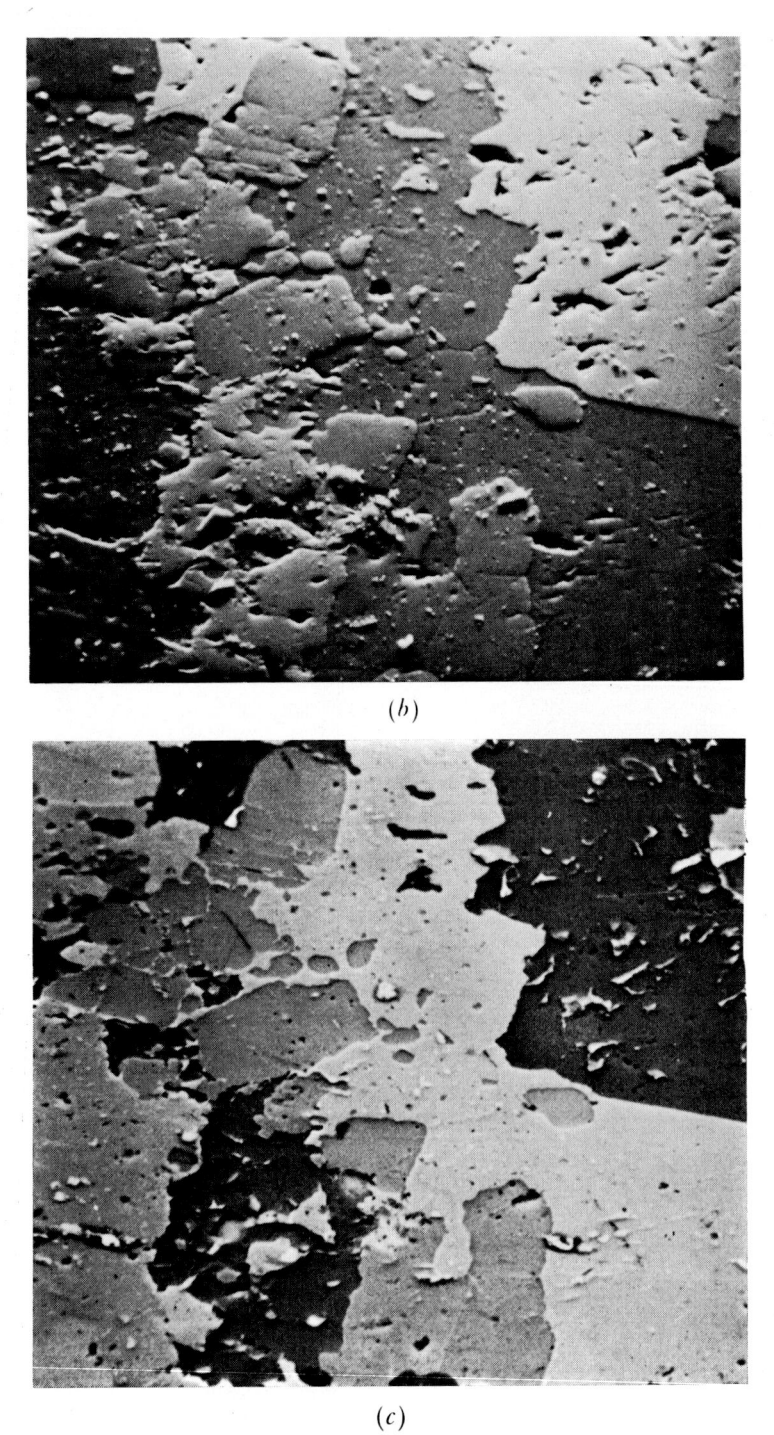

Fig. 4.14 (continued).

(*d*)

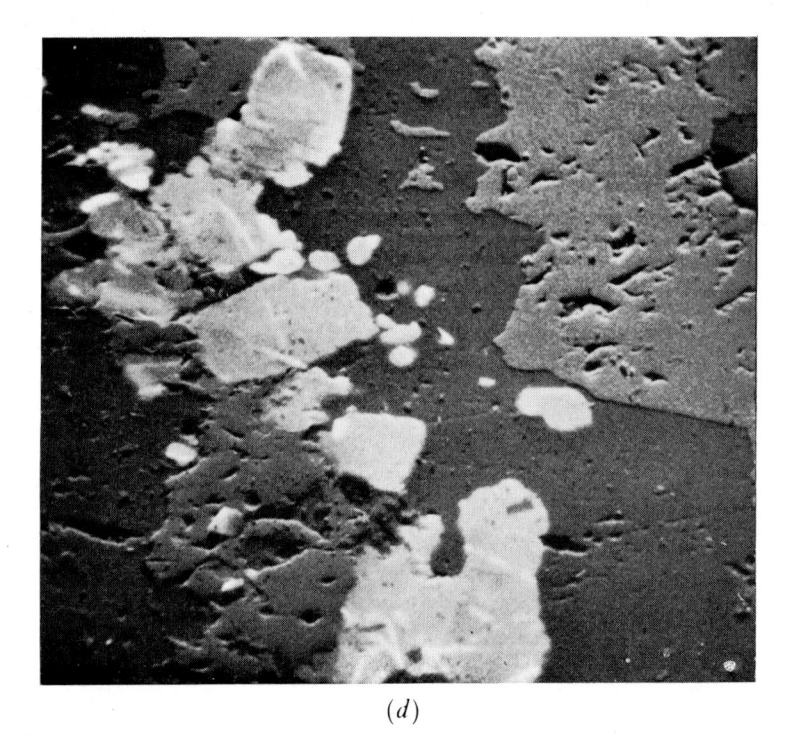

Fig. 4.14 (continued).

possible to produce a signal generated by the visible light (or cathodoluminescence, page 96) which is generated by certain materials under electron bombardment, and hence to identify their presence in the specimen.

Finally there is an X-ray mode in which the image signal is produced by the characteristic X-rays which are generated within the specimen. The advantage of this mode is that it is possible to reveal the relative distribution of each of the chemical elements making up the specimen, simply by selecting in turn only those X-rays which are characteristic of these elements, to form the image. In addition, by measuring the intensities of these X-rays, it is possible to obtain a quantitative determination of the concentration of these elements.

Here the scanning electron microscope begins to overlap with the somewhat similar technique which is known as the electron probe microanalyser (page 140). The latter instrument is primarily designed to yield this kind of information using X-rays, and employs a number of integral crystal spectrometers (page 129) by means of which the various X-rays are separated according to their wavelength. In

Fig. 4.15. Scanning electron micrographs of the surface of a fractured galena specimen. Magnifications (a) ×30, (b) ×135, (c) ×700, (d) ×2700.

the scanning electron microscope, on the other hand, X-ray detection is very much a subsidiary aspect, and is usually accomplished by means of a separate, and optional, detector which differentiates the X-rays this time on the basis of their difference in energy. Hence further discussion of this particular mode will be deferred until the following chapter.

The most visually dramatic application of the scanning electron microscope is in the study of surface relief. Considerable variations in surface height may be accommodated owing to the large depth of field and in addition, since it is the low energy secondary electrons which are used for imaging in this mode, it is possible for electrons arising out of the direct line of sight of the collector to be attracted and caught, thus giving rise to a remarkable 'three-dimensional' effect. Figure 4.15 reveals the ability of the scanning electron microscope to 'zoom in' on to a feature of interest, while fig. 4.16 shows the impression of solidity that may be gained, this time with a biological specimen.

(b)

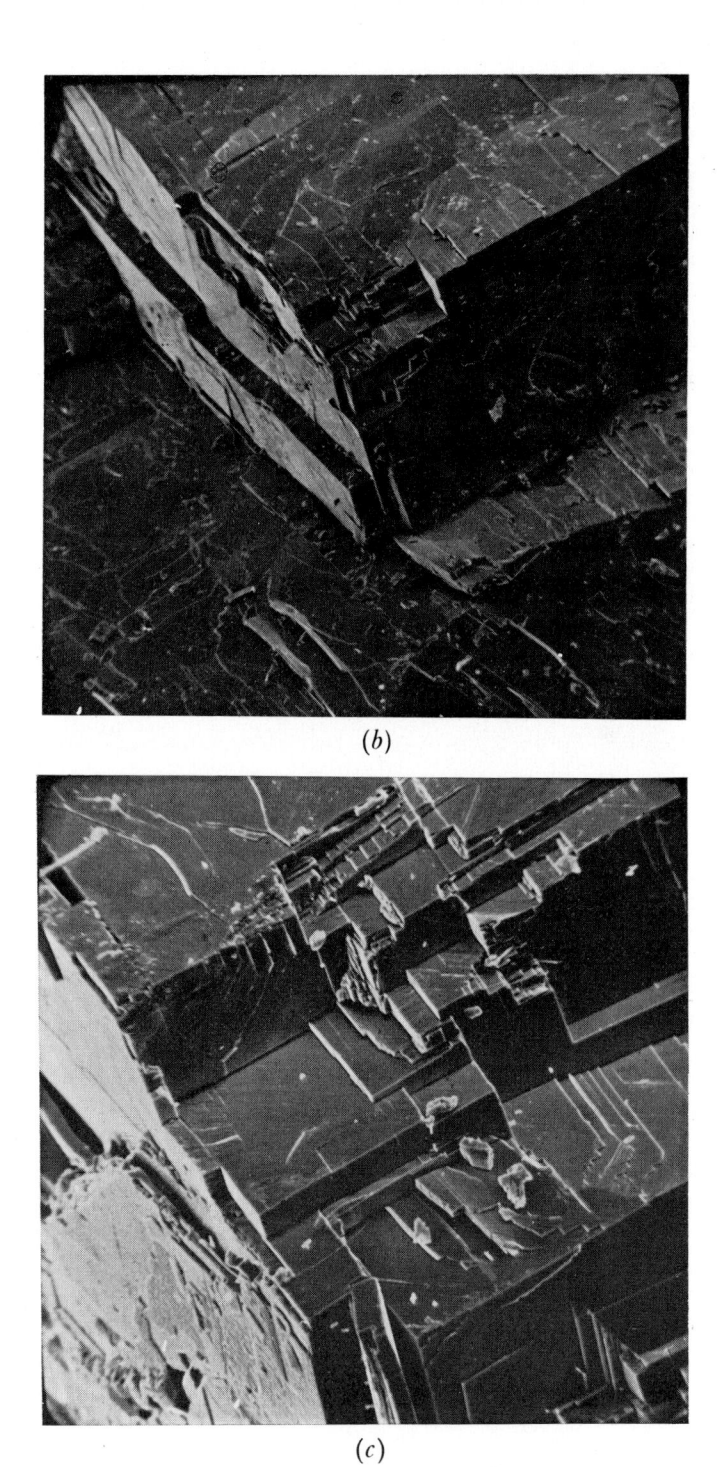

(c)
Fig. 4.15 (continued).

(*d*)

Fig. 4.15 (continued).

With biological and other non-conducting specimens it is necessary to evaporate a thin layer of metal on to their surface before they are examined. Beyond this no further preparation may be needed, except drying in certain cases, and specimens up to 10 mm in diameter may be used. Thus some quite macroscopic organisms have been studied in this way, including one or two small living creatures which are capable of withstanding a vacuum environment for short periods of time. Considerable application of the technique to metallurgical studies has been made, and an example of particular importance is the examination of microelectronic devices incorporating semi-conductors, in which surface potential differences may be used to give image contrast. Finally, it is possible to obtain some sort of crystallographic information by analysing patterns rather similar to Kikuchi lines (page 108) which arise due to electron channelling effects, and which can be observed at very low magnifications.

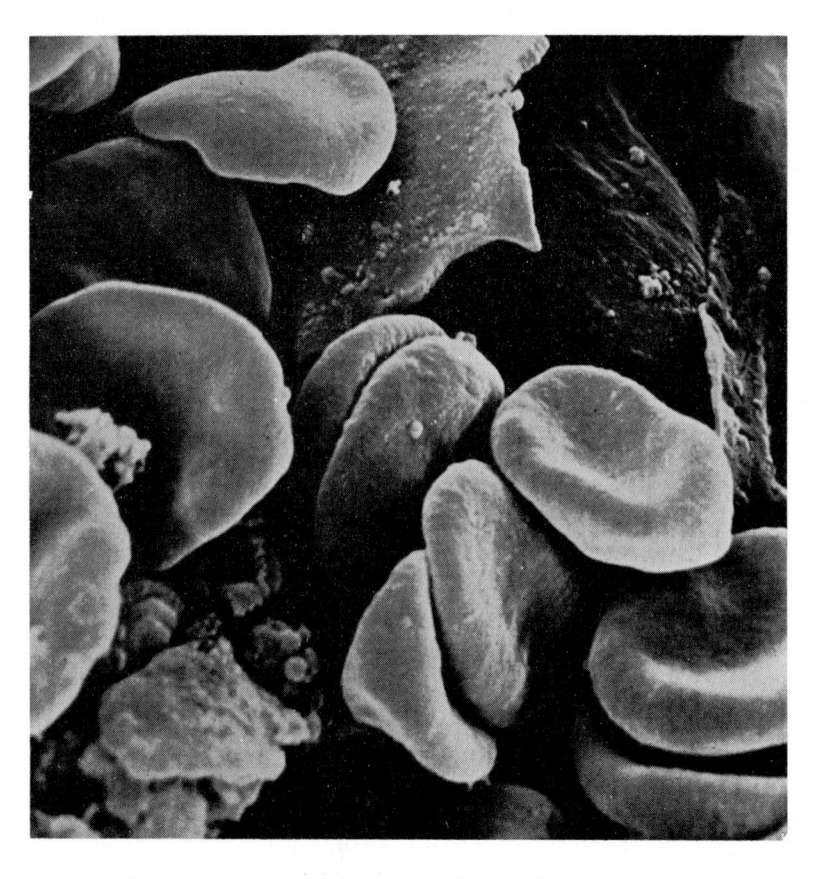

Fig. 4.16. Scanning electron micrograph of red blood cells on cell debris. ×7000. *C. G. Fick.*

Table 3. Variation of electron wavelength with accelerating potential difference

Accelerating p.d., in kV	Electron wavelength, in nm
50	0·0054
80	0·0042
100	0·0037
500	0·0014
1000	0·0009

CHAPTER 5
x-ray microscopy and microanalysis

5.1. Introduction

X-RAYS were discovered in 1895 by the German physicist Röntgen, who was later to become the first person to be awarded the Nobel prize for physics, in honour of his discovery. Röntgen himself was at a loss to understand the nature of X-rays (hence their name), finding that they were unaffected either by magnetic or electric fields (and hence were electrically neutral), and were neither reflected nor refracted as visible light is. However he did find that they were able to penetrate such 'opaque' materials as wood and metal, the amount to which they were absorbed by the material depending on its density, and also that they were registered by a photographic film.

It was not until 1912 that it was established that X-rays are a form of electromagnetic radiation of wavelength much shorter than that of light, typically around 0·1 nm. This is comparable with the interatomic spacings in solids and hence X-rays, like electrons, are strongly diffracted by crystalline material. This property is made use of in two ways. By studying the diffraction patterns formed using X-rays of known wavelength, it is possible to determine the structure of unknown crystals. This is known as X-ray crystallography. On the other hand, if crystals of known dimensions are employed, it is possible to identify unknown X-ray wavelengths. This technique is known as X-ray spectroscopy (page 129) and may be used to obtain a chemical analysis of the different atomic species present in a specimen, since they will each emit X-rays of quite different, and hence characteristic, wavelengths under suitable excitation. These various X-rays may be individually detected and their intensity measured. Indeed, a variation of the scanning electron microscope uses characteristic X-rays to form a direct image of the specimen (page 140).

In terms of more conventional microscopy, however, X-rays are a disappointment. If one considers the Abbe diffraction limit then their short wavelength promises considerably better ultimate resolution than can be obtained using light, although not quite as good as that obtained using electrons. The difficulty lies in finding some way of focusing X-rays. Refraction cannot be used since for X-rays the refractive index of all known materials is almost equal to unity, typically 0·99998. This leads to a focal length some 10 000 times the radius of curvature of the lens and, for a useful magnification, an image distance of up to a hundred times this extremely long focal length, rendering the concept unworkable. Since X-rays carry no electric charge, neither magnetic nor electrostatic lenses have any effect either.

Nevertheless considerable ingenuity has gone into devising techniques whereby X-rays might be used to form an image, since they do possess some particular advantage over light or electrons, notably the possibility of achieving high resolution. The principal advantage of X-rays however lies in the nature of the image contrast that they produce. Such contrast arises as a result of differential absorption of the incident X-rays between different regions of the specimen. This is analogous to the way in which contrast is obtained in the transmission optical microscope. However in the case of X-rays the degree of absorption depends very specifically both on the species of atoms which are present and on their number, and hence it is possible not only to reveal the presence of different microstructural features, but also to gain some measure of their composition.

A further advantage is the comparatively deep penetration of X-rays into thick objects, enabling internal details of opaque biological and metallurgical specimens to be seen. Coupled with this is a correspondingly greater depth of field permitting a complete three-dimensional view of the structure to be obtained. Furthermore, since X-rays, like electrons, are readily diffracted by crystalline material, techniques analogous to selected area electron diffraction (page 102) may be used to add crystallographic and structural information to that obtained by direct image formation. An example of how this is achieved is described on page 144.

Before describing the various techniques used to form X-ray images, it will be useful to consider the nature and detection of X-rays in rather more detail.

5.2. *The nature of X-rays*

Generation

X-rays are produced when any material is bombarded by very high energy particles or radiation. Usually this takes the form of electrons but in certain circumstances ions, γ-rays or indeed X-rays themselves (as in X-ray fluorescence analysis, page 182), may be employed.

When X-rays are required for either diffraction or microscopy they are generated using apparatus of the type shown in fig. 5.1. Electrons produced by a heated tungsten filament are focused on to a metal target (the anode) set into a copper block. The electrons are accelerated to high energy by applying a potential difference of up to 50 kV between the anode (at earth potential) and the filament or cathode (negative). Less than 1 per cent of their energy is actually converted into X-rays, most of the remainder being dissipated as heat, for which reason the anode must be water-cooled.

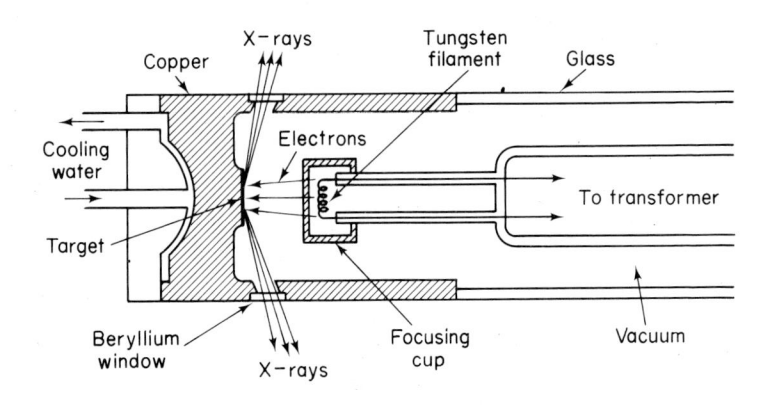

Fig. 5.1. Cross-section of an X-ray tube.

Under the electron bombardment X-rays are generated and are emitted in all directions, being allowed to escape from the tube through two or more windows, typically made of beryllium, set in the tube housing. The whole tube must be evacuated down to a pressure of about 10^{-4} Torr in order to avoid electron absorption (the X-rays are largely unaffected) and it is usually found convenient to use a permanently sealed tube in order to avoid the need for cumbersome vacuum pumping equipment, although it is then necessary to possess as many such units as the number of different target materials which will be required.

The X-ray spectrum

The electron current through the X-ray tube is controlled by varying the current which heats the filament, and it is this which determines the quantity of radiation emitted by the tube. On the other hand, the magnitude of the accelerating voltage determines the type or wavelength of this radiation.

The energy of an electron striking the target is given by
$$E = eV$$
where e is the charge on the electron and V is the accelerating potential difference. If the electron is completely decelerated in an encounter with a single atom, then all its energy will be converted into a single X-ray quantum whose frequency, v, is given by
$$E = hv$$
where h is the Planck constant. Since
$$v = c/\lambda$$
where c is the velocity of light and λ is the wavelength of the X-rays,
$$\lambda = hc/eV.$$
Substituting values for these constants,
$$\lambda = 1240/V$$
when V is measured in volts and λ in nm.

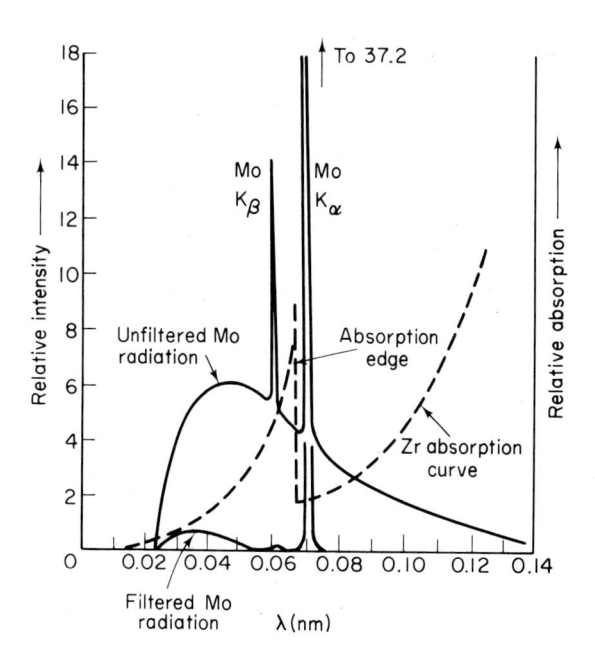

Fig. 5.2. Emission and absorption spectra for Mo radiation and Zr filter.

In practice, however, only a small fraction of the electrons are stopped in single collisions. The majority of the electrons lose their energy in a series of successive collisions with a number of atoms, hence giving off X-ray quanta with energies lower (and hence wavelengths longer) than that calculated above. Thus a continuous spectrum of X-radiation is generated, whose minimum wavelength is determined by the accelerating voltage applied to the tube, and which has the form shown in fig. 5.2. The continuous radiation is known as white radiation or bremsstrahlung (braking radiation) since it is the result of electron deceleration.

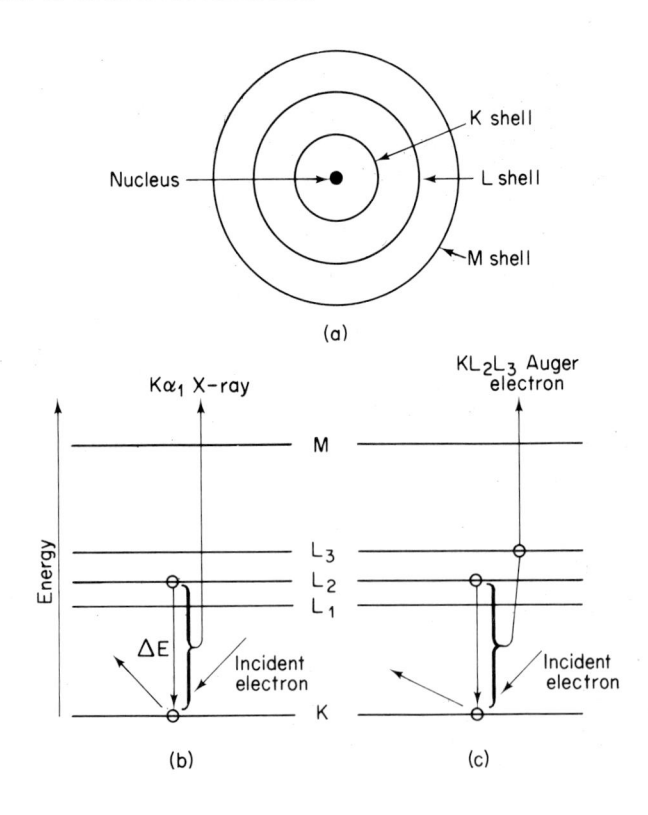

Fig. 5.3. Origin of characteristic radiation. (a) simple electron shell model of the atom (b) energy level diagram showing emission of K_{α_1} X-ray (c) as above showing emission of a KL_2L_3 Auger electron.

Providing the X-ray tube is operated at a sufficiently high voltage there will be an additional line spectrum superimposed on the continuous radiation, as shown in fig. 5.2. These high intensity peaks are known as characteristic radiation, since their wavelengths are a function of the target material.

The origin of this characteristic radiation may be discussed in terms of a simple model of the atom, fig. 5.3 (*a*). Here an atom is represented as a positively charged nucleus surrounded by electrons arranged in a series of discrete shells of different energy (and which may themselves be further subdivided), referred to as K, L, M, ... These may be illustrated schematically on an energy level diagram, as shown in fig. 5.3 (*b*). Sometimes the impinging electrons can make a direct impact upon one of the inner electrons of an atom in the target material, and, if their energy is sufficiently great, knock this electron right out of the atom. The atom is then energetically unstable, and another electron in the same atom will drop down into the space vacated. In doing so it loses energy, ΔE, and a quantum of radiation is emitted whose wavelength, λ, is given by

$$\lambda = hc/\Delta E$$

Since ΔE is a definite quantity associated with the particular energy change occurring in this atom, the wavelength concerned is characteristic of this particular atomic species.

Several such transitions are possible, and if for example, as illustrated by fig. 5.3 (*b*), a K shell electron is displaced and an electron falls from one of the L shells into the vacant site in the K shell, then the resulting X-ray is known as K_α radiation. In practice the L_1–K transition cannot occur and hence L_2–K is known as K_{α_1}, and L_3–K as K_{α_2} radiation. These two peaks are generally very close together, and are often regarded as if they were a single wavelength. Note that if an electron from the M shell falls into the vacant site—a less favoured possibility—then the weaker K_β radiation is produced. This necessarily possesses a shorter wavelength than the K_α. Further transitions may be produced, such as M–L, but these are of less importance. Table 4 on page 145 lists the wavelengths of the characteristic radiation emitted by a number of different target materials. If X-rays of one wavelength only are required, for example the K_α, then a suitable filter must be used, as described on page 128.

It is convenient at this point to discuss a competing process for the dissipation of the energy produced by an electron dropping down from one level into a vacant site in a lower level. This process is shown in fig. 5.3 (*c*). Rather than the energy ΔE being released in the form of an X-ray quantum, it may instead be transferred to yet another electron within the atom, which is then ejected. This electron is known as an Auger electron, and its energy is once again characteristic

of the target material. In the example shown the initial energy made available is given by
$$\Delta E = E_K - E_{L_2}$$
If this is transferred to an electron in the L_3 level an amount of energy equal to E_{L_3} must be expended in ejecting the electron from the atom and its resulting energy is given by $E_K - E_{L_2} - E_{L_3}$. The nomenclature is different to that used in the X-ray case, and this would be referred to as a KL_2L_3 Auger electron. The use of such electrons in analysis is discussed on page 182.

X-ray absorption

When a beam of X-rays passes through a thickness t of a particular material, its intensity is reduced from the initial value I_0 to a value I, following an exponential relationship of the form
$$I = I_0 e^{-\mu t}$$
where μ is a constant whose value depends on the atomic number of the material and on the X-ray wavelength. It is usual to replace μ by the term μ/ρ, where ρ is the density of the material. This new quantity is known as the mass absorption coefficient, μ_m, and is independent of the physical state of the material.

The variation of μ_m with wavelength is shown schematically by the dotted curve in fig. 5.2. It is characterized by a series of abrupt changes known as absorption edges. These arise since as the wavelength of the X-rays decreases (and their energy increases) they reach the point where they are themselves able to dislodge electrons from, for example, the L or K shells of the atoms making up the target material. This results in an abrupt increase in the extent to which they are absorbed.

The existence of absorption edges provides a simple way of obtaining effectively monochromatic radiation from a spectrum such as that shown in fig. 5.2. In general the wavelength of the absorption edge for a given element lies in between the K_β and K_α wavelengths in the emission spectrum of the element with atomic number one or two units greater. Thus, for example, a thin sheet of zirconium foil (atomic number 40) will absorb most of the K_β radiation from a molybdenum target (atomic number 42) but will allow through almost all of the, effectively monochromatic, K_α component. In the process most of the white radiation will also be removed. The effect of such a zirconium filter on the radiation spectrum from molybdenum is illustrated in fig. 5.2.

Detection and measurement of X-rays

In the straightforward techniques of X-ray microscopy the X-rays may be detected using a fluorescent screen, which may then be photographed. Alternatively the X-rays may be allowed to interact directly with the photographic emulsion. However there are several applications (in particular in this chapter the electron probe microanalyser, page 140) where it is necessary to be able to detect, and to measure the intensity of, X-rays of particular wavelengths.

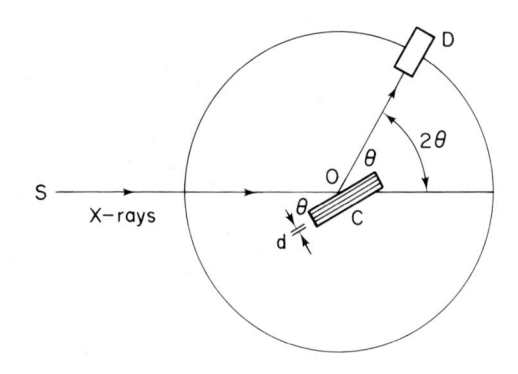

Fig. 5.4. X-ray spectrometer.

Figure 5.4 shows the essential details of an X-ray spectrometer, used for selecting X-rays of a particular wavelength. X-rays originating from the source in question, S, are incident on a crystal, C, which may be set at any desired angle to the incident beam by rotation about an axis through O, the centre of the spectrometer circle. Since d, the interplanar spacing of the atomic planes parallel to the face of the crystal, is fixed and known, we can see that only those X-rays whose wavelength, λ, is given by the Bragg equation

$$2d \sin \theta = n\lambda$$

will be diffracted into the detector set at D. By rotating the crystal C through various values of the angle θ, keeping the detector D at an angle 2θ to the incident beam, the intensities of a whole range of X-rays with different wavelengths may be measured.

Measurement of X-ray intensities is carried out using a Geiger counter, proportional counter or scintillation counter. The first two work in a similar way, as illustrated in fig. 5.5 (*a*). X-rays entering the gas-filled chamber of the counter cause ionization of the gas atoms whereupon the electrons, which are attracted to the positively-biased wire anode, and gas ions, which are attracted towards the negatively biased walls of the chamber, cause a current to flow whose magnitude is proportional to the X-ray intensity. In the scintillation-type counter, fig. 5.5 (*b*), the incident X-rays impinge upon a crystal of sodium iodide which fluoresces, emitting visible light. The latter strikes a photocathode, ejecting electrons whose number is increased using a photomultiplier before the signal is finally recorded. Usually the output of the detector is fed into some form of chart recorder for visual display.

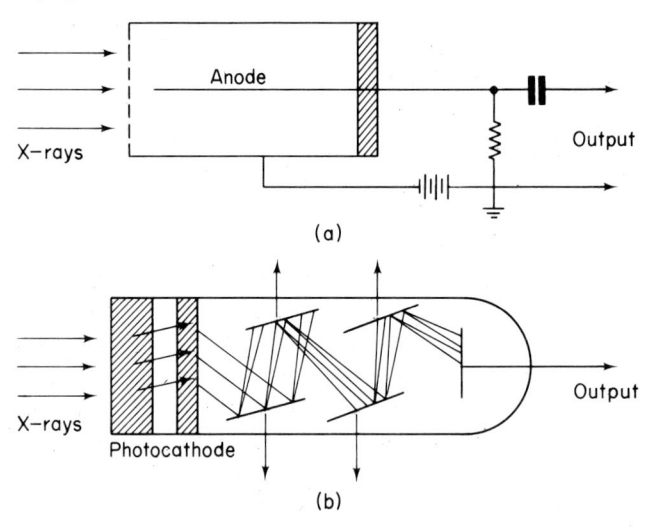

Fig. 5.5. X-ray detectors. (*a*) Geiger or proportional counter (*b*) scintillation counter.

5.3. *X-ray microscopy*

Since conventional methods of image formation cannot be used with X-rays, the two main techniques of X-ray microscopy, contact microradiography and X-ray projection microscopy, work by forming a very simple shadow image of the specimen, rather like that formed when a photographic slide is illuminated by a beam of light, different regions giving rise to different degrees of absorption.

Contact microradiography

Strictly speaking, contact microradiography is not a form of microscopy at all, since on its own it does not produce a magnified

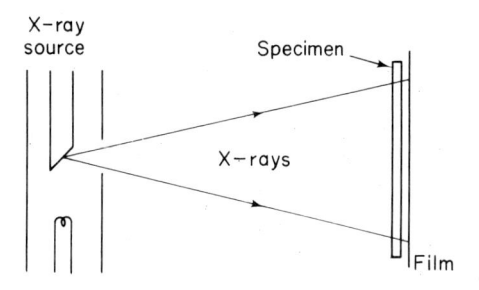

Fig. 5.6. Contact microradiography.

image. The apparatus is extremely simple, and consists of a thin specimen placed as close as possible to a photographic emulsion, and at a certain distance from an X-ray source (fig. 5.6). The X-rays transmitted through the specimen form an image on the emulsion at effectively unit magnification. The resulting negative is then examined under a high resolution optical microscope, and selected areas may subsequently be enlarged photographically. Hence of the three principal microscope parameters, magnification, resolution and contrast, the first is provided entirely by a conventional optical microscope.

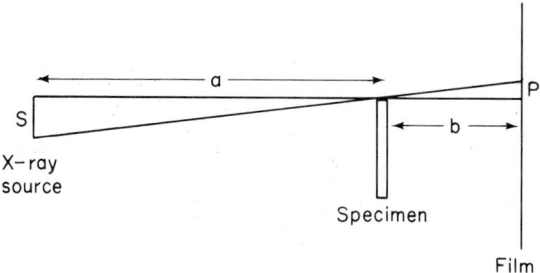

Fig. 5.7. Relative source, specimen and film geometry used in contact microradiography and X-ray projection microscopy.

The resolution that can be obtained is much worse than that permitted by the Abbe diffraction limit. This is due to several factors. Firstly there is geometrical blurring in the primary image due to the formation of a penumbra. From fig. 5.7 it can be seen that the width, p, of the penumbra is given by

$$p = sb/a$$

where s is the width of the X-ray source, b the specimen-to-film distance, and a the source-to-specimen distance. Thus for optimum resolution the specimen is placed in as near contact as possible with the film (reducing b) and an X-ray source of small angular aperture is used. This latter stringency has the undesirable effect of increasing photographic exposure times due to the reduced X-ray intensity; increasing the distance a would carry a similar disadvantage. In practice the degree of geometrical blurring may be reduced sufficiently for it not to constitute the ultimate limit.

A second consideration is that the photographic emulsion must have a grain size that is finer than the detail which it is eventually desired to reveal. This also is fairly readily achieved. The ultimate limitation, therefore, is set by the resolution limit of the optical microscope used to obtain the final magnified image. Attempts have been made to improve on this by examining negatives in the electron microscope, but there are a number of practical difficulties connected with this.

What then is the advantage of contact microradiography over the optical microscope used alone? Firstly there is an effective increase in the depth of field since the X-rays are able to penetrate a sheet of metal, for example, of up to 0·1 mm in thickness, giving a much greater chance of detecting features, such as microcracks or slag inclusions in steels, which form a very small volume fraction of the sample.

The main advantage, however, is the sensitive control over image contrast that may be exercised. The contrast between two structures depends on the difference in their mass absorption coefficients. Since these vary in a known way with the wavelength of the X-rays used (fig. 5.2) it is possible to select the degree of contrast desired for different regions of the microstructure, simply by varying the wavelength of the incident X-rays, especially when the abrupt changes in the absorption coefficient that occur at the various absorption edges are taken into account.

In biological studies contact microradiography has been used on a wide range of animal and plant cells, including such materials as bone and teeth. Since much thicker sections may be viewed than is feasible with the transmission optical microscope it has been possible to examine small structures such as leaves and seeds with virtually no preparation, in addition to small *living* specimens. A wide range of metallurgical microstructures may also be studied, particular interest being centred on small inclusions, defects and segregation effects. Also of interest in this respect is the somewhat analogous technique of autoradiography, wherein a sample containing some radioactive element is placed into contact with a photographic film.

(a)

(b)

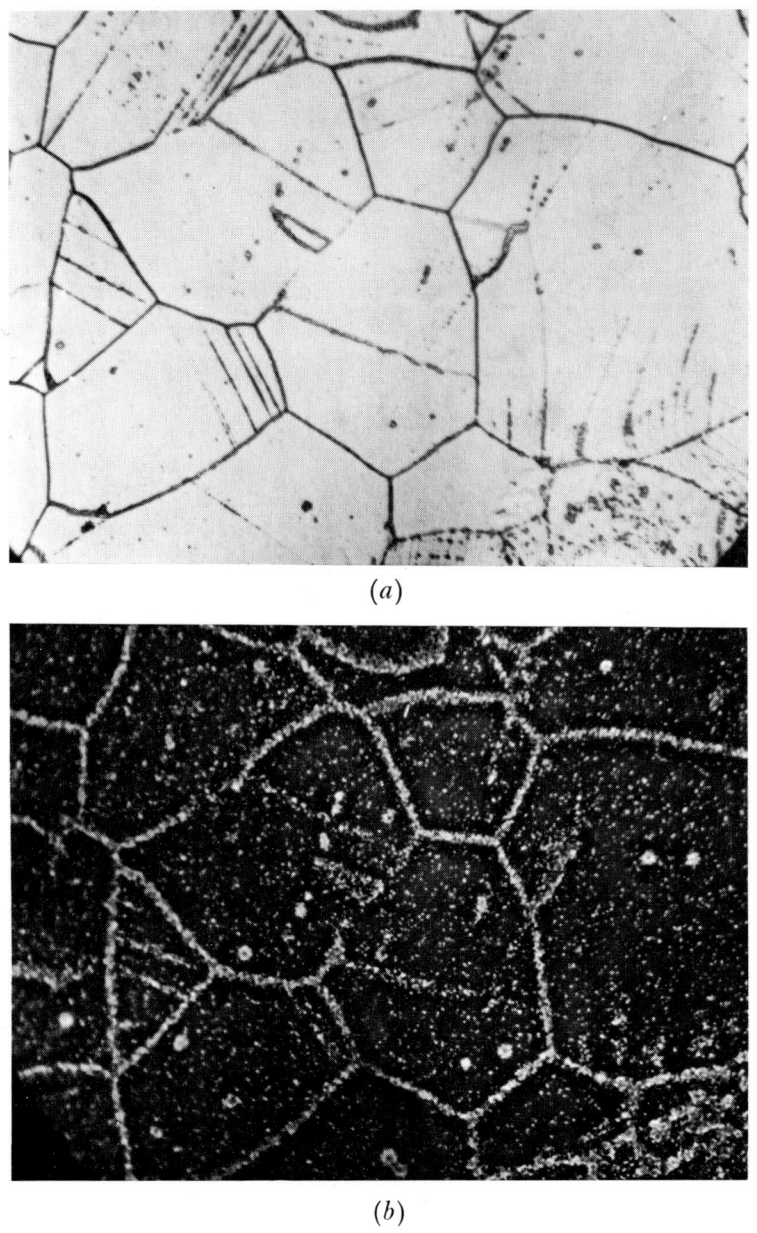

Fig. 5.8. Boron distribution in a heat-treated steel. (a) optical micrograph, (b) autoradiograph, × 500. Comparison of (b) with (a) reveals that the boron has segregated both to the grain boundaries and to small inclusions within the grain. *U.K.A.E.A., A.E.R.E., Harwell.*

The radiation produced by those regions of the specimen which contain the radioactive element produces blackening of the emulsion, and hence image contrast. In the case of biological studies the radioisotope may be administered to the living organism, and tissue samples removed later for examination. With metals the radioisotope may either be added to the melt or produced *in situ* by irradiation. The latter technique was the one used in fig. 5.8, which shows a boron-containing steel. In the autoradiograph, fig. 5.8 (*b*), those areas of the steel which are rich in boron show up white against the dark background.

In addition to revealing direct microstructural information, the microradiography technique may also be used to provide a quantitative chemical analysis, since the amount of X-ray absorption also depends on the total amounts of the elements present. The degree of absorption is measured either by a photometric measurement of the degree of blackening of the photographic emulsion, or directly using a Geiger counter or a proportional counter. The relative concentration of the various elements is calculated by comparing the absorption to that produced by the pure element, or by a standard reference material.

X-ray projection microscopy

The magnification of the image produced by the arrangement illustrated in fig. 5.7 can easily be shown to be:

$$M = (a+b)/a$$

In contact microradiography, since b is very small compared to a, this reduces in practice to unity. However if, instead, a is made very small with respect to b, then a primary magnified X-ray image will be formed whose magnification is effectively equal to b/a. This is the principle of the X-ray projection microscope, fig. 5.9.

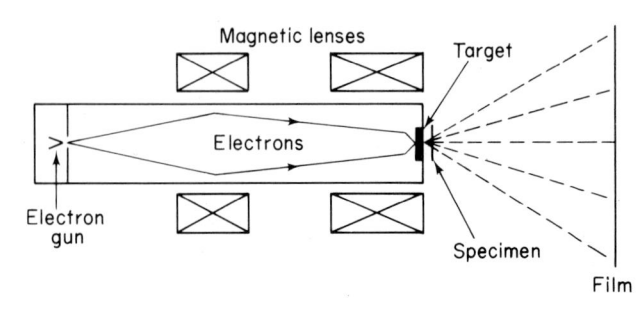

Fig. 5.9. X-ray projection microscope.

Again the primary X-ray image is viewed subsequently at higher magnifications under the optical microscope, but since this primary image already has a certain amount of magnification, the resolution limit of the technique is no longer determined by that of the optical microscope, but by the geometrical penumbra effect referred to above.

As before the size of the penumbra is given by :

$$p = sb/a$$

However since the resolution of a microscope is customarily calculated at the object plane this becomes simply equal to s, since the magnification is equal to b/a. Thus the size of the X-ray source becomes the determining factor, and it is now no longer sufficient to use conventional sources, even with a fine pinhole aperture. Instead, as fig. 5.9 shows, an electron beam is focused to an extremely tiny spot on to a target material which is in the form of a thin foil, so arranged that the specimen can be placed within a millimetre of it. The X-ray source then becomes the tiny area of the target which is being bombarded by the electrons.

With this technique resolutions of 0·1 to 1 μm have been achieved, together with a primary magnification of up to about × 1000, although it is more usually operated at much less demanding values of these two parameters. Image contrast arises in just the same way as with contact microradiography, and the applications of the two techniques are similar. A useful advantage of the projection technique is the even greater depth of field it possesses enabling stereoscopic pairs to be taken even at very high magnifications, and also enabling much larger specimens to be examined, as illustrated by fig. 5.10. It is, however, much more complex and expensive.

Reflection microscopy

It was noted on page 123 that X-rays cannot usefully be focused by refraction through a lens since the refractive index of materials for X-rays is virtually equal to unity. For the same reason the reflection coefficient for X-rays incident *normally* on a polished surface is very small. However since the refractive index is actually *less* than unity this means that at a certain angle of incidence total *external* reflection of X-rays will take place ; that is total reflection occurs in the less dense medium rather than the more dense one as in the case of visible light. Thus the reflection coefficient for X-rays incident at a low angle ($\sim$ 30′) on a polished surface, is very high.

The above property raises the possibility that X-rays may be

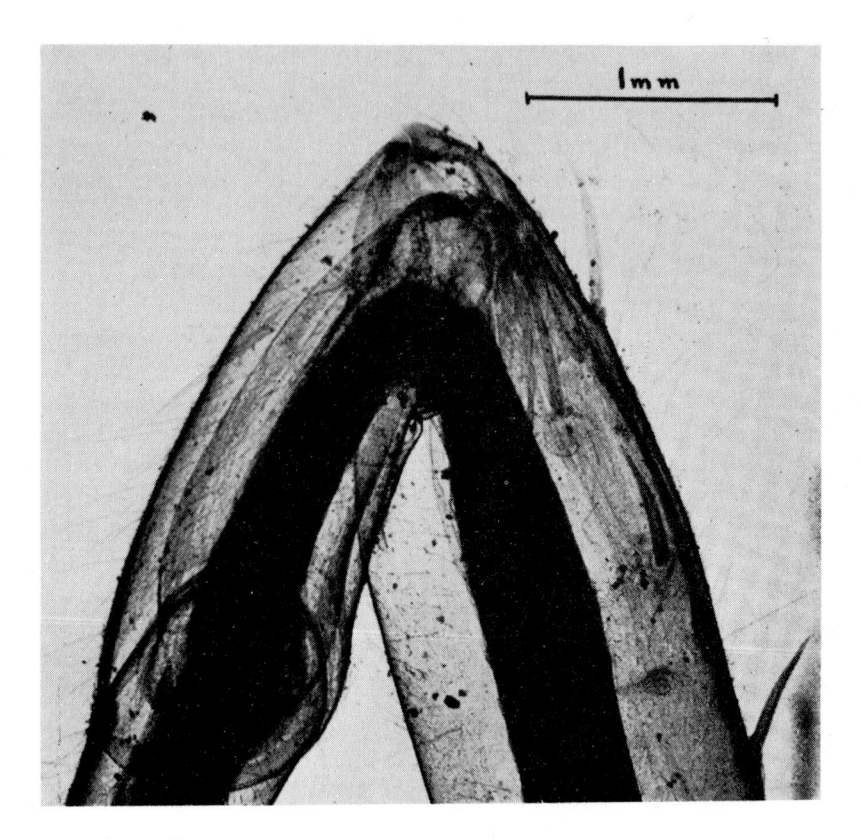

Fig. 5.10. X-ray projection micrograph of spider's knee. *W. C. Nixon.*

focused using a curved mirror surface, as shown in fig. 5.11 (*a*) (the angle of incidence has been greatly exaggerated for clarity). Considerable astigmatism is introduced by this procedure which may be reduced by using two mirrors set at right angles, fig. 5.11 (*b*). Correct alignment of the mirrors for such low angles of incidence is, however, very difficult.

The theoretical limit of resolution for such a system is set by diffraction, just as in the optical microscope. Using an X-ray wavelength of 0·1 nm, and with an effective angular aperture equal to the critical glancing angle of 0·4°, the ultimate resolution would be 8·5 nm. In practice, however, the resolution is actually limited by the accuracy with which the focusing elements, the mirrors, can be constructed—just as it is with the magnetic lenses of the electron microscope. To obtain the above sort of limit would require an

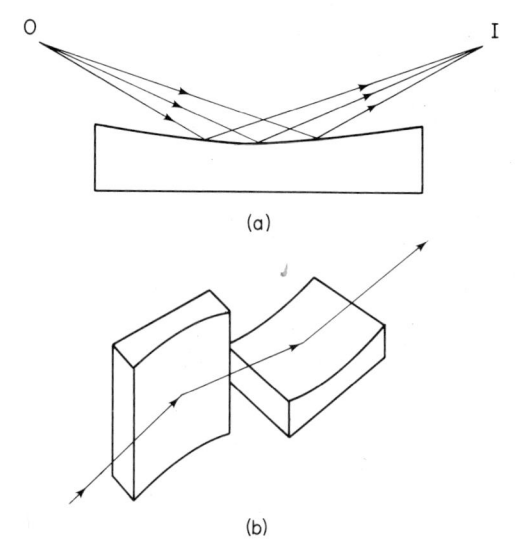

Fig. 5.11. X-ray reflection microscopy. (a) X-rays from a source O form an astigmatic image, I. (b) Use of two mirrors to reduce the degree of astigmatism.

accuracy of better than 0·1 nm in the shape of the mirror surface, a much more stringent requirement than is encountered with optical microscopy. At the present, therefore, such aberrations restrict the useful resolution to some hundreds of nm, and the system finds little practical use. However it is the nearest technique that there is to an X-ray microscope using a conventional method of image formation.

5.4. X-ray diffraction microscopy

Absorption contrast in X-ray microscopy arises from variations in chemical composition, and hence provides information about the composition and distribution of the different phases within the sample. However it gives no information concerning the crystal defects such as grain boundaries and dislocations which are of such great importance in metallurgical studies.

The technique of X-ray diffraction microscopy (known also as X-ray topography) relies on a different method of contrast formation, and is thereby able to reveal the presence of such crystal defects. Essentially it is a dark-field technique—analogous to those discussed previously in connection with both optical and electron microscopy—wherein the direct beam is blocked off after reaching the specimen and only the diffracted beams are allowed to form an image. This may be carried out either in back-reflection or in transmission, and several different modifications of these techniques exist. It will be sufficient here to discuss the two principal methods used in each category.

The Berg–Barrett technique

Figure 5.12 shows the experimental layout used in the Berg–Barrett technique. Radiation from a monochromatic X-ray source is used which is collimated using a fine slit. The specimen, usually in the form of a single crystal, is aligned so that a prominent set of its crystal planes lies at such an angle to the beam as to lead to strong Bragg diffraction. The resulting diffracted radiation forms an image on a fluorescent screen or photographic emulsion placed as close as possible to the specimen.

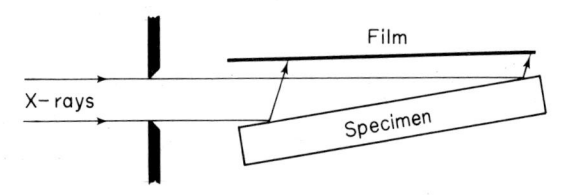

Fig. 5.12. The Berg–Barrett technique.

Just as in electron microscopy, any crystal defect, such as a dislocation, will alter the intensity of the diffracted beam in its vicinity, thus producing image contrast. The presence of individual dislocations may be revealed in this way, providing the dislocation density within the volume studied is not too high. As in contact microradiography, the primary magnification produced by this technique

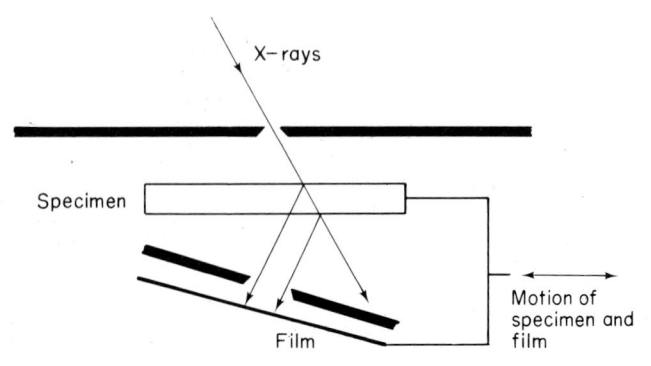

Fig. 5.13. The Lang technique.

is unity, although again subsequent optical enlargement may be used. A useful magnification of up to a few hundred times may be achieved, with a limiting resolution of a few tens of micrometres.

The Lang technique

In the Lang technique, commonly referred to as Lang topography, the specimen is studied in transmission rather than in back reflection, fig. 5.13. Again monochromatic radiation is used, the direct beam being stopped by an absorbing screen while the image is formed by the diffracted radiation. With elements of low atomic number the specimen thickness may be a millimetre or so, but it is more usual to restrict it to a few hundred microns for optimum contrast and resolution. If the specimen and the film are held stationary, then the photograph obtained of the small section of the specimen which is irradiated is known as a section topograph. Alternatively the specimen and film may be mounted on a moving carriage to provide a photograph of a larger volume of the specimen, which is now referred to as a projection topograph. The spatial relationships of the defects within the specimen may be revealed by taking stereoscopic pairs.

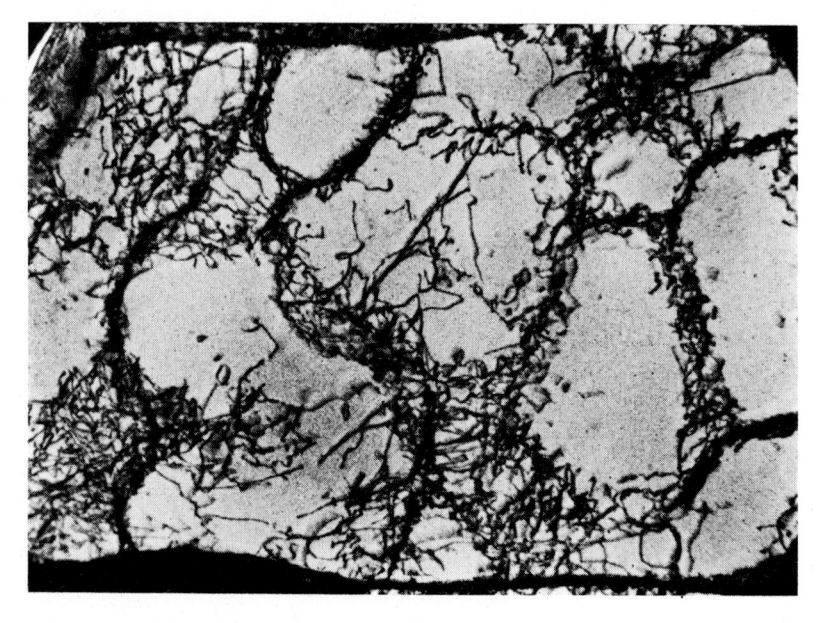

Fig. 5.14. X-ray topograph showing dislocations in magnesium oxide, × 100.
A. R. Lang.

This is accomplished by altering the orientation of the specimen between exposures so that a different set of crystal planes is in the Bragg diffraction position. Figure 5.14 shows an example of dislocation contrast obtained using the Lang technique.

The electron microscope is of course capable of revealing such crystal defects with very much better resolution. However, the X-ray diffraction technique does have the advantage that specimens several thousand times thicker may be studied, and also the specimen thinning processes which may themselves alter the dislocation array in electron microscope specimens are avoided. The major disadvantage of the technique, in addition to its poorer resolution, is the very long photographic exposure times that are needed.

5.5. *The electron probe microanalyser*

Introduction

In principle, the electron probe microanalyser is very similar to the scanning electron microscope, which was discussed on pages 112–120. It will be recalled that in the latter technique a fine electron beam is scanned across the specimen surface, and either the back-scattered primary, or secondary emitted, electrons are used to form an image of the specimen on a synchronously scanned cathode ray tube.

While this is going on, X-rays will also be generated within the region of the specimen being irradiated by the incident electron beam. Superimposed on to the continuous background of white radiation are the peaks occurring at sharply defined wavelengths which are characteristic of the different atomic species which are present in the specimen. In the electron probe microanalyser this characteristic X-radiation is used in two ways. Firstly it may be used directly to form an image: if the wavelength characteristic of a particular element is singled out, then the image will show positive contrast only from those regions of the specimen which contain this element, hence revealing its distribution within the microstructure. Secondly the intensity of the radiation may be measured in order to determine the actual concentration in which the element is present.

This, then, is the basis of the electron probe microanalyser. It is perhaps not a true X-ray microscope, since the incident radiation actually takes the form of electrons, and the image forming X-rays are generated within the specimen itself. Nevertheless its ability to combine direct microstructural information with quantitative chemical analysis makes it by far the most important technique to be discussed in this chapter.

Design

Although in practice its construction may be somewhat different, schematically the design of the electron probe microanalyser is similar to that of the scanning electron microscope, fig. 4.12. Thus it consists of an evacuated column containing an electron gun, electron lenses, and deflection coils to scan the beam across the specimen. The difference between the two instruments stems from the fact that the electron probe microanalyser is designed to provide a quantitative chemical analysis, with image formation of only secondary concern, while in the scanning electron microscope the emphasis is reversed.

In order to increase the sensitivity for X-ray detection, higher beam currents must be used than is necessary in the scanning electron microscope, and this necessitates a primary electron beam of about 1 μm in diameter. The image resolution, therefore, is restricted to this value, thus being over an order of magnitude worse than in the scanning electron microscope. The X-rays are excited from a surface layer about 1 μm thick, and hence the minimum volume which can be analysed is about 1 μm^3.

Incorporated into the design are one or more crystal spectrometers. These are used to select a particular X-ray wavelength for transmission to the detector. The output from the detector may be taken directly to the cathode ray tube to form an image (if more than one spectrometer is employed then the distribution of a number of elements may be monitored simultaneously on a number of viewing screens), or alternatively to some counting device which registers the X-ray intensity via a pen recorder, tape punch, or other print-out facility. As we have seen, similar equipment may also be attached to a scanning electron microscope, and greater beam diameters could be used here as well. However, X-ray intensities are so low that really accurate analyses, especially where only small quantities of a particular species are present, can only be obtained when the entire instrument is designed to this end.

The specimen must be in a form similar to that required for optical microscopy, i.e. highly flat and polished, in order to minimize absorption effects due to surface irregularities. Indeed low-magnification optical microscope viewing is often incorporated into the design. Electron-imaging facilities are included just as in the scanning electron microscope, although the images are not as good due to the inferior resolution.

Operation

Initially, the optical microscope facility may be used to select the general area of interest on the specimen, and then, at higher magnifications, to locate small particles, specific phases, etc. Electron imaging is useful in cases where it is not possible to produce a sufficiently flat surface for the optical microscope, and also provides the opportunity to get the electron spot into its best focus, as judged by the sharpness of the electron image.

The use of the X-ray imaging facility in revealing the distribution of various phases is shown in fig. 5.15. These micrographs are of a section through the mineral bravoite, which consists of interleaved

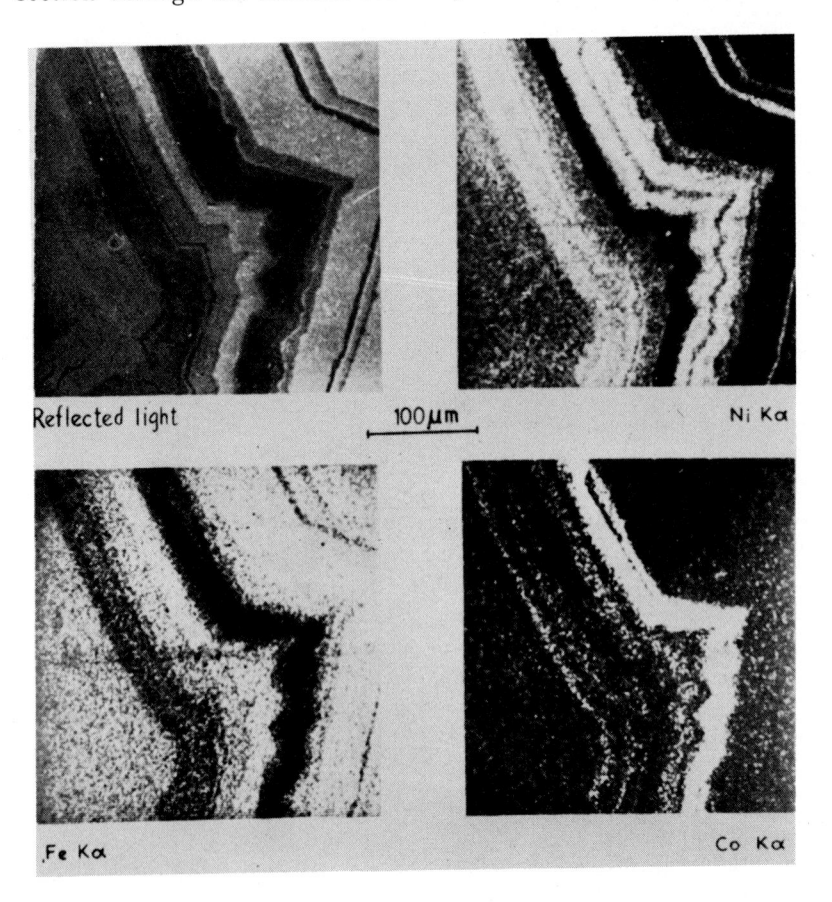

Fig. 5.15. Optical microscope and X-ray images from the electron probe microanalyser showing the distribution of nickel, iron and cobalt in a mineral, bravoite. *J. V. P. Long.*

layers of the sulphides of iron, cobalt and nickel. The appearance of this material under the optical microscope is shown in the top left hand micrograph, while for the remainder the X-ray spectrometer has been set to select the wavelength corresponding to the nickel, iron and cobalt K_α radiation respectively, thereby revealing the distribution of these separate elements in the microstructure.

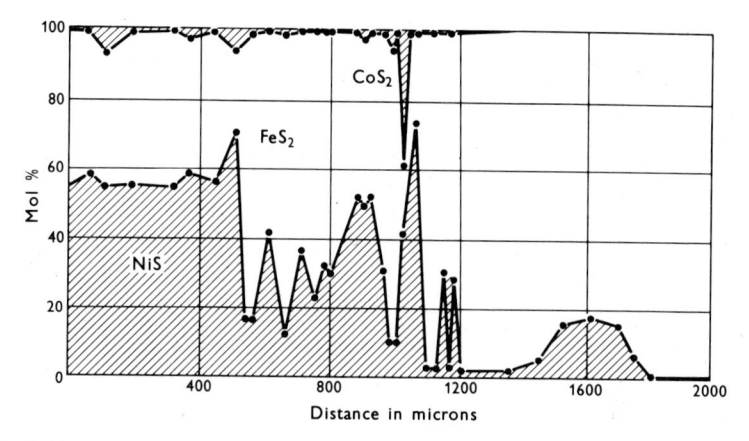

Fig. 5.16. Point-by-point plot of the relative concentrations of the sulphides of nickel, iron and cobalt across a mineral section similar to that shown in fig. 5.15.

In order to obtain a quantitative chemical analysis, the electron spot may be held stationary over successive points of the microstructure while the spectrometer crystal is rotated through a small sweep about the detection angle corresponding to the X-ray peak of the element in question. The area recorded under this peak is then compared with that from a pure sample of the same element in order to obtain the absolute concentration of that species within the area of the specimen studied. Figure 5.16 shows how the results of such a point-by-point determination may be plotted across a section similar to that shown in fig. 5.15. Similar plots could be obtained dynamically by setting the electron beam to scan across a single line on the specimen and presenting the output on a cathode ray tube.

The accuracy of analysis is poorest with elements of low atomic number, in particular for fluorine, oxygen, nitrogen, carbon, boron and beryllium ($Z = 9$ to $Z = 4$). There are several reasons for this. The basic X-ray yield for such elements is inherently low to begin with, and the wavelengths of their characteristic X-rays are comparatively long, resulting in the difficulty of preparing crystals of sufficiently large interplanar spacing for their detection in the spectrometer. These light elements apart, the relative sensitivity of the technique is in the range 10–100 parts per million, with an absolute detection sensitivity of about 10^{-14} of a gram.

Applications

There are several other methods of analysis which have a greater sensitivity than that quoted above. What makes the electron probe microanalyser such a powerful tool is its ability to perform chemical analysis on such a fine scale. Thus it is particularly suited to specimens which contain a fine aggregate of very small particles or grains, which cannot physically be separated in order to carry out more accurate analyses.

In minerals and ores in particular it may be important to know not only the percentage of a given metal that is present, but also how it is distributed, and hence whether its extraction is commercially feasible. Thus the technique has received extensive use in the minerals field in both identification and analysis, and it is perhaps appropriate that one new mineral, castaingite, has been named after the originator of the technique, the French scientist Castaing. Equal application is made of the technique in metallurgical studies, where it may be used to study the segregation and diffusion of alloying elements, the formation of precipitates and of corrosion products such as oxide scales.

As well as information on the composition and distribution of the various phases, crystallographic data may be obtained using the Kossel microdiffraction technique. The normal microanalyser sample is covered with a very thin foil of a metal which will emit X-rays of a *known* wavelength when irradiated by the primary electron beam. Some of these X-rays enter the region of the specimen under the beam and there are diffracted in the normal way to form a selected area diffraction pattern. This may be used to reveal the relative orientations of the different phases present, and also to provide very accurate measurements of their crystal structure.

The applications of the electron probe microanalyser in biology are more limited, since the elements which mainly compose both plant and animal tissues—carbon, nitrogen and oxygen—are very difficult to detect, as already noted. One method of overcoming this, borrowed from optical microscopy, is to 'stain' different constituents by the addition of some metallic compound which attaches itself preferentially to the structure of interest, and hence promotes image contrast from that region. Another application is the detection of toxic elements, for example zinc, which may be present in certain tissues.

Table 4. Characteristic K series X-ray wavelengths emitted by some common target materials

Element	K_{α_2}	K_{α_1}	K_β
	nm	nm	nm
Cr	0·229351	0·228962	0·208480
Fe	0·193991	0·193597	0·175653
Co	0·179278	0·178892	0·162075
Ni	0·166169	0·165784	0·150010
Cu	0·154433	0·154051	0·139217
Mo	0·071354	0·070926	0·063225
Ag	0·056378	0·055936	0·049701
W	0·021381	0·020899	0·018436

CHAPTER 6
emission microscopy

6.1. *Introduction*

ALL forms of microscopy depend upon some kind of radiation which conveys information from the specimen to the eye, or to some other recording medium. Conventionally the radiation, which may be light, electrons or X-rays, is produced by some external source, directed on to the specimen, where it is modified in a way directly related to the microstructure, and then on leaving the specimen is used to form an image. To some extent the electron probe microanalyser and the scanning electron microscope (at least when used in the secondary emission mode) depart from this scheme, in that the image forming radiation originates within the specimen itself, although it is still produced by the action of some other radiation incident upon the specimen.

In this chapter we shall consider a group of techniques in which the imaging radiation again originates within the specimen, but this time is not excited by external radiation, but by raising the specimen either to a high temperature or to a high electrical potential. Since biological materials do not in general lend themselves well to this kind of treatment, the principal applications of these techniques are to be found mainly in metallurgy and materials science. Their importance lies in the particular kinds of information that they are able to supply, and, in the case of the field-ion microscope (page 156), the fact that, for the first time, the individual atoms which make up the crystal structure may be directly revealed.

6.2. *The thermionic emission microscope*
Design

The design of a thermionic emission microscope closely resembles that of a conventional transmission electron microscope from the specimen position onwards, fig. 6.1. Since the electrons which are used for imaging originate within the specimen itself, there is no requirement for an electron gun or condenser lens system. The specimen, which is similar in form to that used in the optical microscope, is maintained at a high negative potential with respect to the earthed anode in order that electrons emitted from the metal surface may be accelerated away towards a series of objective and projector lenses which focus an image of the surface on to a fluorescent screen or camera plate. The magnifications normally obtained are rather less than in the electron microscope, ranging between ×100 and ×12 000.

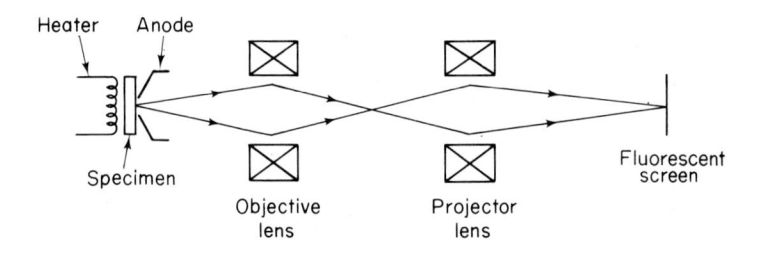

Fig. 6.1. The thermionic emission microscope.

In order to release electrons from the metal surface some sort of excitation is required. In the thermionic emission microscope this may be supplied simply by heating the specimen to a temperature in the range 1200–2000°C. Many metals would of course melt at this kind of temperature, and with such metals it is necessary to 'activate' the metal surface by coating it with a thin layer of caesium or barium. This reduces the temperature required to promote substantial electron emission to a minimum of about 500°C, for reasons which are discussed in the following section. If even this temperature is too high the electron emission may be produced instead using ion bombardment or irradiation with ultraviolet light (photoemission). The results obtained are essentially the same as those using thermionic emission and indeed the photoemission variation is becoming a powerful technique in its own right.

Historically, the thermionic emission microscope actually predates the transmission electron microscope. The early experiments on electron lenses and magnetic focusing were carried out using the electron radiation generated by a heated filament cathode ray tube and the images that were produced were of the cathode surface itself, the concept of a thin specimen through which the electrons were transmitted not being introduced until later. The principle of thermionic emission is still employed in the heated filament electron guns which are used today, although it is interesting to note that a new type of gun, based instead on field emission (page 150) is now coming into use.

Resolution and contrast

Although the lens optics are similar to those in the electron microscope, the limit of resolution in the thermionic emission microscope is not determined either by the wave nature of the electrons (the Abbe limit) or by aberrations in the electron lenses. The limit is set by the fact that, at the surface being imaged, the electrons have comparatively low emission energies and a proportionately large energy spread. In all the previous electron optical techniques the energy spread of the electrons has always been a very small fraction of their total energy at the object plane. Thus the practical limit on resolution is set by the energy spread of the electrons from a given region; in other words by a kind of chromatic aberration. Actual values of the resolution obtained range between 20–100 nm, the former being comparable with that of the scanning electron microscope, and rather better than that of the optical microscope.

Image contrast arises out of differences in electron emission between different regions of the microstructure, which in turn may be related to differences in the *work function* of the regions. The concept of work function may be explained in terms of the Sommerfeld model for the behaviour of electrons in a metal, fig. 6.2. The electrons can occupy energy levels within the metal up to the energy E_F, which is known as the Fermi energy. The energy difference between an electron at infinity and an electron in this topmost filled level is the work function, ϕ, and this is the amount of energy that must be supplied to an electron if it is to escape from the metal. It may be supplied by heating, ion bombardment or ultraviolet irradiation, as described above.

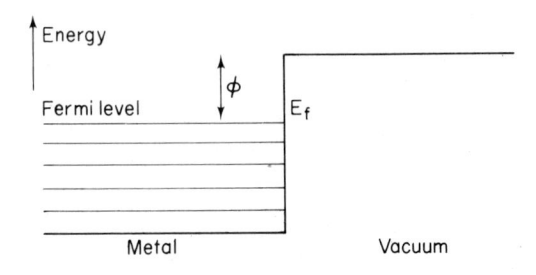

Fig. 6.2. The work function of a metal surface.

The value of ϕ for most metals is around 4–5 eV. However it is very low for both caesium ($\phi = 1\cdot8$ eV) and barium ($\phi = 2\cdot2$ eV), which explains why electron emission becomes so much easier if the specimen is coated with such an 'activating' layer. Even within a given metal, the magnitude of ϕ varies with the crystallographic orientation of the atoms forming the surface layer. Thus differently oriented grains in a polycrystalline microstructure give rise to quite striking image contrast, fig. 6.3, rather resembling that obtained with the optical microscope. Since the orientation of the crystal surface governs the extent to which the caesium or barium atoms are adsorbed on to the surface, the activation process still permits such contrast to be obtained.

Fig. 6.3. Photoemission micrograph showing austenite grains in an alloy steel, ×1000. *A. J. Baker.*

Composition is another factor which affects the value of ϕ. For example, in the case of iron, ϕ is decreased by the presence of silicon and chromium solute atoms, while carbon and copper increase it. Thus different phases can give varying image contrast due to differences in composition, crystal structure or orientation. Even within a single phase, differences in solute concentration may be revealed.

Since work function is a concept related to the surface state of the metal its value will be altered further by surface reactions such as adsorption, oxidation and corrosion.

Applications

The principal application of the thermionic emission microscope lies in the *dynamic* observation of processes occurring at high temperature, thereby capitalizing on the fact that the technique depends for its actual operation on the specimen being held at such temperatures. Such studies may of course be made using a high temperature stage with an optical microscope. However the resolving power of the thermionic emission microscope allows higher useful magnifications to be achieved, and the technique also is capable of revealing structures which do not give rise to good optical contrast.

High temperature reactions that have been studied include recrystallization and grain growth, phase transformations, diffusion and segregation, together with surface reactions themselves, such as surface adsorption of gases and the initial stages of the oxidation of metals under controlled conditions. Since stress gradients within the metal also give rise to changes in work function, dynamic loading studies may also be made.

6.3. *The field emission microscope*

Field emission

Two methods of promoting electron emission from a metal have already been discussed, with reference to fig. 6.2. The electrons may either be supplied with an additional amount of energy, for example by heating the metal, or alternatively the height of the potential energy barrier to their escape may be reduced by activation with a low work function material. The third method, known as field emission, is rather more subtle, and involves the application of

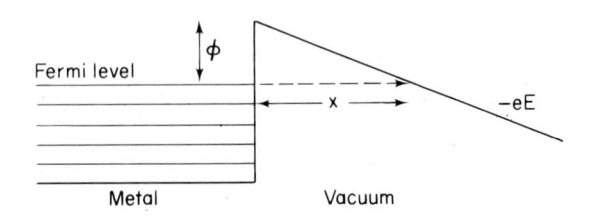

Fig. 6.4. The mechanism of field emission.

an external electrical potential, thereby decreasing the *width* of the potential energy barrier, so that the electrons may penetrate through it by means of a process known as ' tunnelling '.

The effect of applying a negative electric potential to the metal surface is shown in fig. 6.4. The potential gradient away from the metal surface may, to a first approximation, be represented by a straight line of gradient $-eE$. Thus the potential barrier is reduced from one of height ϕ, and infinite width, to one which is triangular in shape, and of width x at an energy corresponding to that of the Fermi level.

A complete description of the tunnelling process requires the application of quantum mechanics, and lies beyond the scope of this book. Qualitatively it may be explained as follows. The Heisenberg uncertainty principle tells us that it is not possible to determine both the position coordinate x and the momentum p of a particle at any one moment more closely than is given by the relation $\Delta x \Delta p \simeq h$, where Δx and Δp are the uncertainties. As a consequence, providing the width of the energy barrier in fig. 6.4 is less than the uncertainty in position of the electron, there is a finite possibility of finding the electron on the other side of the barrier, without it having to be supplied with the energy ϕ that would be necessary for it actually to surmount the barrier. If one calculates the potential gradient that is necessary for the barrier width, x, to be reduced sufficiently for this tunnelling process to occur, it comes out to the order of 5×10^9 V/m or 5 V/nm. This is an enormous value, but can readily be achieved when the specimen takes the particular form described below.

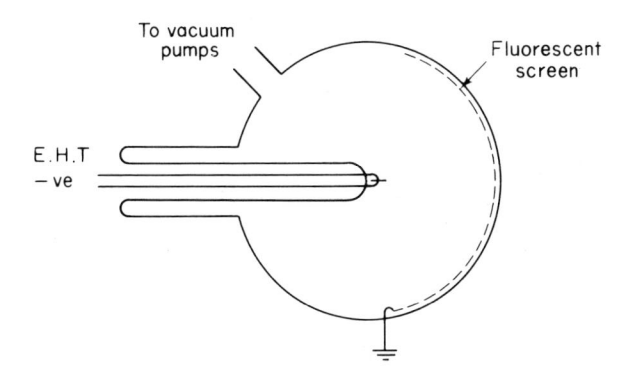

Fig. 6.5. The field emission microscope.

Image formation

The basic design of the field emission microscope is shown in fig. 6.5. The specimen is a metal wire which has been electropolished to a fine point, 0·1 to 1 μm in diameter. This is situated within a vacuum chamber, facing a fluorescent screen, and is mounted on to a filament loop which allows the specimen to be heated when a current is passed.

With the specimen in this form it is possible to generate at its tip the kind of potential gradient described above by applying a potential of a few kV. The field emitted electrons are then accelerated away from the emitter surface, following radial paths to strike the screen, which is at earth potential, where they produce a magnified image of the specimen surface. Thus the technique does not rely upon lenses and focusing in order to form an image, but rather resembles the X-ray projection microscope (page 134) in being a projection device.

The magnification that is obtained may be deduced from fig. 6.6, assuming the projection to be radial. To a close approximation it is simply the ratio of the emitter-to-screen distance divided by the radius of the emitter itself. Thus for an emitter of radius 0·5 μm, situated 10 cm from the screen, the magnification is approximately × 200 000.

Figure 6.6 may be compared with the projection geometry shown in fig. 5.7. Since the field emission microscope is a *point* projection device, the magnitude of the quantity s in fig. 5.7 is zero. Hence there can be no penumbral limit on the resolution obtained. Instead the principal limiting factor is again the energy spread of the emitted electrons, just as in the thermionic emission microscope, although in

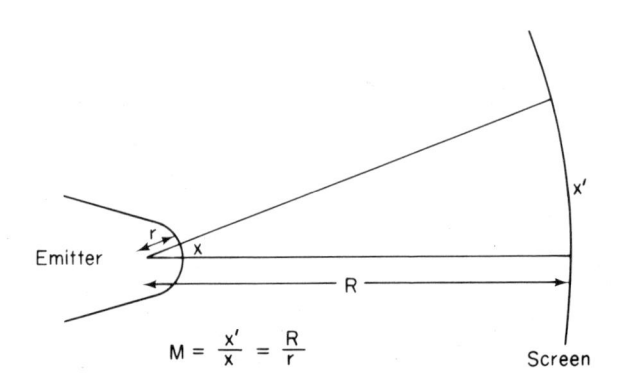

Fig. 6.6. Projection diagram showing the magnification obtained in the field emission and field-ion microscopes.

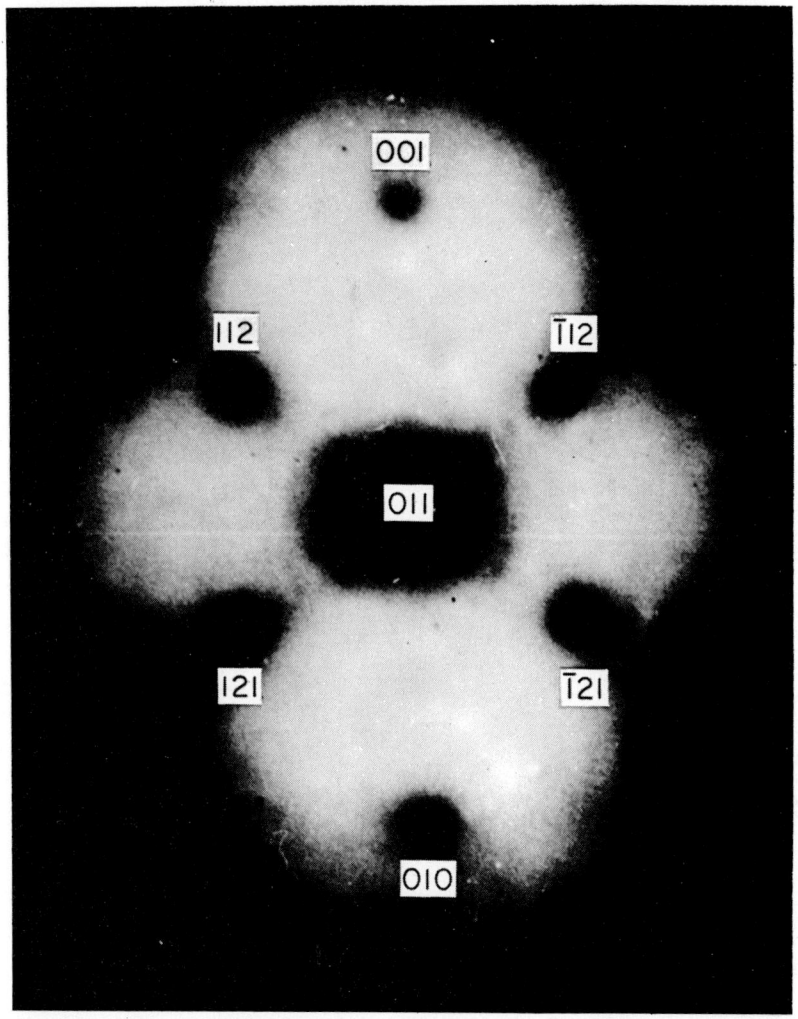

Fig. 6.7. Field emission image from a clean tungsten surface. *A. D. Martin.*

the field emission technique values as low as 2–3 nm may be achieved, almost comparable with the transmission electron microscope.

A field emission image from a tungsten specimen is shown in fig. 6.7. Its appearance may be understood in terms of a ball model of the atomic structure of the emitter surface such as that shown in fig. 6.13 (*a*), later in this chapter. At such small emitter radii, the hemispherical shape is actually approximated to by a series of terraced facets. These facets develop where comparatively closely packed planes of atoms within the structure occur parallel to the emitter surface. These planes are indexed crystallographically in fig. 6.13 (*a*), and also where they appear in the image in fig. 6.7. The more closely packed the plane, the higher is its work function, and hence the more difficult becomes the process of electron emission. Such planes therefore appear dark in the image. Thus the image

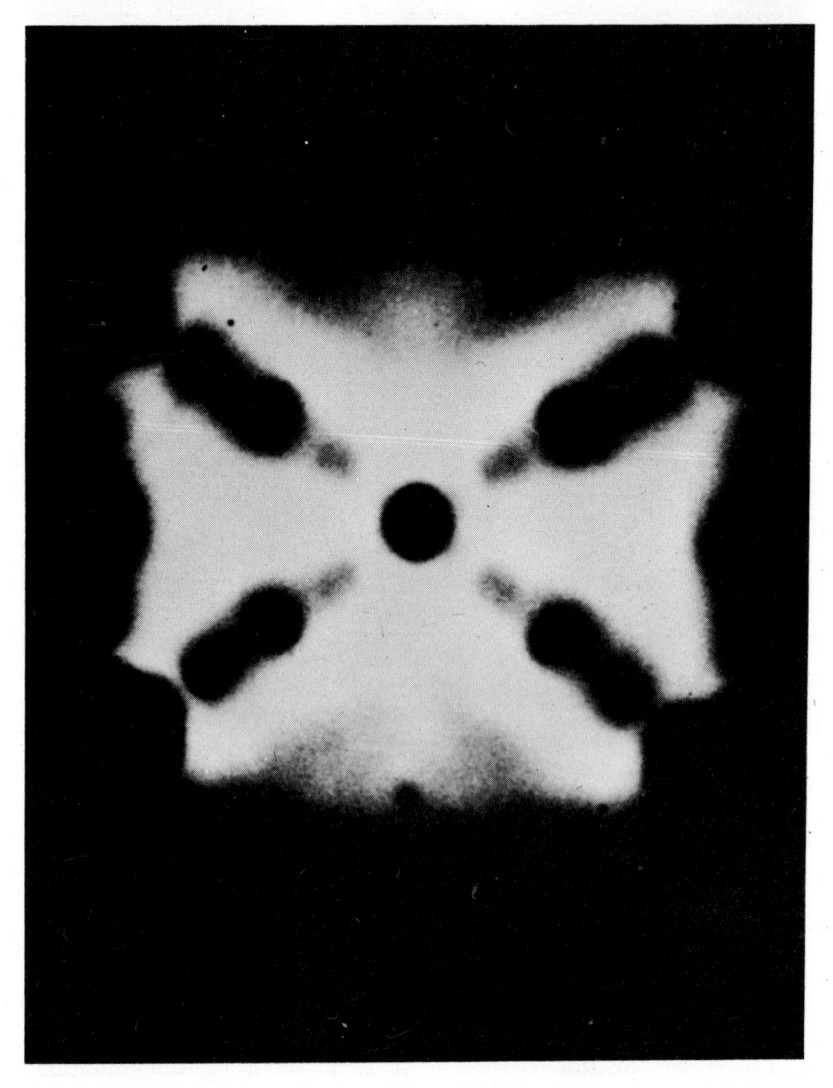

Fig. 6.8. As in fig. 6.7., but with a thin layer of platinum deposited onto the specimen surface.

displays variations in the value of the work function over the emitter surface, which are related to variations in the surface orientation.

With such a small field of view it is rare to have a grain boundary traversing the image, and hence essentially one is imaging a single crystal. Normally only pure metal specimens are used and hence the image contrast arises only from this orientation dependence of the work function. It is essential that the specimen surface should be totally clean and free from all contamination, in order that alterations in image contrast brought about by subsequent experiments may be referred back to an image known to be representative of an untouched surface. This cleaning may be accomplished either by heating the specimen to a high temperature, or by a process known as field desorption, which is effectively the same as that of field evaporation, described on page 162.

If, during controlled experiments, small clusters of atoms are deposited on to the clean surface, then they may give rise to recognizable changes in the image contrast, either due to their different work function, or to the local enhancement in field that occurs at their site, leading to greater emission. Figure 6.8 shows a tungsten specimen on to which a thin layer of platinum has been evaporated and allowed to diffuse over the surface at a temperature of 300°C.

Applications

By now it will have become apparent that the field emission microscope is primarily a technique for studying reactions occurring at solid surfaces. In particular the effects of surface crystal orientation on reactions may be studied, since the image is that of a number of differently oriented facets. Thus the main applications to date have been in the field of surface chemistry, although they have a strong metallurgical flavour as well.

Topics studied include the adsorption and desorption of gases on various metal surfaces, together with the early stages of oxidation and corrosion reactions. The nucleation and growth of thin films produced by vapour deposition is an important area, as illustrated in fig. 6.8, and closely allied to this are studies of surface diffusion. All of these are experiments carried out within the microscope chamber.

The progress of experiments such as these may be followed either by simply observing the changes in image contrast that are produced, or, in a more quantitative fashion, by actually measuring the changes in work function that occur.

In principle there is no reason why microstructures similar to those examined in the thermionic emission microscope should not be investigated, and with similar image contrast. A difficulty here is the very small field of view that is associated with the form that the specimen must take. However if the phenomena to be studied were selected to be those occurring on a reasonably fine scale, such as phase transformations in alloys, then there appears to be no reason why the applications of field emission microscopy should not be extended here as well. While it is true that the field-ion microscope, which is described in the following section, is capable of giving considerably greater information in such areas, the range of materials which may be studied is not so great.

6.4. *The field-ion microscope*
Field ionization

The physical principle on which the operation of the field-ion microscope depends is that of field ionization. This is again a quantum mechanical 'tunnelling' process, whereby individual gas atoms may lose an electron, i.e. become ionized, under the influence of an electric field. Figure 6.9 (*a*) represents the potential energy of an electron around its parent ion, in field-free space. For ionization to occur, energy equal to I eV, where I is the ionization potential must be supplied to the electron. In the presence of a positive potential gradient, the energy barrier is reduced both in height and width, as shown in fig. 6.9 (*b*). Now ionization may occur without the supply of any further energy, merely by the electron tunnelling out *through* the energy barrier, following the route A–B. This process is extremely similar to that occurring during field emission,

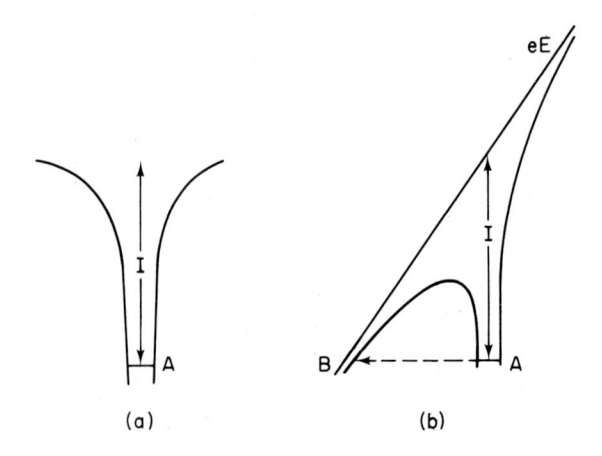

Fig. 6.9. The mechanism of field ionization.

although here it occurs from atoms in the gas phase rather than in the specimen.

Image formation

The basic design of the field-ion microscope is quite similar to that of the field emission microscope and is illustrated in fig. 6.10, while fig. 6.11 shows the appearance of a sophisticated commercial instrument. Again the specimen is in the form of a sharply pointed metal wire facing a fluorescent screen, and situated within a vacuum chamber. This time, however, a *positive* potential is applied to the specimen, and, since field strengths about ten times greater must be generated, the tip is generally more finely pointed (0·01 to 0·1 μm diameter), and the applied potential somewhat higher.

During operation of the microscope, a small amount of gas, usually helium, is leaked into the microscope chamber, and in the regions of highest field, just above the surface of the specimen tip, these gas atoms undergo field ionization. The positive ions thus formed are then repelled away from the tip surface, to strike the screen. Here they excite a magnified image of the atomic configuration of the tip surface, fig. 6.12. In this micrograph each white spot is the image of a single atom on the specimen surface.

Strictly speaking this technique should perhaps not be described

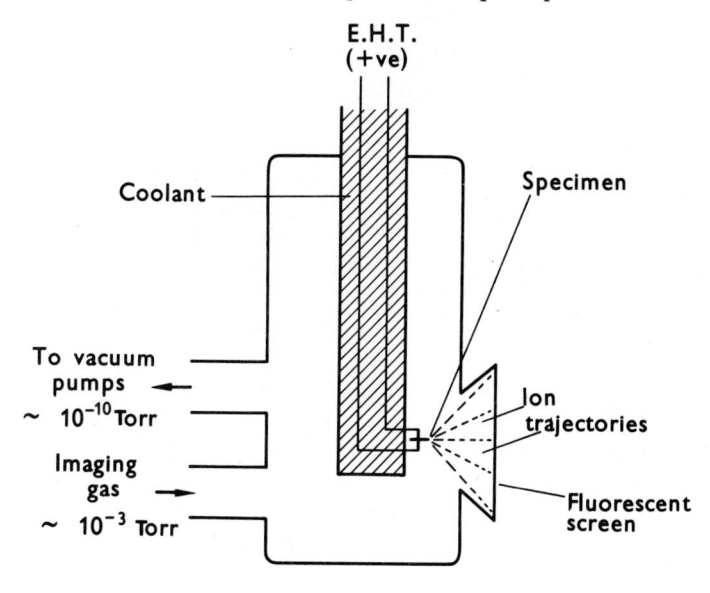

Fig. 6.10. Schematic arrangement of the field-ion microscope.

as an emission one, since the 'imaging' radiation—the ionized helium gas—does not actually originate within the specimen itself. However the mode of image formation so closely resembles that of the field emission microscope that it is only reasonable to treat them at the same time. Note that it is quite easy to perform field emission microscopy using a field-ion microscope, simply by pumping out the imaging gas and reversing the potential applied to the specimen.

Fig. 6.11. A modern commercial field-ion microscope. *Vacuum Generators Ltd.*

The magnification obtained with the field-ion microscope may be calculated in just the same way as on page 152. For a tip of radius 0·03 μm situated 10 cm from the screen, the magnification is approximately × 3 000 000.

Contrast and resolution

If the specimen surface were a perfectly smooth hemisphere then field ionization would be expected to occur uniformly over it, resulting in a featureless white image. In fact, each white spot in the image results from a single atom on this surface. This is because, on the atomic scale, the surface is actually very highly contoured. Thus the site of each atom is effectively a protrusion of small radius on the nominally hemispherical surface. This results in a local enhancement in the field over these sites, and, since the rate of ionization is very strongly dependent on the field strength, beams of ions arise solely from above the individual atom positions. Not every atom exposed at the surface protrudes sufficiently to give rise to an image point, however, as is discussed in the following section.

In order to obtain such atomic resolution in the image, it is necessary to ensure that the pattern of ion beams leaving the specimen surface is preserved until it reaches the screen. In other words the ion beams must not overlap or merge significantly during transit. The main limiting factor here is the random thermal motion of the imaging atom at the moment of ionization. Hence the specimen is cooled to as low a temperature as possible so that the incoming gas atom accommodates itself to the temperature of the tip surface before ionization occurs. Liquid nitrogen (78 K) is the most commonly used coolant since it is cheap and readily available, unlike liquid neon (27 K) or liquid helium (4 K).

When other factors, such as the finite size of the imaging gas atom, are taken into account, the resolution of the field-ion microscope comes out to be about 0·2–0·3 nm. This is sufficient to be able to resolve neighbouring atoms in all but the most closely packed atomic planes, and even these may be distinguished using the lower temperature coolants.

Image interpretation

At first sight the image shown in fig. 6.12 may appear to be extremely complex, although the symmetry and regularity of the atomic pattern are quite apparent. However a closer examination reveals

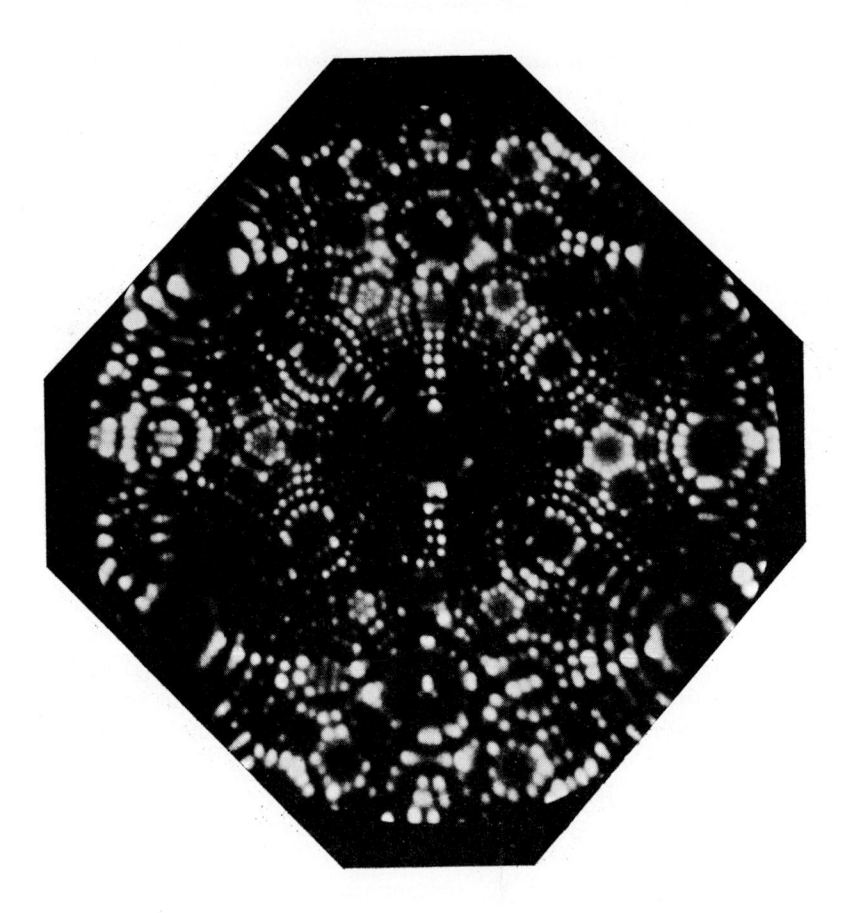

Fig. 6.12. Field-ion micrograph of tungsten. *G. G. Summers.*

that it is simply composed of a series of concentric rings of image points, in sets each containing up to 8 or 9 rings, with the sets overlapping to some extent. This configuration may be understood by once again considering the ball model of the specimen surface, fig. 6.13 (*a*).

Each facet on the tip surface is made up of a series of ledges and steps, and it is the atoms at the edges of the ledges which protrude the most from the surface, and hence experience the highest field. Fig. 6.13 (*b*) shows the same model as in fig. 6.13 (*a*) but with these most protruding atoms highlighted. Owing to the strong dependence of the field ionization process on the magnitude of the local field, it is these atoms alone which actually contribute to the image. In the case of the not too densely populated planes, each atom in the centre of the

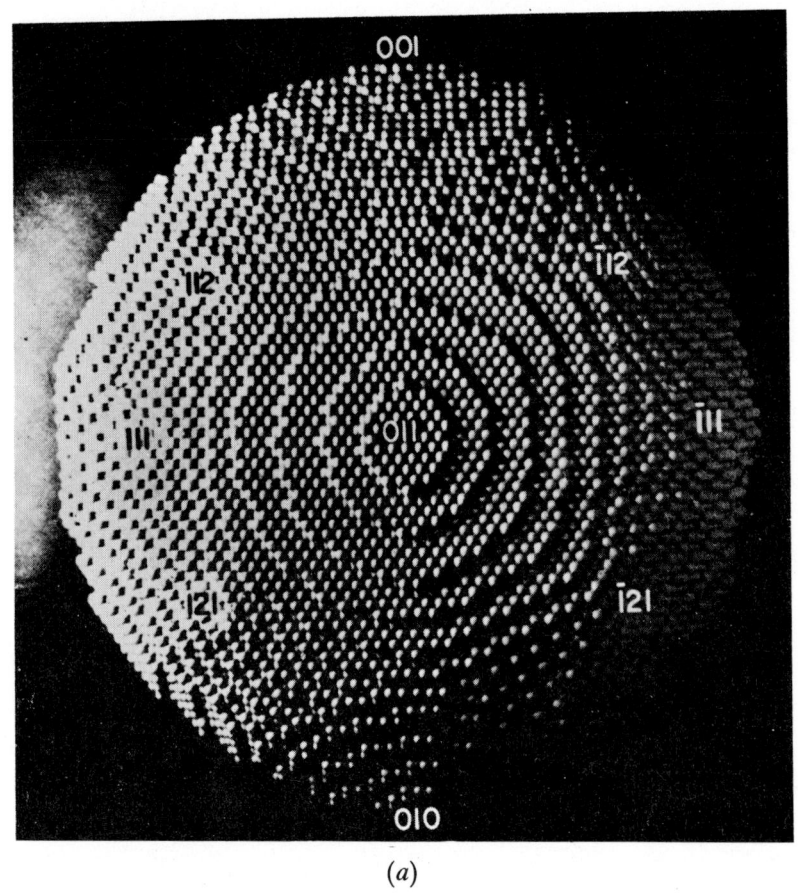

Fig. 6.13. Ball model of the surface of a field-ion or field emission specimen, (a) showing the regular terraced structure, with various facets indexed crystallographically; (b) with the most protruding atoms illuminated. E. W. Müller.

topmost 'ledge' may image as well. Comparison of figs. 6.13 (a) and (b) with fig. 6.12 should make these points clear. These figures correspond to an emitter whose radius at the tip is about 15 nm. At larger tip radii the number of rings of image points defining each plane becomes greater.

Thus the field-ion image represents the locus of those atoms which are left protruding the furthest when a hemispherical section is taken through the crystal structure. With practice it becomes very easy to recognize departures from the ideal image regularity arising from particular features in the microstructure such as dislocations.

(b)

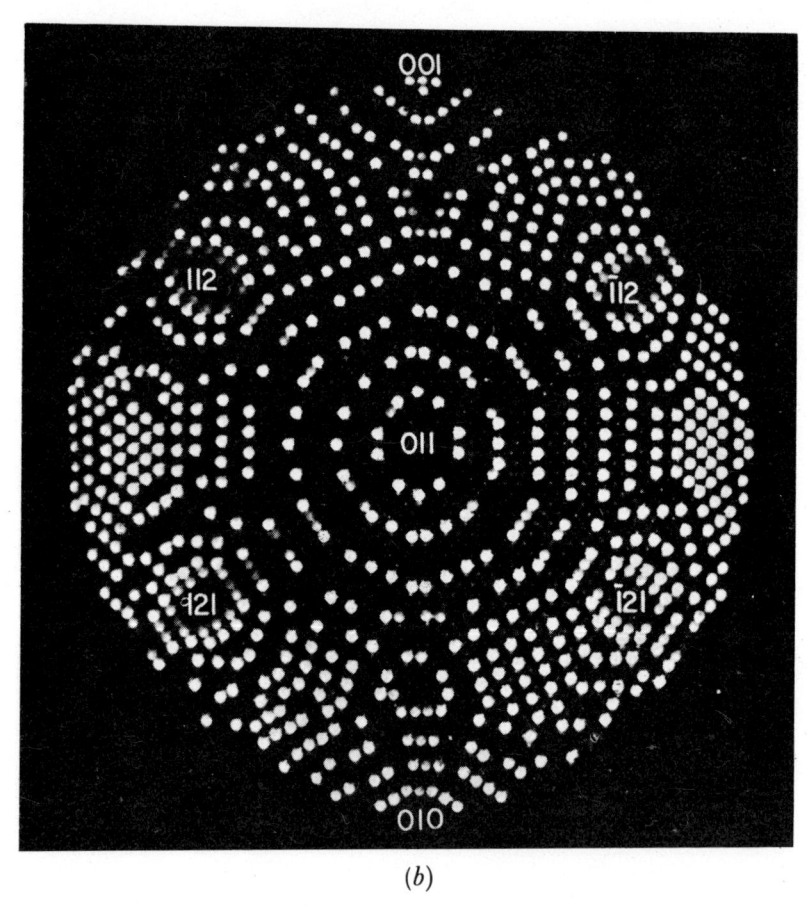

Fig. 6.13 (continued).

Field evaporation

Once the image from the specimen surface has been photographed, the atoms composing the surface are removed in a controllable way to expose a fresh surface, which may then be imaged. This is accomplished by increasing the potential applied to the specimen up to a critical amount. This process is termed 'field evaporation', and it is this facility which makes field-ion microscopy such a powerful tool for investigating the internal structure of solids. It is possible to control the process so that atoms are removed one or two at a time, but also it may be continued so that thousands of complete atomic layers are removed. In this way a complete volume of material can be examined, in the form of successive surface sections.

The mechanism of field evaporation may be understood by reference to fig. 6.14. Figure 6.14 (a) describes the potential energy, V_I, of a metal ion, as a function of its distance from the other atoms making up the surface in which it lies. Energy of amount Q_0 would have to be supplied in order to evaporate the ion from the surface. The corresponding curve for an atom rather than an ion would be similar in form, but with a smaller value of Q_0, equal in fact to the sublimation energy of the metal. Thus under thermal activation alone the metal evaporates, or sublimes, in the form of atoms rather than ions.

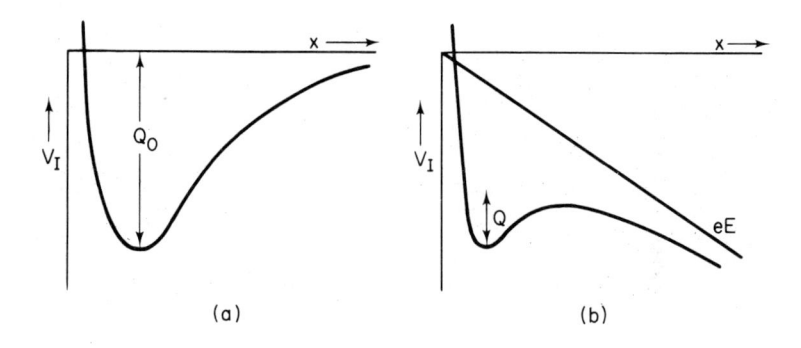

Fig. 6.14. The mechanism of field evaporation.

Under the influence of an applied potential the potential energy curve for the ion is modified as shown in fig. 6.14 (b) : that for the (neutral) atom would be unaffected. So now only a very small amount of thermal activation energy, Q, suffices to remove the metal in the form of an ion. If the field is raised to a sufficiently high value this process may occur even at the very low temperature at which the specimen is maintained.

Figure 6.15 illustrates how a single layer of atoms, belonging to just one of the planar facets composing the top surface, may be field evaporated in successive small stages. In principle, therefore, every single atom in the region of the specimen examined may be imaged, and by comparison of successive micrographs, the exact configuration of a crystal defect, or other microstructural feature may be ascertained.

Applications

There are three categories of information that may be obtained using the field-ion microscope.

Firstly there is structural information, combined with atomic resolution.

Secondly there is crystallographic information. The projection relationship between the three-dimensional distribution of crystallographic planes forming the faceted tip surface, and their image on the screen, is very close to being *stereographic*. This projection is a familiar one in crystallographic work and the techniques for manipulating such data are well established. Thus, for example, it is possible to deduce the misorientation between two grains separated by a grain boundary which crosses the image.

(a)

(b)

(c)

(d)

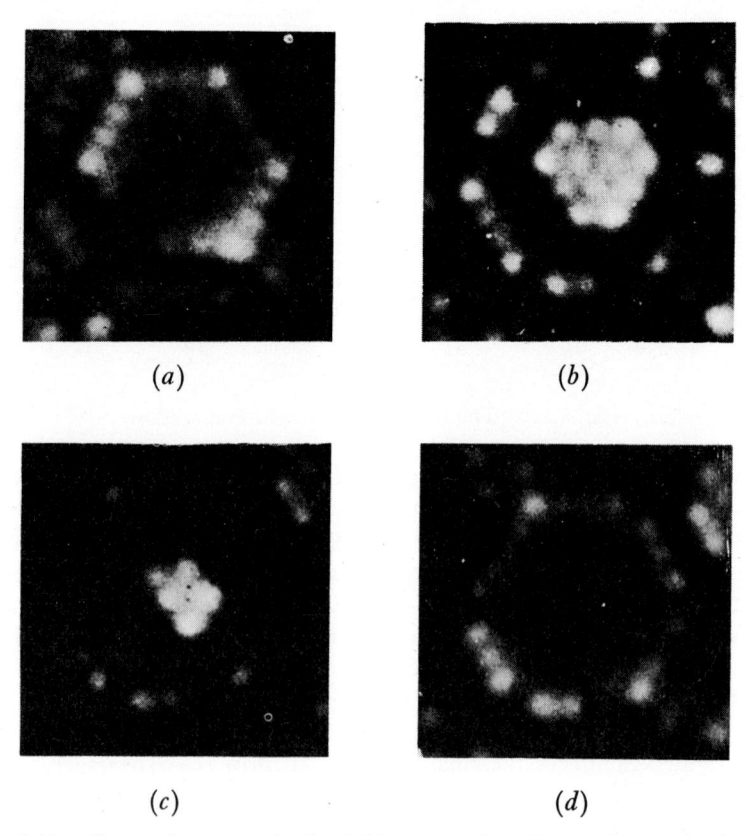

Fig. 6.15. Successive stages in the field evaporation of a single atomic plane.

Thirdly there is the possibility of chemical analysis, either inferentially, by recognizing differences in image spot intensity due to different atomic species, or directly, using a modification known as the atom probe field-ion microscope, which will be described in Chapter 8.

The technique has the dual advantage of being able, like the field emission microscope, to study surface properties and reactions, and also the internal structure of the metal, via the process of field evaporation. Once again, in connection with surface studies, the existence of differently oriented crystal facets on the imaged surface, makes it possible to study the crystallographic dependence of various reactions.

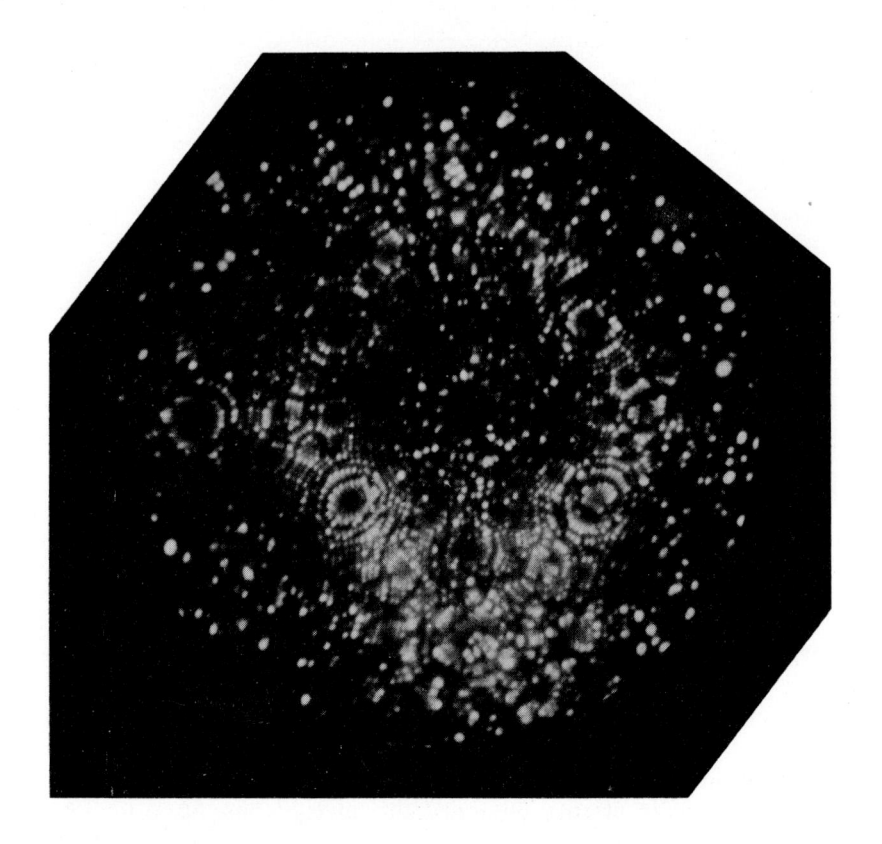

Fig. 6.16. Field-ion micrograph of an ion-bombarded tungsten surface. *J. M. Walls.*

The surface investigations that have been made have covered more or less the same ground as with the field emission microscope, but of course with much greater resolution, viz. adsorption, surface diffusion, oxidation, vapour deposition. Figure 6.16 illustrates a further application in this area, and shows the kind of surface damage

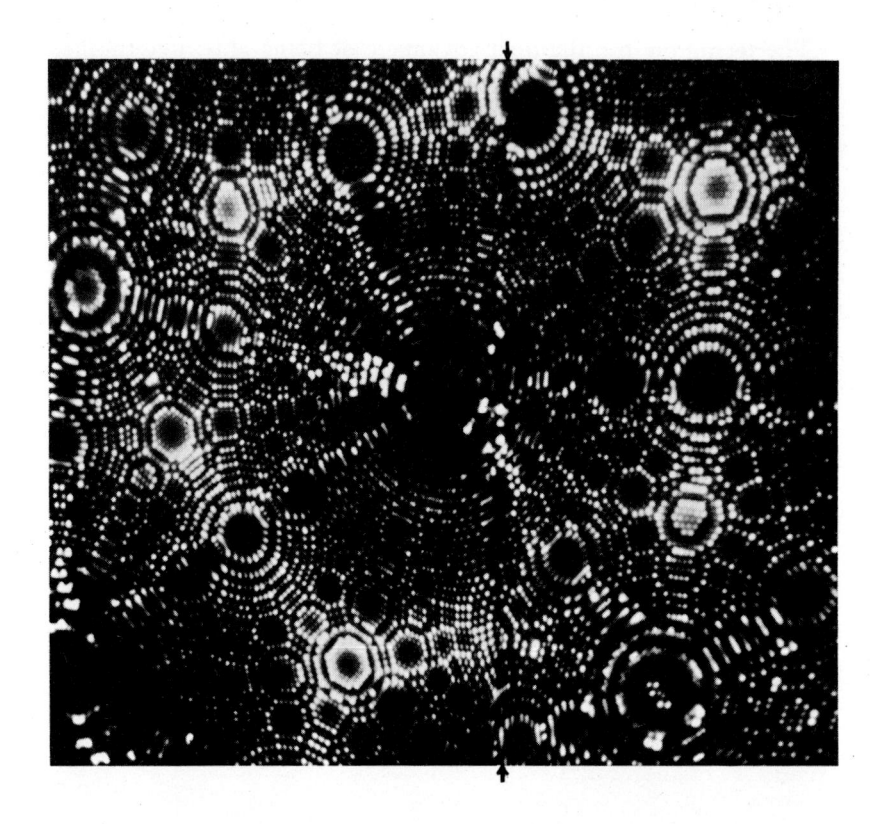

Fig. 6.17. Field-ion micrograph of a grain boundary in tungsten. *J. J. Hren.*

which is caused when a tungsten specimen, similar to fig. 6.12, is subjected to bombardment by medium energy argon ions.

In connection with bulk studies, the recognition of crystal defects is quite easy. Vacancies may be detected directly; dislocations cause spiralling of the image rings; grain boundaries are seen as abrupt changes in orientation across the micrographs, fig. 6.17. An important area has been the study of alloying effects, such as randomness and order in solid solutions, together with the early stages of precipitation in both steels and non-ferrous alloys.

The limitations of field-ion microscopy stem from its high degree of specialization. The form that the specimen must take is rather restricted, as is the field of view studied. The imaging conditions are themselves rather extreme. This is a drawback with the less strongly bound metals, since they may field evaporate at a field strength *below* that required to cause field ionization of the imaging gas. In such cases the specimen surface would be continuously changing while being imaged. This may be overcome by using gases of lower ionization potential, such as neon or argon, for imaging.

Over the last two or three years the range of materials that may be studied has been extended from tungsten, iridium and platinum, for which helium imaging is suitable, to include iron, gold, cobalt and nickel, together with their alloys.

CHAPTER 7
diffraction and spectroscopy

7.1. Introduction

THE preceding chapters will have given a good idea of the powerful techniques which are at the disposal of the microscopist. However even the most sophisticated microscope goes no further than revealing a picture which is in some way representative of the object under investigation and even this representation can itself be indirect. One obtains 'image contrast' from, for example, grain boundaries in the optical microscope, or from dislocations in the electron microscope, but in neither case are these structures being observed directly. Even in the field-ion microscope, where image points corresponding to individual atoms may be observed, these images are strictly representative only of the variations in electric field over the surface of the specimen, although there is, of course, a one-to-one correspondence between these variations and the atoms making up this surface. Bearing these limitations in mind, however, we are still justified in referring to microscopy as a 'direct' technique for investigating matter.

In contrast, there are two indirect techniques which we should consider, which are capable of providing information which microscopy alone cannot, since it is not possible to determine either the internal atomic dimensions of a crystal, or its chemical composition, merely by looking at it. Instead we need to use some form of *diffraction* or *spectroscopy*, respectively.

Diffraction techniques allow extremely accurate measurements to be made of the dimensions of the crystal structure, and can also be used to deduce its detailed atomic configuration. Indeed most of the complex chemical and biological structures that have been determined to date have been solved using diffraction techniques rather than microscopy.

X-ray diffraction is the most important technique which comes into this category, although from the point of view of the microscopist it suffers from rarely being linked directly with microstructural studies. In contrast the great power of selected area electron diffraction (page 102) is that the pattern obtained is related directly to a previously selected small area of the microstructure, which itself can be imaged in the electron microscope. This is of course no accident since it will be recalled from Chapter 1 that the Abbe theory of image formation involves the production of a diffraction pattern, which contains all the information concerning the periodicity of the specimen, and which then acts as a secondary 'object' from which the final image is obtained. In the case of optical microscopy the diffraction pattern cannot be observed (except in trivial cases such as a diffraction grating), while in the case of X-rays image formation cannot take place by this method, and hence in neither of these two cases can this combination be achieved.

Spectroscopic techniques are used to analyse radiation emitted from the specimen which is characteristic of the chemical elements comprising the specimen, and hence to determine both the presence and amount of the latter. Several examples of compositional analysis using some form of X-ray spectroscopy have already been encountered, and there are a number of other techniques involving either electrons or ions (the latter are discussed in Chapter 8). However, spectroscopic analysis tends to be even more divorced from primarily microstructural considerations, the results obtained being more representative of a bulk specimen as a whole than of localized regions, and only one or two selected examples of these techniques will be discussed here. In any case the descriptions of the various forms of diffraction and spectroscopy will be kept brief and are included mainly for the sake of completeness. A particularly good description of X-ray diffraction is given in the companion volume in this series by Lipson, which is referred to in the reading list at the end of the book.

7.2. X-ray diffraction
Introduction

The general idea underlying the operation of the various X-ray diffraction techniques is that an effectively parallel beam of X-rays is directed at the (crystalline) specimen, and these X-rays are then scattered by its component atoms (or rather by their surrounding electrons). We have seen in Chapter 1 that when the X-rays scattered by successive parallel atomic planes are originally incident on the specimen in certain specific directions relative to these planes, they will mutually reinforce each other to give a strong emergent beam. This is termed a diffracted beam. The *directions* in space of these diffracted beams may then be related to the *dimensions* of the specimen crystal structure. The latter are commonly expressed as the lengths of the sides of the smallest repeating unit, termed the unit cell, which, when repeated in three dimensions, can be seen to build up the entire structure. Furthermore, the *intensities* scattered in these diffracted directions can be related to the *atom positions* within the unit cell.

These points may be elaborated as follows. The Bragg diffraction equation

$$2d \sin \theta = n\lambda$$

relates the wavelength λ of the X-radiation and the spacing d of the various parallel crystal planes involved to the orientation θ of these planes with respect to the incident beam. It is usually possible to deduce the overall symmetry of the crystal structure from the general appearance of the diffraction pattern, and individual points in the pattern can then be identified as originating from particular sets of crystal planes. If λ is known and θ has been measured it is now possible to calculate the d-spacing of the planes and hence to relate this to the dimensions of the unit cell.

If the size and shape of the unit cell are known it is possible to calculate the number of atoms which make up the unit cell, provided that the chemical composition and density of the specimen have been determined. The detailed configuration of the atoms within the unit cell may then be deduced from the intensities of the various diffraction points. This is because each species of atom has its own *atomic scattering factor*, which dictates how efficient it is at scattering X-rays, and hence how intense this scattered radiation will be. The intensity scattered by the entire unit cell, which is what is actually recorded, is determined by the sum of the scattering factors of all the individual atoms within the cell, taking account of their relative positions, and possible interference of the scattered waves with one another. Hence by careful comparison of the intensities of a number of diffraction points one may in principle work back to discover what this configuration is. In practice the determination of crystal structures may not be quite as simple as this, particularly where complex organic structures are concerned. In recent years, however, the application of Fourier analysis techniques to diffraction pattern data has greatly facilitated such investigations, and in some cases the structures of molecular proteins, containing several thousand atoms, have been successfully worked out.

Not all the applications of X-ray diffraction are aimed at determining unknown crystal structures of course, and various techniques have been developed in order to provide other kinds of information. These may be divided into two main categories depending upon whether radiation containing a whole range of X-ray wavelengths (white radiation), or just a single wavelength (monochromatic radiation) is used. In order to gain the maximum amount of information we want to produce as many diffraction points as possible. However if X-radiation of a single wavelength were to be used in conjunction with a single crystal which was in a fixed orientation with respect to the incident beam, then it is unlikely that many of the sets of parallel atomic planes within the crystal would be so oriented as to make the correct Bragg angle with the incident beam. Hence very few diffraction points would be observed.

The solution is to use white radiation, so that whatever the (fixed) value of θ that a particular plane of spacing d makes with the incident beam, there will generally be an appropriate value of λ present in the beam to give diffraction points. This is the basis of the Laue single crystal technique. Alternatively monochromatic radiation can be used, and the value of θ varied by varying the orientation of the single crystal with respect to the incident beam. Effectively the same solution is being used in the powder technique in which monochromatic radiation is employed, this time with the specimen in the form of a powder (which is effectively a collection of a very large number of single crystals in random orientations), or a polycrystalline metal specimen. Here, although λ and θ are both fixed, for each set of planes considered some of the small crystals making up the specimen will usually be oriented so that they satisfy the Bragg condition.

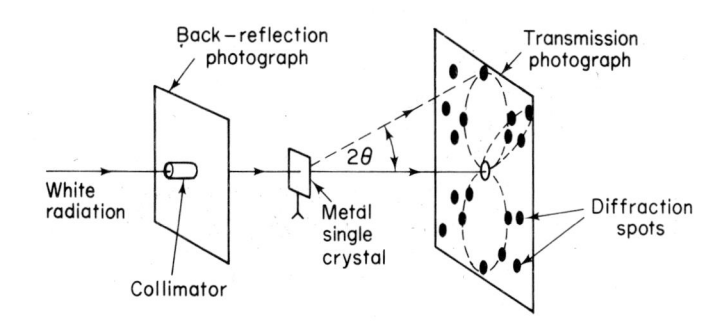

Fig. 7.1. The Laue method.

The Laue method

In the Laue technique the specimen is a single crystal and is exposed to a collimated beam of white radiation as shown in fig. 7.1. This is effectively the same arrangement as that used by Friedrich and Knipping in 1912 when they were first able to demonstrate that X-rays could indeed be diffracted by crystalline material. In the modern versions of the method either a transmission or back-reflection photograph may be taken, and the diffraction pattern gives rise to spots which lie either on ellipses or hyperbolas.

If the incident beam is parallel to an axis of symmetry of the crystal then the Laue photograph will display this symmetry, and hence the technique may be used to align crystals along such axes, for example for subsequent investigation using the rotating crystal method described in the following section. Alternatively, if the crystal is of a known material and aligned in an arbitrary manner with respect to the incident beam, then its orientation may be deduced by plotting the positions of the diffraction spots on to a stereographic projection and comparing the angles measured on this projection with known interplanar angles for this structure.

The technique is rarely used except in these rather qualitative ways, chiefly because each diffraction spot is formed from a different wavelength of the continuous X-ray spectrum and, since the atomic scattering factor is a function of wavelength, spot intensities cannot readily be compared in order to extract further information.

The rotating crystal method

In this method a single crystal is again used, this time with monochromatic radiation. The specimen is mounted vertically on a rotating spindle around which is placed a sheet of film in the form of a cylinder whose axis is parallel to that of the specimen.

If the specimen were stationary it is possible that very few or even no crystal planes would be suitably oriented to produce a diffraction spot. However if the crystal is rotated on its axis then at various positions a particular set of crystal planes will, for an instant, make the correct Bragg angle with respect to the incident beam, and a diffracted beam will result which can be recorded on the film. After exposure the film is opened up flat, a typical example being shown in fig. 7.2.

Conventionally the crystal is oriented so that its axis of rotation corresponds to one of the axes of the unit cell (as determined, for example, using a Laue photograph). When the film is rolled out flat, the diffraction spots all lie along straight lines, called layer lines, normal to the axis of rotation. From the separation of these layer lines it is possible to calculate the dimensions of the unit cell along this axis. The procedure may then be repeated for each of the other two axes.

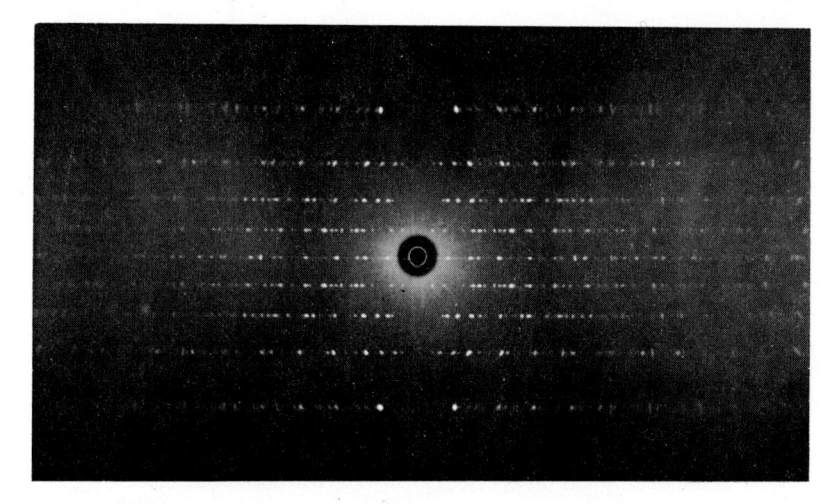

Fig. 7.2. X-ray photograph taken using the rotating crystal method. A. W. Nichol.

The powder method

The powder method (sometimes called the Debye–Scherrer technique, after its originators) is probably the most widely used of all the X-ray diffraction techniques. The specimen is either in the form of a fine powder, made into a thin cylinder, or, in the case of a metal, it is a polycrystalline wire. Monochromatic X-radiation is used. Just as in the rotating crystal method, a cylindrical film is placed around the specimen, although here it is sufficient merely to use a fairly narrow strip. The experimental arrangement is illustrated in fig. 7.3.

Although monochromatic radiation is being used, some crystals will always be suitably oriented with respect to the incident beam for each type of crystal plane to satisfy the Bragg equation. Often the specimen is rotated during the exposure of the film in order to maximize this effect. The resulting diffracted beams in each instance form a cone, which makes a constant angle, 2θ, with the incident X-ray axis, and which intersects the film along a symmetrically located pair of arcs, as illustrated schematically in fig. 7.3.

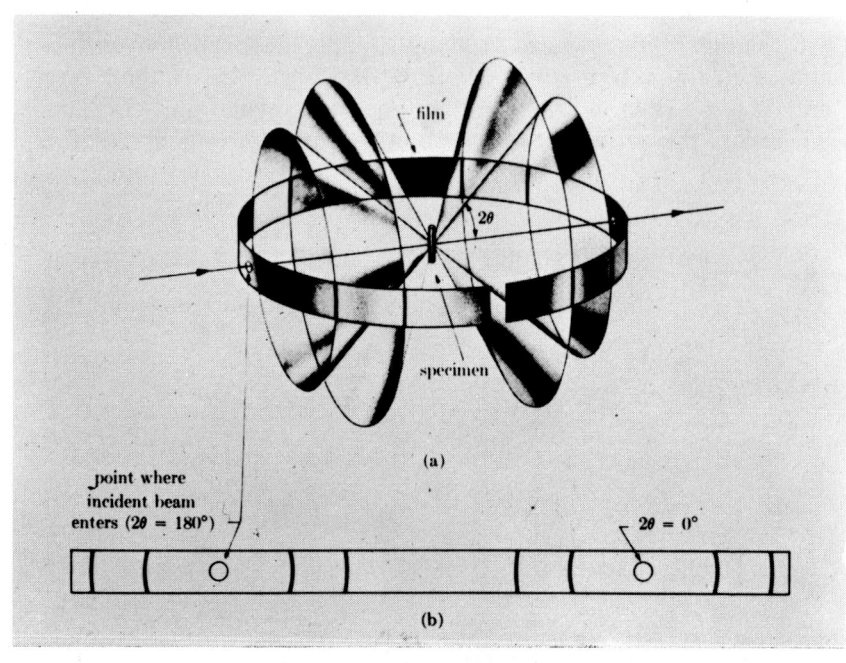

Fig. 7.3. The powder method: (a) relationship between film, specimen and incident beam (b) appearance of film when laid out flat.

A number of X-ray powder photographs of metals, each possessing a different crystal structure, are illustrated in fig. 7.4. By observing the sequence of diffraction lines which are present, it is possible first to identify the type of crystal structure which the specimen possesses and then to relate each line to the particular set of crystal planes responsible for it. By measuring the line positions it is then possible to obtain accurate values for the unit cell dimensions, and, from the line intensities, to gain some idea of the actual atomic distribution within the cell. An alternative design uses an X-ray spectrometer, or diffractometer (page 129), rather than a film, to record the positions and intensities of the diffracted X-rays, and this method permits rather greater precision to be obtained, particularly in the measurement of line intensities.

One important application of the technique is in the identification of an unknown sample. The sample's powder pattern is effectively its 'fingerprint', and files are available of the powder patterns for a wide variety of substances. By checking the crystal type, dimensions and most prominent line intensities against those in the file, it is usually possible to obtain an unambiguous identification, particularly

(a)

(b)

(c)

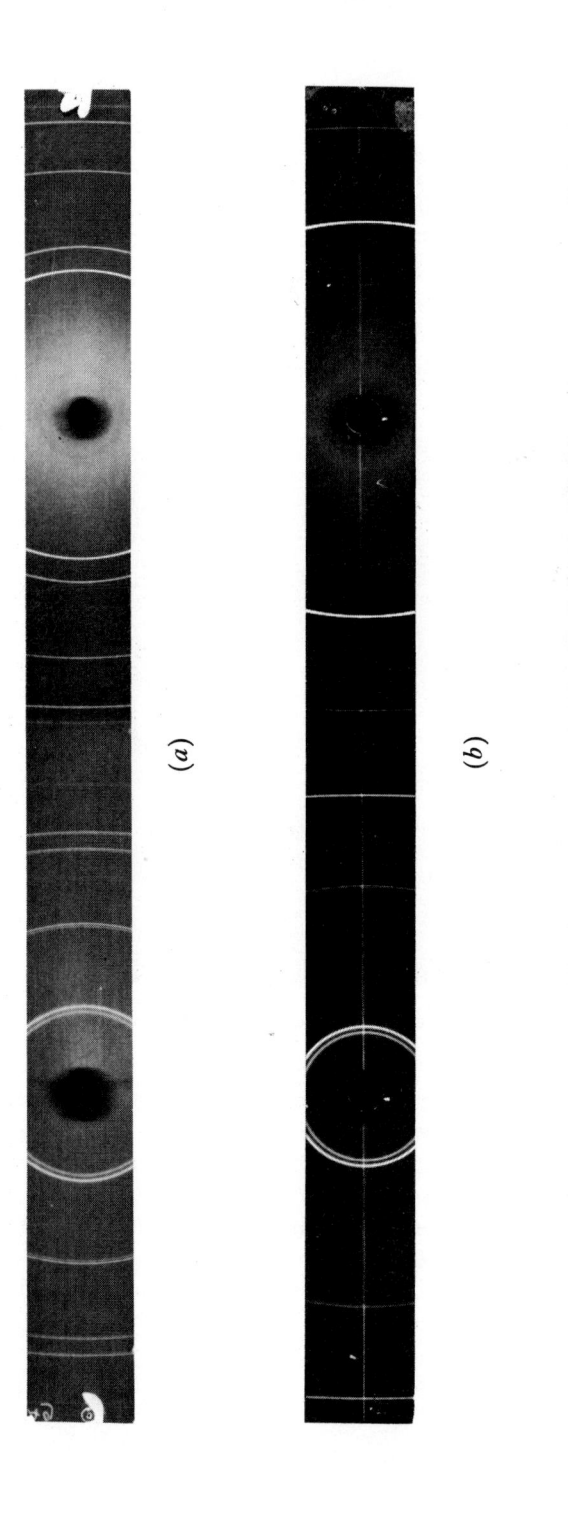

Fig. 7.4. Powder photographs from (a) silver (b) iron (c) zinc. *I. R. Harris.*

if some idea is already available as to its nature, e.g. that it is a metal oxide, rather than an organic compound. The technique is also very widely used for determining phase diagrams and for following the mechanism of phase transformations in metals and alloys. A further application relies on the fact that under certain conditions the lines formed on the film become broadened and this broadening can be measured. It may be caused either by the presence of stress within the sample, distorting the crystal structure, or by the presence of particularly fine crystals. In either case some quantitative idea of their extent may be gained.

Fig. 7.5.   X-ray texture photograph from cold-rolled copper.
W. B. Hutchinson.

If only a comparatively few crystals are present within the specimen then, rather than following continuous arcs, the powder lines will be made up of a series of discrete spots. In particular, if the orientation of the crystals is not completely random, then the spots will be grouped together in some regions of the arc, and less densely spaced in others. This factor is made use of in a somewhat related technique for determining what is known as 'texture' or 'preferred orientation' in cold-drawn metal wires or cold-rolled sheet. During the deformation process the metal grains tend to become aligned along similar crystallographic directions, and hence their orientation is no longer random. The apparatus used to detect this effect is rather similar to that used in the Laue technique (fig. 7.1). The difference here is that one is now using a polycrystalline specimen, together with monochromatic radiation, and so is effectively recording the entire diffracted cone of fig. 7.3 on to a flat plate, rather than the two intercepted arcs as in the powder technique. An example of such a texture photograph is given in fig. 7.5. By measuring the regions of the diffraction rings which are the most heavily exposed it is possible to construct a crystallographic diagram which illustrates the degree of preferred orientation which is present.

7.3. Electron diffraction
High-energy electron diffraction

High-energy electron diffraction has already been encountered in connection with electron microscopy in Chapter 4, and when the two techniques are used in conjunction it is possible, using a suitable aperture, to select a small area in the image and then to record its diffraction pattern. However there is no fundamental reason why the technique should only be used on small areas, and with many electron microscopes it is possible to obtain a diffraction pattern from the entire area that is illuminated by the electron beam. Indeed there is a device marketed simply as an ' electron diffraction camera ' which, while designed in much the same way as the electron microscope itself, has no facility for image formation and merely produces a diffraction pattern. However although it is somewhat cheaper than the electron microscope it is rarely preferred on account of the latter's much greater versatility.

The kind of information that results from electron diffraction is essentially similar to that obtained using X-rays. One practical difference is that diffraction of electrons is much stronger than that of X-rays, and hence electron diffraction patterns can be seen directly on a fluorescent screen rather than requiring the several hours' photographic exposure time that characterizes X-ray methods. This difference is actually more of a disadvantage than an advantage since a complete understanding of electron diffraction must also take into account the further diffraction of the diffracted waves themselves, since they are almost as strong as the incident beam. Thus the theory is extremely complicated and it is not possible to work out crystal structures as easily as with X-ray diffraction.

A further difference arises from the much smaller extent to which electrons can penetrate matter. Hence if electron diffraction patterns are required in transmission, the specimen must take the form of a thin film, as it does in the electron microscope. This carries the advantage that, since the Bragg condition is relaxed to a certain extent when the specimen is thin (page 102), a good number of diffraction spots—and hence a good deal of information—is produced without the need to rotate the specimen. If the technique is used instead in back-reflection the diffraction patterns formed are much more representative of the surface layers than are those obtained using X-rays, which relate to depths of several hundred nm. This surface sensitivity can be exploited to a much greater extent, however, in the specialized kind of electron diffraction equipment which is described in the following section.

Low-energy electron diffraction

In discussing high energy electron diffraction we have been concerned with electron energies in the 100 keV region as encountered in a conventional electron microscope. In the technique known as LEED (Low-Energy Electron Diffraction), on the other hand, we are concerned with electrons whose energies lie in the range 10–200 eV, so that the (back-reflected) diffraction patterns formed by such

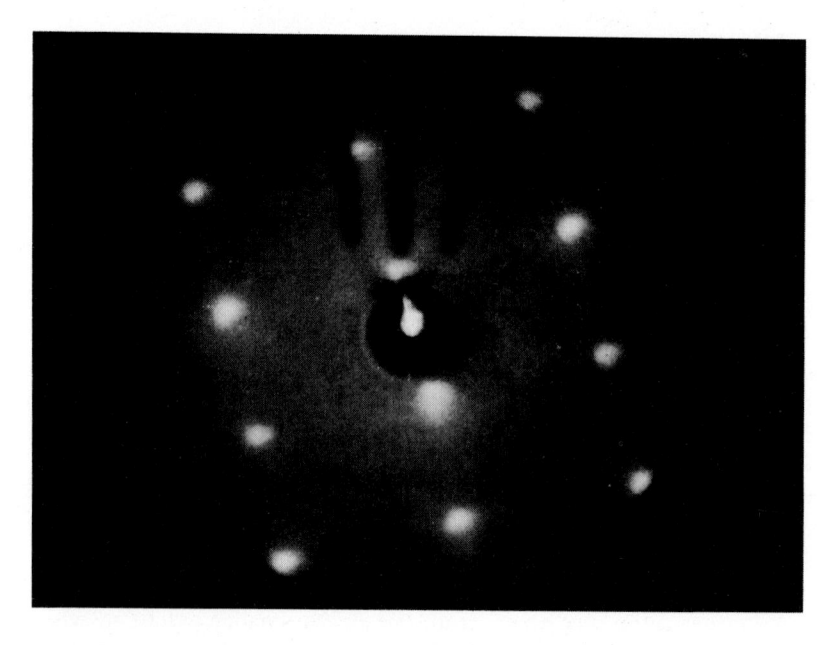

Fig. 7.6. LEED pattern from the surface of a single crystal of the intermetallic compound NiAl. *D. D. Hall.*

electrons are representative only of the first one or two atomic layers at the surface of the specimen. Hence this technique is complementary to field emission and field-ion microscopy (Chapter 6) in providing a very sensitive method for studying surface reactions.

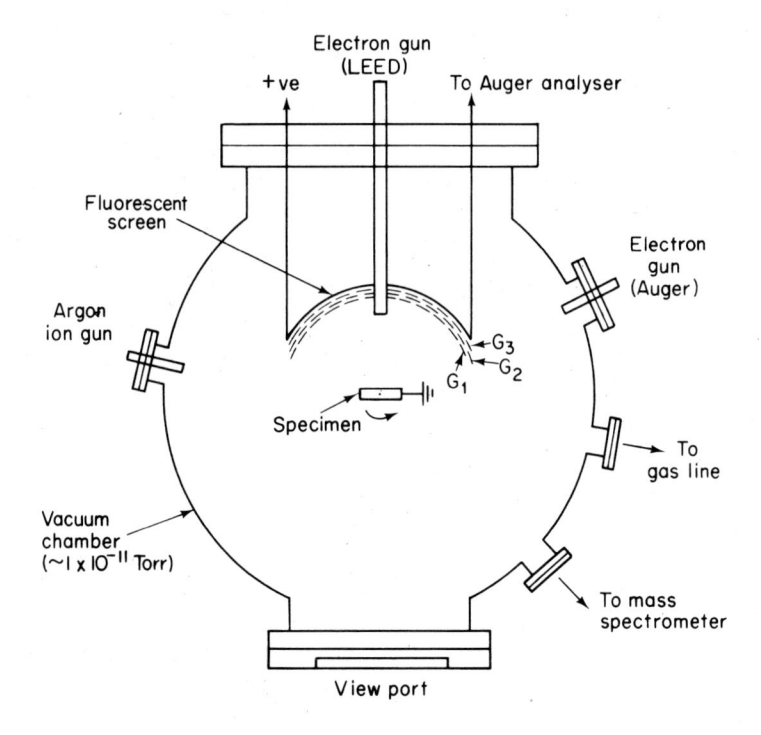

Fig. 7.7. Schematic diagram of LEED/Auger apparatus.

A typical LEED pattern is shown in fig. 7.6, its symmetry reflecting the symmetry of the essentially two-dimensional crystal structure of the specimen surface. Typically this technique is used to study fine-scale adsorption reactions, since an adsorbing species will tend to occupy only certain very specific sites on the crystal surface, thereby altering its symmetry, and hence the LEED pattern. By studying successive changes in the LEED pattern as the adsorbed material builds up it is often possible to deduce the precise mechanism of adsorption. One shortcoming of the technique, however, is that the diffraction process is extremely difficult to analyse quantitatively, and the interpretation of spot intensities, and in some cases even precise spot positions, is very uncertain.

The apparatus used in LEED work is quite sophisticated, but it

Fig. 7.8. A commercial LEED/Auger system.

will be quite useful to discuss the 'vacuum hardware' and electron optics in some detail, since they are essentially the same as those used in the complementary technique of Auger electron spectroscopy. A schematic diagram of a typical LEED/Auger system is shown in fig. 7.7, while fig. 7.8 shows a particular commercial instrument. The apparatus consists primarily of an ultra-high vacuum chamber, at the centre of which is placed the specimen (which for LEED, although not for Auger spectroscopy, must be a single crystal), which can be rotated about a vertical axis. In order to produce the diffraction pattern the specimen is turned to face an electron gun which is mounted centrally within a hemispherical screen and grid arrangement. The diffracted electrons strike the fluorescent screen and the resultant pattern may be photographed through the view port located behind the specimen (hence the specimen itself partially obscures the screen, as may be seen from fig. 7.6).

The grid nearest to the specimen, G_1, and the specimen itself, are both earthed so that the region in between the specimen and the screen contains no electric field and hence the paths of the (very low energy) incident and diffracted beams are undistorted. In the LEED mode grids G_2 and G_3 are coupled together and are held at a negative potential just less than that of the electron gun so that only the elastically scattered (diffracted) electrons are able to pass through these grids to reach the screen, the lower energy inelastically scattered electrons, and secondary emitted electrons being repelled.

Since the technique is so surface-sensitive, before any actual experiments can be carried out on the specimen, any atmospheric contamination that may be present on its surface must be removed so that it starts off clean, and this is usually accomplished by a combination of argon ion bombardment and heating. Facilities are also available for the introduction of various gases into the system, and for the mass spectrometric analysis of all gaseous species which may be present.

7.4. *Neutron diffraction*

One disadvantage of X-ray diffraction is that the atomic scattering factors of elements which are very close to each other in the periodic table are very similar. Hence it is difficult to distinguish between them on the basis of X-ray intensities, and this makes studies of alloys of metals such as iron and cobalt, or copper and zinc, very difficult. In some cases this difficulty can be overcome by using neutron diffraction instead. Neutron beam technology has been developed since the advent of atomic reactors, and in the diffraction experiments a particularly narrow band of the neutron energy spectrum is selected corresponding to a neutron wavelength of the order of 0·1 nm.

Neutrons are scattered by the *nucleus* of the atom, and not by its surrounding electrons, and it turns out that the scattering factors of different chemical elements vary quite irregularly over the periodic table, and hence the above limitation encountered with X-rays may often be avoided. Furthermore the light elements, such as hydrogen, scatter neutrons as strongly as do the heavier ones. This is in contrast to X-ray studies where the contributions of the light elements are often swamped by those of the heavier ones. The disadvantage of the neutron technique is that it is so very much more expensive; nevertheless in situations when X-ray diffraction is inadequate it has proved to be an extremely valuable tool.

7.5. *X-ray spectroscopy*

Several examples of X-ray spectroscopy have already been encountered in Chapter 5. Absorption analysis was discussed in connection with contact micro-radiography, and X-ray emission analysis in connection both with scanning electron microscopy (Chapter 4) and electron probe microanalysis. The latter technique is perhaps the most powerful since it combines reasonably high resolution microscopy with an accurate determination of chemical composition.

In the electron probe microanalyser the X-rays characteristic of the atomic species present in the specimen are excited by means of an incident electron beam. Clearly characteristic X-rays could also be produced using other forms of excitation, and when X-rays themselves are used in this way, the phenomenon is termed X-ray fluorescence. This has now become a separate and valuable technique in chemical analysis since its accuracy is substantially greater than that of the electron probe technique, and in addition, as electron beams are not involved, it does not require vacuum apparatus. Its disadvantage lies in the fact that a considerably greater area and depth of the specimen is sampled, and it should really be considered as a highly accurate bulk analysis technique, and not one that is concerned with microstructure.

7.6. Electron spectroscopy

Auger electron spectroscopy

The mechanism by which characteristic X-rays may be generated using electron excitation, as for example in the electron probe micro-

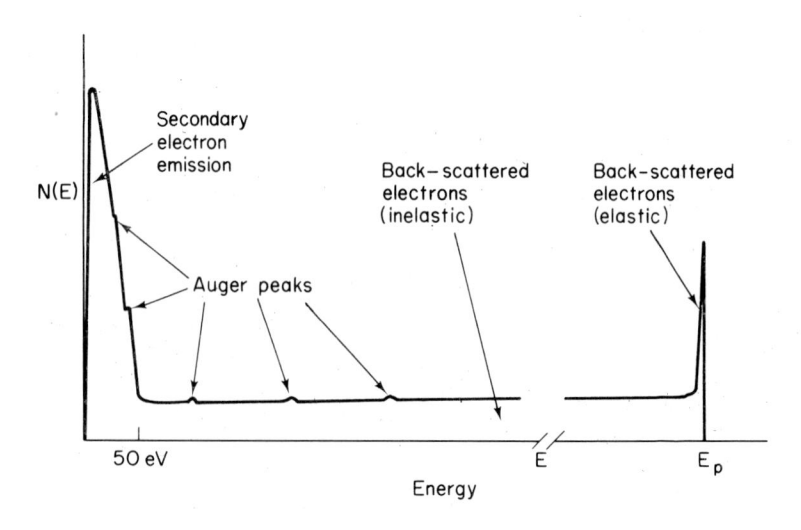

Fig. 7.9. Energy spectrum of electrons emitted from a specimen being irradiated with electrons of primary energy E_p.

analyser, was discussed on page 127. At the same time it was pointed out how an alternative de-excitation process could produce characteristic Auger electrons instead, and it is these which are made use of for chemical analysis in the technique of Auger electron spectroscopy.

The entire electron energy spectrum that results from a specimen which is excited by a primary electron beam of energy E_p is illustrated in fig. 7.9. Several different regions can be recognized. First the peak at the extreme right shows that there are a number of electrons which are scattered elastically, that is with no change in energy. This in practice corresponds to electron diffraction, and it is these electrons which are used, for example, in LEED, all the electrons of lower energy being deliberately retarded from reaching the detection screen. Second, there is a range of energies corresponding to electrons which have been scattered inelastically. This extends from E_p down to about 50 eV, where these electrons become indistinguishable from the secondary emitted electrons. It is these back-scattered primary electrons that are used, for example, for image formation in the scanning electron microscope (page 114). The very large secondary electron peak is caused mainly by electrons which were originally present within the specimen and which are

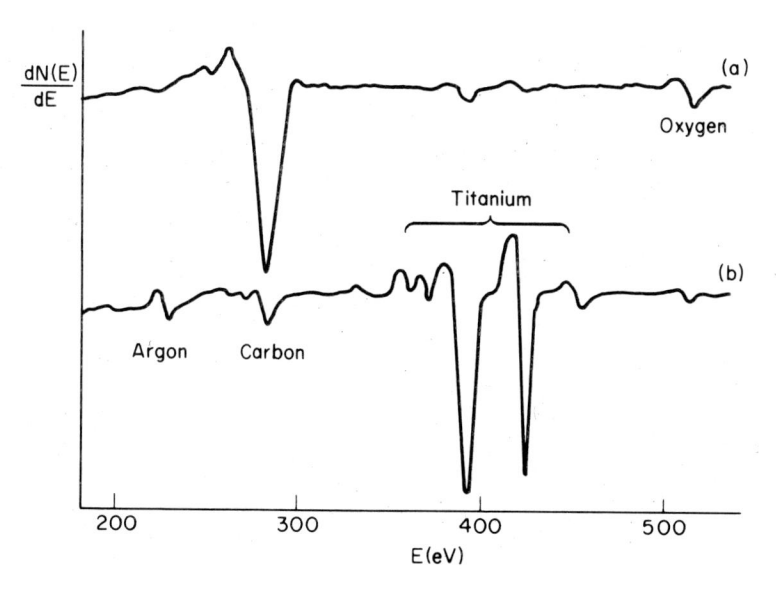

Fig. 7.10. Auger spectra from titanium (a) showing surface contamination (b) after cleaning.

ejected under the primary excitation. These also are used for image formation in the scanning electron microscope. Superimposed on the overall spectrum are the extremely small Auger electron peaks, which occur at energies which are characteristic of the atomic species giving rise to them.

The apparatus which is used to detect these Auger electrons is essentially similar to that used for LEED (fig. 7.7), although with certain modifications made to its operating conditions. For one thing a glancing incidence electron gun is generally employed, and the electron energy may be raised to as high as 3 keV. The electron detection system must also be operated in a different manner in order to permit the entire electron energy spectrum to be recorded, and some sophisticated electronic circuitry is added in order to facilitate the detection of the Auger peaks themselves.

At first sight these Auger peaks do not appear to be very promising in terms of analysis, since they are present only as minute fluctuations on a relatively high background. However while they may be small, they do represent quite abrupt changes in the *gradient* of the electron energy distribution curve. The trick is to obtain the *differential* of this energy distribution, whereupon these abrupt changes in gradient become pronounced maxima and minima, which are readily detected. This may be illustrated by comparison of figs. 7.9 and 7.10. In the former, $N(E)$, which is the number of electrons with a given energy E, is plotted against E, to produce the normal electron energy distribution with its single Auger peaks. Figure 7.10, on the other hand, shows the effect of differentiating such a curve, to produce a plot of $dN(E)/dE$ versus E. Now very prominent double peaks are present (since two changes in gradient are involved), and their recognition and measurement becomes very easy. In practice this operation is accomplished by varying the retarding potential (applied in this case to G_2 while G_1 and G_3 are earthed) from E_p down to zero, hence allowing the entire spectrum to be swept, and then by electronically differentiating the resultant signal before feeding the output to a pen recorder.

Whereas characteristic X-rays can come from some considerable depth in the specimen, Auger electrons originate only from the first two or three atomic layers below the surface. Hence they provide a chemical analysis which is extremely surface-sensitive, and the technique is frequently used in conjunction with LEED in order to obtain both chemical and structural information from the same specimen. As in LEED, ion bombardment is used in order to clean off atmospheric contamination before experiments can be performed, and fig. 7.10 shows the difference between a specimen freshly inserted, where the predominant species present are oxygen and carbon, and one which has been cleaned. A further advantage of the ion bombardment facility is that it can be used to erode away successive surface layers of the specimen itself, and hence the composition at different depths below the surface can be determined.

In the form illustrated in fig. 7.7 the technique does not possess much spatial resolution in terms of analysing particular regions of the microstructure, since the incident electron beam is about one millimetre in diameter and its position on the specimen is not precisely determined owing to the absence of any imaging facility. Recently, however, the development of more sensitive analysers has led to their being incorporated into scanning electron microscopes, which use a much finer beam, and with this design it is possible to form a direct image of the specimen, using characteristic Auger electrons, in much the same way as one uses characteristic X-rays in the electron probe microanalyser. The full spectrum may also be recorded graphically as before, and quantitative analyses carried out.

Photoelectron spectroscopy

Auger electron spectroscopy is a relative newcomer to the general field of electron spectroscopy, although it is probably the one most relevant to the overall theme of this book. Both characteristic Auger electrons, and characteristic X-rays are produced as the result of an electron de-excitation process. A primary beam knocks an electron out of one of the inner electron levels in the atom, and a second electron drops down to fill this vacancy from a higher level. The energy thereby released appears either as an X-ray photon or as an Auger electron. In photoelectron spectroscopy, on the other hand, it is the energy of the first ejected electron which is measured, since the difference between its energy and that of the incident radiation is directly equal to the energy of the electron level excited. This energy is itself characteristic of the atomic species concerned, and providing the energy of the incident radiation is accurately known, and that of the ejected electron accurately measured, a very sensitive measurement of such electron energy levels may be made.

Two versions of the technique exist. The first uses comparatively low-energy ultraviolet excitation, for example from a helium discharge tube, and is capable of exciting only the outer valence electrons. The second uses characteristic X-rays and the resulting spectra are much more representative of the inner electron levels. The great power of photoelectron spectroscopy is that one is able to determine not only the presence and concentration of various elements, but also their state of chemical combination (and hence, for example, whether iron is present as ferrous or ferric). The reason for this is that electron energy levels are extremely sensitive to the chemical environment of the atom, and since these levels are measured with a high degree of accuracy, any changes in them due to chemical combination are readily detected. The apparatus used is somewhat similar to that used in the Auger technique, although as yet there has been no extension made towards direct microscopy.

CHAPTER 8
future microscopy

8.1. *Introduction*

IN the earlier chapters we have concentrated on describing a wide variety of microscopical techniques, primarily in terms of their basic design and operation, pointing out those factors which one would expect to encounter in routine use. However the unceasing demands of fundamental research have ensured that more and more sophisticated variations on these techniques have been developed, together with a number of new ones aimed at exploiting yet more physical properties which may be manipulated in order to provide new levels of information. A prime example of the latter category are the various forms of ion beam technique discussed in section 8.4. Ion beams are one form of ' radiation ' which we have not so far encountered (except indirectly in the field-ion microscope), but the several ways in which they can interact with solids are proving to be a most important source of information.

At any one time there are a large number of such new ideas, each exciting in its own right, and it is often very difficult to foresee which will survive to become established techniques, and which will languish due to lack of interest or support. Hence the techniques which will be described in this chapter have been selected on the basis that, while they may be very new, they have already achieved firm recognition, usually as measured by the hard-headed fact that they are in commercial production, rather than still being at the stage of the laboratory prototype.

Beyond this it would be foolish to predict. The history of science is littered with authoritative pronouncements on what would or could never come about, and which are now in ridicule. Who, for example, would have predicted the renaissance in optical microscopy which was brought about by the various interference techniques described in Chapter 3 ? Indeed since the present book was begun there have been a number of extremely important innovations which demand inclusion, and the only thing about which there *can* be little doubt is that the future will bring many more.

8.2. Optical microscopy

Technical developments

The recent advances to be found in optical microscopy are divided fairly evenly between purely technological improvements, and the application of new optical concepts. For example, better and more versatile sources of illumination have become available, such as the quartz–iodine lamp, and the use of colour and Polaroid film techniques has increased as facilities for them have become more widely available. A major advance has been the widespread application of computer methods in the design of lens systems which are more effectively corrected for lens aberrations, a great improvement over the previous, and laborious, ray-tracing methods. From the point of view of new optical concepts, the development of laser beam technology has enabled the successful development of the technique of holography, which offers some fascinating applications to microscopy. Another area of importance is the development of electronic image processing techniques, such as the image analysing computer described in the following section. Nevertheless it should always be remembered in connection with the optical microscope that its resolution is strictly limited to a comparatively poor value, and hence that its potential usefulness, at least at the research level, must continue

Fig. 8.1. The image-analysing computer. *Metals Research Ltd.*

to decrease as interest centres more and more on the molecular and the atomic scale.

The image analysing computer

Conventional optical microscopy is primarily a qualitative tool. However there is often a need to obtain quantitative information from the object under investigation, and some simple techniques for performing some kind of *measurement* on the image were discussed in Chapter 2. Manual *counting*, for example of particle distributions, can be another, and laborious, task.

Now, however, there is a device—known as the image analysing computer—which will perform such operations automatically. A simple version of this instrument is illustrated in fig. 8.1. It consists of a conventional optical microscope equipped with both a normal eyepiece viewing facility and a television monitor. The latter may be used to scan a selected area of the image and then to determine various kinds of information contained within this area. In its most sophisticated form the technique may be used to make

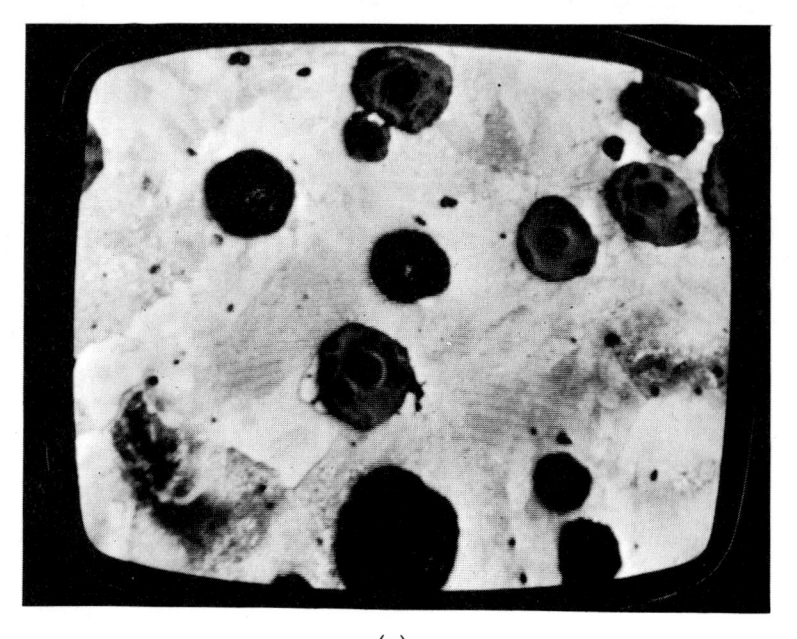

(a)

Fig. 8.2. Application of the image analysing computer (a) region of image selected for analysis: a number of particles can be observed (b) selection of these particles for subsequent counting etc.

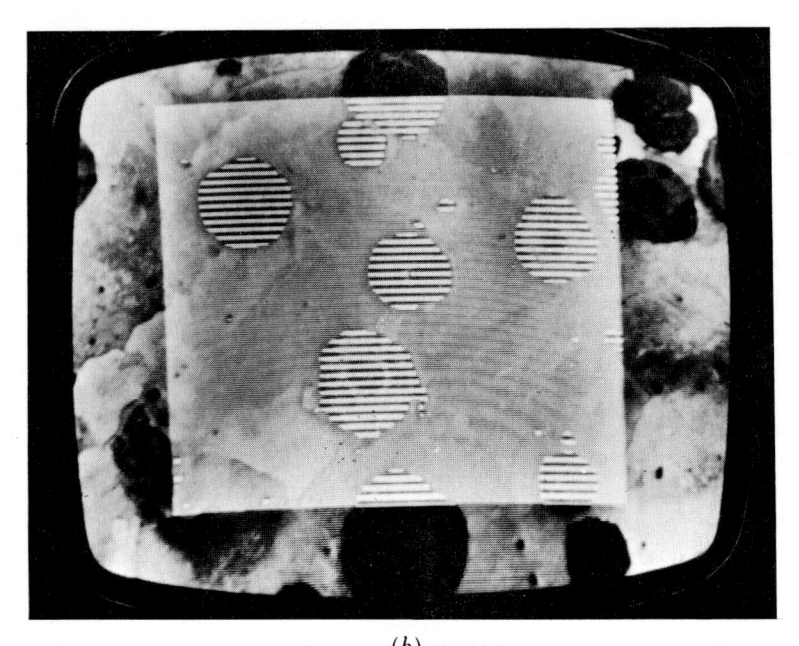

(b)

Fig. 8.2 (continued).

quite complex judgements, for example selecting particular levels of intensity within the image, or even particular patterns, and then representing the size and dimensions of these regions on a standard computer print-out.

In this way it becomes possible to obtain such geometrical information on microstructural features as their area, length and shape, as well as on their number, average size and size distribution. Figure 8.2 illustrates a typical such application. Figure 8.2 (a) reveals a fairly simple microstructure containing a number of particles which are easily distinguished because their image intensity differs from that of the background. In fig. 8.2 (b) a region of the image has been marked out, and the detection circuits of the instrument adjusted so as to pick out these darker areas, which now appear cross-hatched. The analysing circuits can now be used to determine the number, area and distribution of these particles. The technique may also be used to analyse electron micrographs in a similar fashion.

Holography

One of the most interesting developments in recent years has been the extension of holographic techniques to optical microscopy.

However, before we discuss this association, we must consider how conventional holography itself operates. The basic idea is actually extremely simple, and can be understood very readily in terms of the wave ideas put forward in Chapter 1.

The original concept of holography was first put forward by Gabor in 1947, although it was not until the introduction of the laser that a sufficiently powerful, and, above all, coherent light source became available for the technique to become a practical possibility. The term 'hologram' refers simply to an intermediate photographic record in a two-step method of image formation. In a sense the same definition is fulfilled by the conventional photographic 'negative' and indeed holograms themselves are recorded directly on to photographic film or plate. The difference is that when a conventional negative is illuminated it produces a two-dimensional image of the original object, which may then, for example, be recorded on to a photographic print. When a hologram is illuminated (usually laser light must again be employed), it produces a *three-dimensional* image of the object.

The reason for this distinction is that the hologram contains information on the *phase* of the light reaching it from the object, while the conventional negative does not. Photographic film (in common with the human eye) responds only to differences in the intensity of the light which reaches it. Since the intensity is proportional to the square of the amplitude, the emulsion cannot differentiate between two waves of equal amplitude but different phase. Hence, for example, light reflected with equal amplitude from two regions of the object lying at slightly different distances from the emulsion (and hence differing in phase) would be recorded in an identical manner on the emulsion, and therefore the information referring to the three-dimensional nature of the object would be lost. Since the hologram, on the other hand *is* able to store this information, the three-dimensional nature of the object can be reconstituted in the image.

To see how this is accomplished consider fig. 8.3 (*a*). Some form of beam-splitting device can be used to separate a laser beam into two parts. One of these illuminates the object under consideration, and light scattered or reflected by this object (now to be called the object beam) then falls on to a photographic plate. The other beam, called the reference beam, passes directly to the photographic plate, where its wavefronts are then superposed on those originating from the object. This results in an interference pattern which, when the plate is developed, appears as regions of varying light and dark

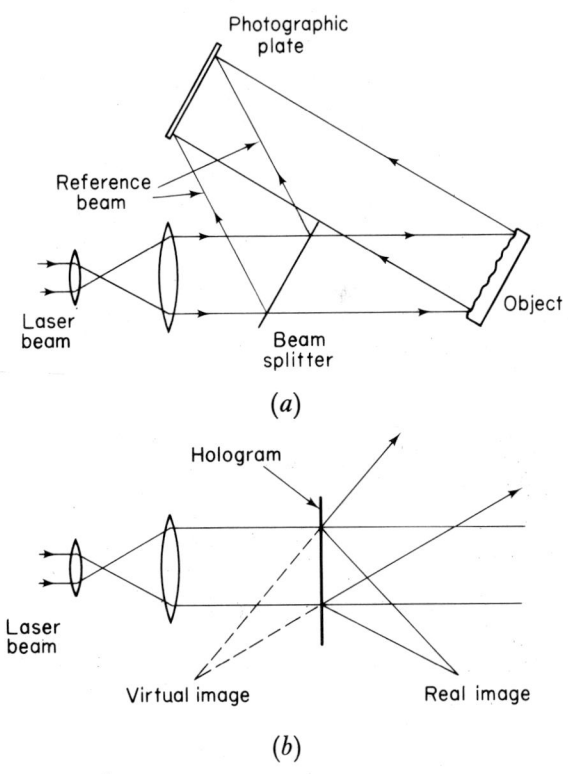

Fig. 8.3. Holography: (a) formation of the hologram, (b) reconstitution of the image.

where the two waves interfere either constructively or destructively. Effectively the object wave modulates the amplitude of the reference wave, and thereby is able to pass on its phase information encoded in these amplitude variations. Hence the record which is formed on the photographic plate—the hologram—is merely a complex interference pattern and bears no apparent resemblance to the original object. This should be compared with the intermediate stage in the conventional photographic process, where the photographic negative reveals a perfect (reversed contrast) image of the object.

In order to reconstruct the image of the object the hologram is re-illuminated as shown in fig. 8.3 (b). The interference pattern on the film acts rather as a complex diffraction grating so that on the far side of the hologram from the illumination two sets of diffracted waves emerge. One set of these forms a real image which can be projected on to a screen, photographed or viewed, provided the eye is placed well beyond it; the second appears to come from a virtual image located behind the plate, and can therefore be observed directly by the eye from a position close to the hologram. Since the image is three-dimensional, it is possible to focus on to any plane through it, or by viewing it from various positions, to observe different aspects of it. In fact it is just like observing the original solid object, an effect that appears totally uncanny when obtained by illuminating a two-dimensional film.

The advantages of this kind of image formation in connection with microscopy are enormous. It is possible, by taking a single hologram from an object, to come back time and time again perhaps to observe it from a slightly different angle, even though the original specimen may now no longer be available. This is particularly advantageous with objects which may be moving about, or otherwise varying, during the course of their examination. Possibly the major advantage, however, is that using the holographic technique it becomes possible to reproduce many of the complex image contrast enhancement effects which were discussed in Chapter 3. The latter techniques depend essentially upon artificially altering the interference balance of the various light waves which come together in the image plane, particularly where phase effects are concerned. Since the hologram itself contains all the phase information concerning the object, it is possible, by controlling the illuminating conditions, to produce image contrast effects which are analogous to bright field, dark field, phase contrast and interference contrast. Hence after taking a single hologram the microscopist can decide, possibly at some much later date, whether it might be useful to use any other of these contrast techniques, and then proceed to carry them out just as if the specimen itself was still available.

At the moment these ideas represent potential rather than routine achievements. The technique is of course more complex in operation than the conventional microscope alone, and a disadvantage of using coherent laser radiation is that the microscope resolution is impaired. It remains to be seen whether this extremely elegant application can become a viable possibility.

8.3. *Electron microscopy*

Resolution and contrast

In recent years improvements in technical design have pushed the resolution limit of the transmission electron microscope to below 0·1 nm. At this level it would, in principle, be possible to resolve individual atoms. That this has not, except in rather special circumstances, been achieved is due to the difficulty in obtaining atomic *contrast*, rather than atomic resolution ; the individual atoms in, say, a thin foil of a metal specimen, simply do not perturb the incident electron beam sufficiently for them to be imaged separately. (Compare this with the field-ion microscope, page 156, where the individual atoms perturb the *surface* electric field to a marked extent, and hence are able to give rise to individual contrast.) In any case, even if atomic images could be obtained, it is apparent that, for any practical specimen thickness, their images would overlap to an impossible extent when projected through the entire thickness of the specimen on to the image plane. These problems are not encountered in the technique for the direct resolution of parallel crystal planes discussed on page 100. Here the image is effectively an interference pattern formed between the direct and diffracted beams, and the crystal planes are oriented parallel to the incident beam in order to avoid overlap effects.

Considerable ingenuity has, however, gone into creating situations in which it might be possible to image isolated single atoms, and fig. 8.4 illustrates one of these. The technique is a sophisticated extension of the staining techniques discussed on page 101. Here thorium

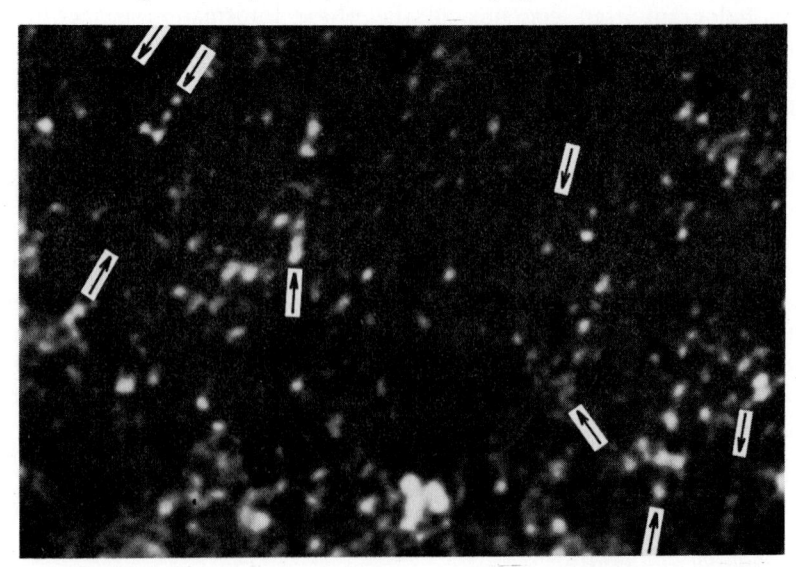

Fig. 8.4. Dark field electron micrograph showing individual thorium atoms located within a specimen of benzenetetracarboxylic acid, × 5 000 000. *H. Hashimoto.*

atoms have been incorporated into a complex organic compound in very specific atomic sites. The electronic scattering power of these very heavy metal atoms is then sufficiently greater than that of the background for them to be imaged as individual bright spots under dark field imaging conditions. Far though this achievement is from total atomic resolution of the specimen, it does hold exciting possibilities for studying the structure of such molecules by defining the sites at which such ' tagging ' atoms are located.

Of equal interest is the ' weak beam ' imaging technique, which enables remarkable improvements to be made in the resolution obtainable with dislocation images. It will be recalled from the discussion on page 107 that dislocations can be revealed in electron microscope images by means of diffraction contrast. Here the specimen is oriented such that one particular set of crystal planes is close to the Bragg diffraction condition, and the strain fields that extend around the dislocation give rise to enhanced diffraction, and hence

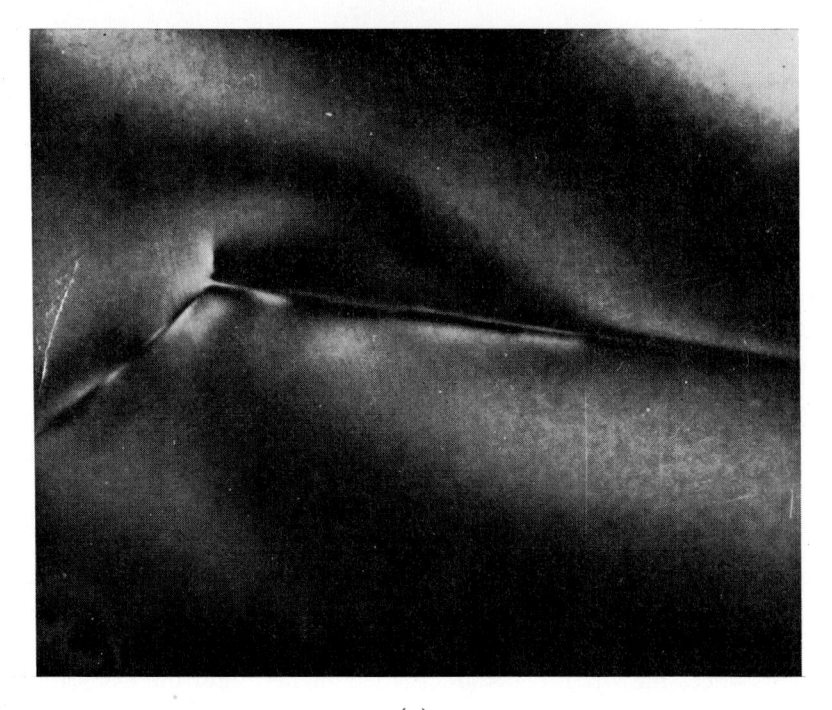

(a)

Fig. 8.5. The ' weak beam ' technique (a) conventional dark field electron micrograph showing a dislocation in silicon (b) the same dislocation imaged under weak beam conditions. *I. L. F. Ray.*

(*b*)

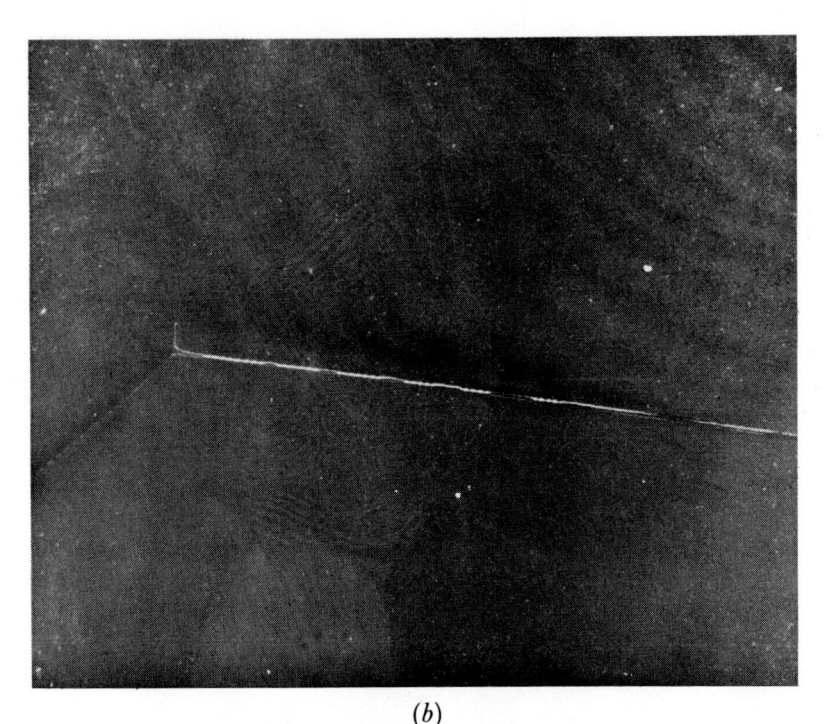

Fig. 8.5 (continued).

to dark or bright contrast (depending upon whether a bright field or dark field image is being observed) at the site of the dislocation. The difficulty is that these strain fields extend for a distance of several nm around the centre of the dislocation, and hence the diffraction ' image ' of the dislocation must also possess these dimensions. In practice this means that if two dislocations are any closer than about 10 nm, then their images cannot be resolved from each other, whatever the conventional resolution of the instrument may be.

In the weak beam technique this is rather neatly avoided by setting the specimen orientation a long way from the diffraction condition necessary for the particular diffracting beam which has been selected to form the dark field image. Now sufficiently strong diffraction to give rise to image formation only occurs very close to the dislocation core, where the strain fields are at their highest, and the dislocation is now imaged as a much narrower line. Figure 8.5 illustrates the power of the weak beam technique. Figure 8.5 (*a*) shows the image of a dislocation in silicon using conventional dark field electron microscopy, while fig. 8.5 (*b*) shows the same field of view imaged

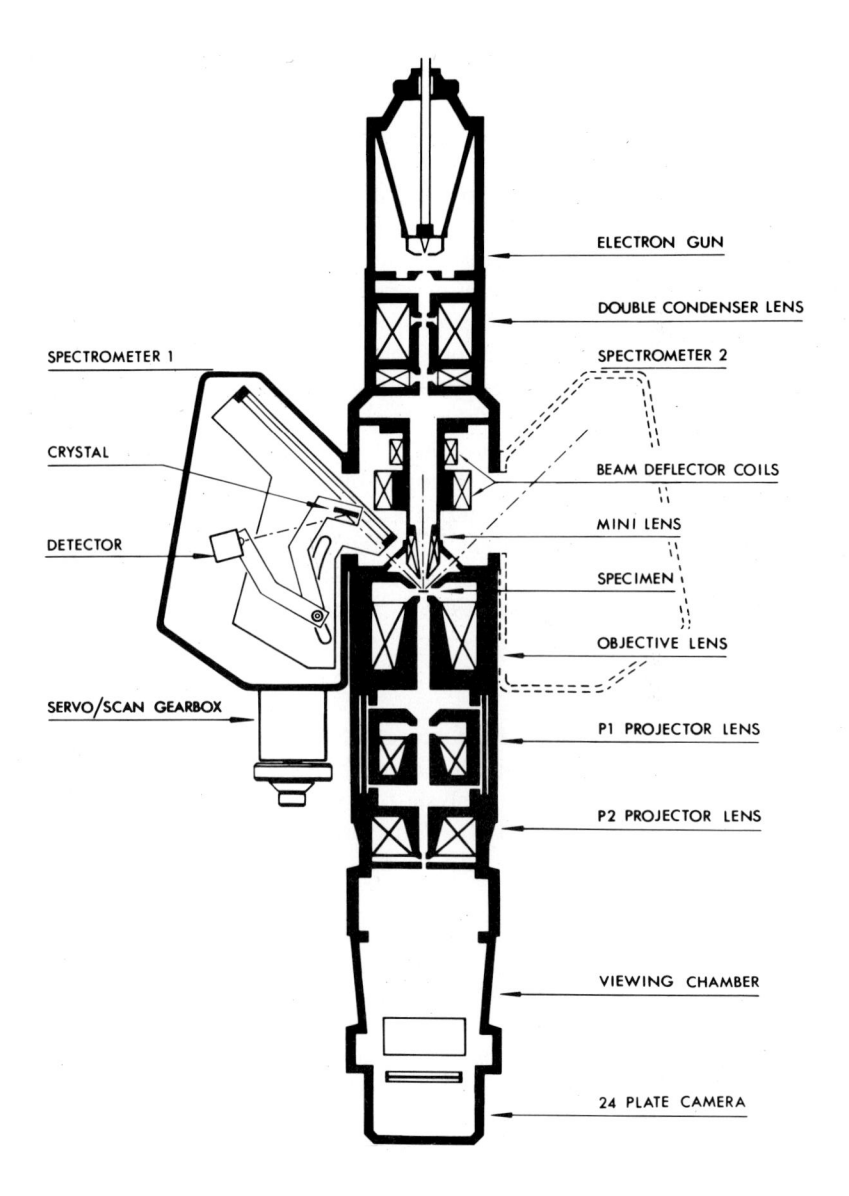

Fig. 8.6. Schematic diagram of the EMMA-4 instrument for combined electron microscopy and microanalysis. *A.E.I. Scientific Apparatus Ltd.*

using the weak beam method. The resolution is sufficiently enhanced for the dislocation to be seen to be split into two ' partial ' dislocations along certain segments of its length.

A rather different approach is used in the two remaining techniques which will be discussed in this section. The first of these uses a computer to simulate the image contrast that a particular microstructural feature is predicted to show. Such features may then be recognized when they occur in electron images by comparison with these simulated images. The other approach makes use of a variety of optical processing techniques in order to extract even further levels of information from existing micrographs, a technique which can also be applied to optical microscope images. In some cases it is possible to deduce information about crystal periodicities from apparently random images, using optical transforms and Fourier techniques, while in others the overall image sharpness, and hence effectively its resolution, may be increased either by eliminating background ' noise ' or by reducing ' blurring ' effects due to lens aberrations. This latter technique is particularly valuable in the case of certain biological specimens in which it is only possible to get adequate image *contrast* by deliberately defocusing the image, with a concomitant sacrifice in resolution.

Chemical analysis

As we have already seen, the feature that makes electron microscopy such a powerful technique is that it combines high resolution microscopy with crystallographic analysis obtained by means of selected area electron diffraction. It is not surprising, therefore, that attempts should have been made to add to these the facility for fine scale chemical analysis.

Two quite different approaches have been made to this problem. The first borrows extensively from the existing technique of electron probe microanalysis (page 140). Although in the latter technique extremely accurate chemical analysis can be made, the image resolution is only about 1 μm, about one thousand times worse than that of the electron microscope. The alternative, therefore, is to start with a high resolution electron microscope, and then to add X-ray detection and analysis systems to it. It is possible to obtain separate microanalyser attachments to fit on to standard commercial microscopes (just as it is for the scanning electron microscope), but the best solution to the problem has been the specially designed hybrid microscope known as EMMA—the Electron Microscope Microanalyser.

A schematic diagram of the EMMA-4 commercial instrument is shown in fig. 8.6. The design is based on a conventional 100 kV transmission electron microscope giving 1 nm resolution and 0·2 μm selected area diffraction. The addition of a special 'minilens' allows a fine (static) electron beam to be focused on to a selected area of the specimen and the characteristic X-rays which are emitted are detected using two built-in crystal spectrometers. Just as the electron probe microanalyser itself is a much more accurate instrument than merely a modified scanning electron microscope, so EMMA gives a considerably higher performance than a modified conventional microscope. While the accuracy of the analysis it yields is not as high as with the electron probe technique, its image resolution (in the analysis mode) is a factor of ten better.

The combination of selected area diffraction and microanalysis is particularly valuable. An important application of the diffraction technique lies in the identification of unknown particles in the microstructure from their diffraction pattern. If a reasonably accurate chemical analysis can be performed at the same time, then this identification becomes very much more certain. Thus to the microscopist EMMA adds the important advantage of microanalysis to his existing capabilities, while to the microanalyst who is prepared to accept some loss in accuracy the technique offers a number of extremely important advantages. Much smaller particles can be detected and identified, and in particular those which give rise to poor contrast in either the electron or X-ray scanning modes in the conventional microanalyser, and there is the opportunity to perform high resolution microscopy and diffraction on them as well.

A more subtle approach involves detecting characteristic energy losses in the electron beam used to form a conventional electron microscope image. As we have already seen, when electrons interact with matter they can be scattered either elastically or inelastically. It is the former electrons with which we are concerned when we talk about diffraction contrast. The inelastically scattered electrons, on the other hand, are those which have suffered an energy loss in being transmitted through the specimen, the extent to which this occurs increasing with the specimen thickness. These electrons contribute generally to the image background, but since they effectively constitute a form of chromatic aberration, can cause a deterioration in image resolution in thick specimens.

The point is though that these electron energy losses are also a function of the chemical composition of the region of the specimen through which they are transmitted. Hence if these energy losses can be detected they offer the opportunity to perform fine-scale chemical analysis. The techniques used to capitalize on this are as yet fairly new and their range of applications limited. However they are beginning to yield some interesting results. One method, termed *energy analysis microscopy*, uses a slit aperture to select a narrow region of the microstructure, and then produces an energy spectrum of the electrons emerging through this slit. Figure 8.7 shows this technique in operation. The slit, S-S' is located across the image of a small precipitate particle in fig. 8.7 (*a*), while fig. 8.7 (*b*) shows the resultant electron energy spectrum, the vertical axis of which corresponds spatially to that of the slit. The left hand line of the spectrum corresponds to electrons which have undergone no energy loss, while the lines to the right of this correspond to electrons which have lost certain specific amounts of energy on passing through the specimen. The energy loss spectrum across the precipitate particle can be seen to be quite different from that across the matrix. An effective image resolution of 10 nm can be achieved using this technique, considerably better even than with EMMA, although it cannot compare with the latter in terms of ease of operation or accuracy of analysis.

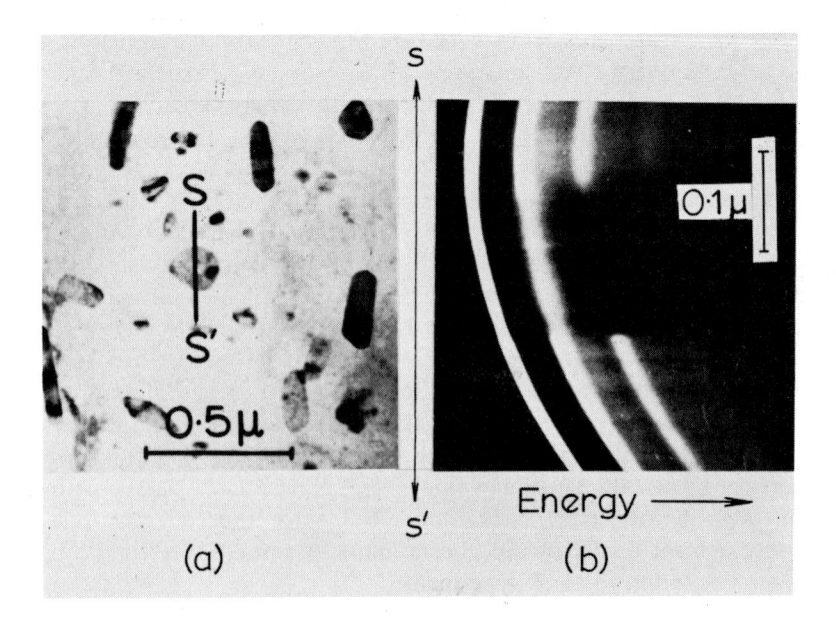

Fig. 8.7. Application of the energy-analysing electron microscope (*a*) micrograph showing the position of the analysing slit, SS', across a θ phase particle in an aluminium–copper alloy (*b*) corresponding electron energy loss spectrum. *A. J. F. Metherell.*

Fig. 8.8. High voltage electron microscope. *A.E.I. Scientific Apparatus Ltd.*

An alternative method, termed *energy-selecting microscopy*, forms a direct image of the specimen using only electrons from a particular band of the energy spectrum, in much the same way as in the image formed by characteristic X-rays in the electron microanalyser, or by characteristic Auger electrons in the scanning electron microscope version of the Auger technique discussed on page 185.

High voltage electron microscopy

One problem encountered in conventional transmission electron microscopy is that the limited penetrating power of a 100 kV electron beam means that the image quality resulting from specimens whose thickness is much greater than about 200 nm is unacceptably reduced. This limitation may be overcome by going to higher and higher accelerating voltages, and it is with this aim in mind that a series of high voltage electron microscopes has been developed. Although one million volts is the most usual operating potential, the range does extend right up to 3 MV. In this way specimen thicknesses up to 5–10 times greater than those used in conventional electron microscopy can usefully be examined.

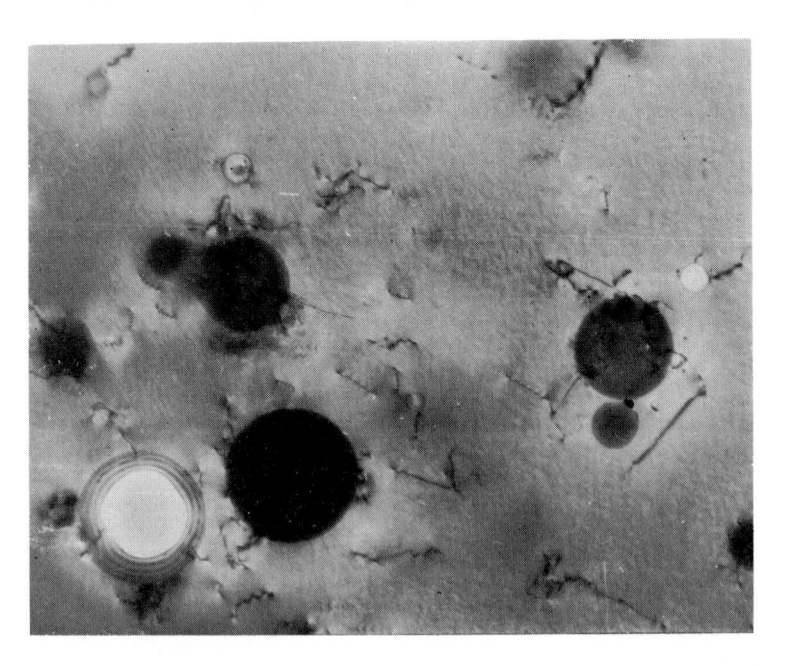

Fig. 8.9. High voltage electron micrograph showing particles of SiO_2 in copper, ×13 000. *M. H. Loretto.*

The differences in design between the 100 kV and 1 MV instruments are largely technical. The 1 MV model is vastly scaled up both in cost (this may be as much as £250 000) and in size—it may weigh some 10–20 tons and usually requires to be housed in its own separate building. Figure 8.8 gives some idea of its scale in relationship to the operating console and screen (cf. fig. 4.2). The major technical difficulty lies in producing the high voltage itself, and for this a Cockroft–Walton type of generator is required.

The advantages of the increased penetrating power are particularly apparent in the case of metallurgical specimens. When one is restricted to using very thin foils it is never certain that the microstructures seen are truly representative of the bulk specimen, or whether they might have been altered in some way by the thinning process. Furthermore, if dynamic experiments, such as heating or mechanical deformation, are carried out *in situ*, the resultant changes in the microstructure may again fail to be characteristic of those which would have occurred in the bulk, due to the large surface to volume ratio of a thin foil, and the possibility of stress relief normal to its surface. In any case some materials (ceramics, mineral specimens) are difficult to produce in thin enough form for study using 100 kV electrons.

These difficulties are very much reduced in high voltage electron microscopy, and metallurgical applications include dynamic studies of recrystallization, grain growth and phase transformations. An example of the latter is shown in fig. 8.9. Several spherical particles can be seen whose diameter, at 1–3 μm, is much too great for them to be studied using 100 kV microscopy. Here they are readily observed, and more importantly, the interaction of dislocations with them can be noted. The much greater physical dimensions of the high voltage microscope also make it feasible to install quite complicated internal apparatus, such as mechanical straining stages, which would be quite impractical in the 100 kV design. It is also possible to carry out oxidation and corrosion experiments under controlled environmental conditions by enclosing the specimen within a small reaction chamber containing two windows through which the electron beam is able to pass.

Similar problems of specimen preparation arise with biological specimens. In particular the possibility of using 'environmental cells' such as described above is a great benefit since it opens up the possibility of studying heavily hydrated materials which would otherwise degrade very rapidly when exposed to a vacuum. It also becomes possible to study living organisms, something which is impossible with the 100 kV instrument, since with this even the smallest living organism is too thick for worthwhile electron images to be produced. Hence the possibilities that the technique opens up on biological research are probably even more far reaching than those in metallurgy.

The major disadvantage of the technique is the radiation damage that the high energy beam causes to the specimen. This may take two forms. Firstly electron–atom collisions may lead to atoms being knocked out of their normal sites within the crystal, leading to the formation of defect clusters which in time can begin to obscure the image. To some extent this may be turned to advantage in that *in situ* radiation damage studies may themselves be carried out, but in general it is a disadvantage, particularly with the lighter elements which suffer proportionately greater damage (hence this is a problem that is encountered with biological materials even at 100 kV). The second kind of radiation damage involves *ionization* of the atoms making up the specimen, and does not occur in metals owing to the free electron nature of their bonding. However in organic materials this effect can lead to serious deterioration, leading one biologist to comment, somewhat sourly, that the technique does not so much open up the possibility of studying living organisms as dying ones ! However it appears that the situation may be improved, somewhat paradoxically, by going to even higher voltages still, at which point the damage begins to decrease again. At a simple level this may be explained by saying that the damage caused is proportional to the time that the electrons spend within the specimen, and at the higher voltages they are travelling that much faster.

The scanning transmission electron microscope

The conventional scanning electron microscope, although normally used to study the surface of bulk specimens, can equally well be used in transmission with a suitably thin specimen. However, its much inferior resolution makes it unable to compete in any way with the conventional transmission electron microscope. The reason for the poor resolution of the scanning microscope is that the diameter of the electron beam used in the scan is restricted to the comparatively high value of 10–20 nm owing to the low beam intensity of a conventional heated filament electron source. This is of little importance in the normal transmission electron microscope where the entire specimen is illuminated at once, and the brightness of the resultant image is adequate for photographic exposure times of the order of a second to be used. In the scanning instrument, however, each point of the specimen is illuminated for only a tiny fraction of the time taken to record the entire image, and, even with relatively long exposure times, it is necessary to use a beam size of the kind described above in order for an adequate signal to be received.

In the last few years, however, a new kind of electron source has become available, which is some 10 000 times brighter than the heated filament variety, and this has made possible the development of a new generation of scanning transmission electron microscopes which are more than able to compete with the more conventional kind of transmission microscope. The new electron source is effectively a pointed field emission specimen, virtually identical to that discussed on page 152. Not only is its current density sufficiently high for beam sizes of the order of 0·2–0·3 nm to be used, but, since it operates at room temperature, the spread in energy of the electrons, and hence the chromatic aberration, is also that much lower. The main disadvantage of the technique is that, for the field emission source to operate satisfactorily, an ultra-high (rather than merely a high) vacuum environment must be provided.

It might be wondered why it should be thought worth while to produce such an instrument which, whilst matching the conventional transmission microscope in resolution, does not exceed it. The

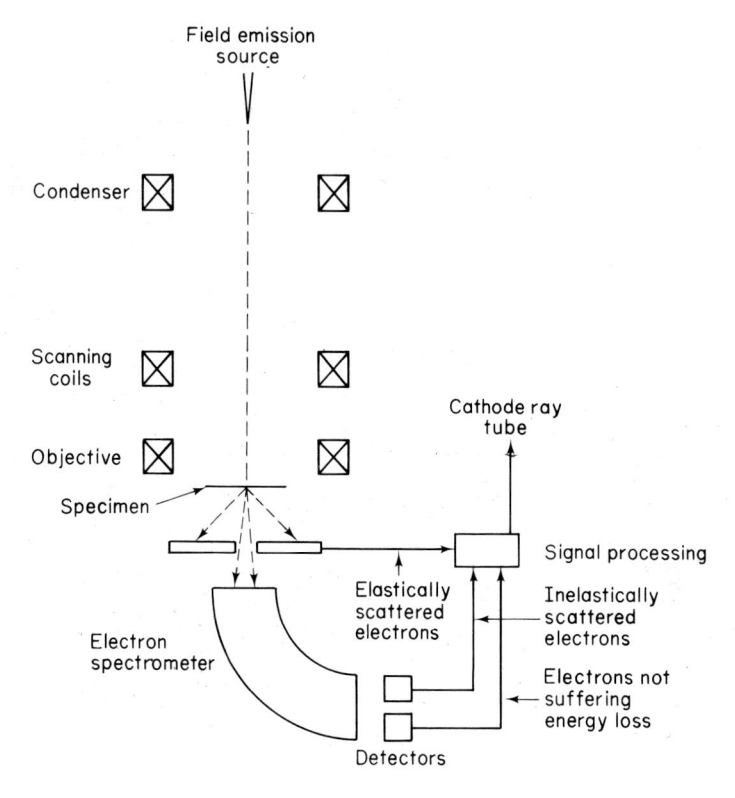

Fig. 8.10. The scanning transmission electron microscope.

answer lies in the unique advantages that can be obtained by using the scanning principle of image formation. Since the electrons are not focused after leaving the specimen, there are no problems about objective lens aberrations, and in particular about the form of chromatic aberration that arises with thick specimens due to electron energy losses. In the conventional transmission microscope these energy-loss electrons contribute to the general image blur, although they may, as we have seen on page 199, be turned to advantage in giving chemical information.

Using the scanning principle, on the other hand, it is possible, at least in principle, to collect each electron as it emerges from the specimen, and to assign it to a particular group according to the kind of interaction which it has experienced. The resultant signal may then be amplified and processed electronically in a number of ways before being fed to the cathode ray tube for display. This is done point by point as the beam is scanned across the specimen. Figure 8.10 shows how this may be accomplished in practice. A circular electron detector is located underneath the specimen, with a small hole through its centre through which both the unscattered electrons and the inelastically scattered electrons can pass (equivalent to the 'direct beam' in the conventional microscope). The elastically scattered, or diffracted electrons, with their much larger deflections, strike the disc where they are then collected and can be used to produce a signal. The electrons that pass through the hole enter a spectrometer where they may be separated according to their energy, and hence classified. Energy losses can then be analysed to provide chemical information in much the same way as was described on page 200. Even more valuable is the fact that other detectors may also be installed to collect characteristic Auger electrons, or characteristic X-rays, and hence to form images or provide quantitative analyses in the ways that have already been discussed in connection with these radiations.

Versatility, therefore, is the keynote of this instrument, particularly in the way that the various electron signals may be processed and combined. For example it is known that the signal from the elastically scattered electrons is proportional to $Z^{4/3}$ where Z is the atomic number of the atoms of which the specimen is composed, while that of the inelastically scattered electrons is proportional to $Z^{1/3}$. Hence, electronically dividing the former signal by the latter produces an output which is proportional simply to the atomic number of these component atoms. This facility has been made use of in forming images of single atoms of some heavy metal which has been induced to react with specific sites in various organic compounds, the heavier atoms being rendered visible as bright spots, in much the same way as illustrated in fig. 8.4.

So significant are these advantages that it is probable that the scanning transmission electron microscope will become the dominant electron-optical technique over the next few decades, and it is likely that its true capabilities are still nowhere near to being fully recognized. For example, a further advantage of the instrument is that it can be used with very much thicker specimens than can the conventional variety, since it is necessary only that transmission can be obtained, without the subsequent need for adequate image formation by focusing. In this respect it becomes a serious competitor to the high voltage electron microscope, since, although costing nearly twice as much as the conventional transmission microscope (about £80 000, with full analytical facilities), it is still very much cheaper than the high voltage instrument.

Perhaps inevitably, the next step is to produce a high voltage scanning transmission electron microscope, and indeed this objective is already actively being pursued. One advantage of the combination may be that, since both techniques separately are noted for their increased specimen penetrating power, and since, using the scanning principle, there are no electron optics beyond the specimen, it may be possible to arrange for the electron beam to pass through a special window completely *out* of the microscope chamber, and hence to interact with a specimen which is simply located in the outside air, a much more convenient arrangement than having to enclose it within some double windowed environmental cell inside the microscope.

8.4. *Ion beam techniques*

Ion back-scattering

In recent years a number of techniques have been devised which depend in some way on detecting or measuring ions which have been back-scattered after colliding with a solid surface. In the simplest of these, the *proton scattering* technique, a beam of protons in the energy range 20–100 kV is directed at a single crystal target as shown in fig. 8.11 (*a*). A substantial fraction of these protons will be scattered back from the crystal due to collisions which occur within the first hundred or so atomic layers. These back-scattered protons may be detected on a fluorescent screen or suitable emulsion. If the target has no regular crystal structure the scattered protons will

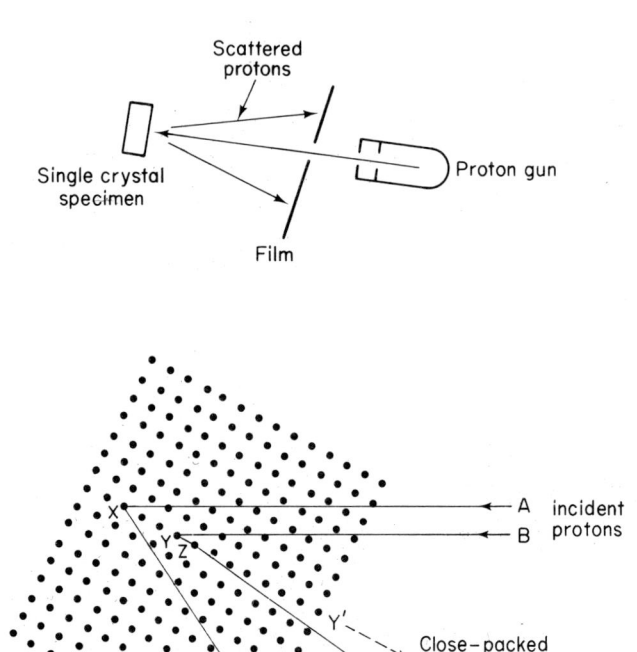

Fig. 8.11. The proton scattering technique: (a) schematic diagram of the apparatus (b) illustrating proton blocking.

emerge in a completely random manner, and the screen will be uniformly illuminated. However if the target is crystalline then the directions which the back-scattered protons can take are strongly influenced by the regular nature of the atomic array.

Figure 8.11 (b) illustrates two possible trajectories taken by protons scattered by a crystalline specimen. Proton A is scattered through a comparatively large angle on colliding with the atom at X, and then passes right back out of the crystal without suffering any further deflection. Proton B, on the other hand, is scattered by Y into the direction of a densely packed atomic row and its further path in this direction is blocked by atom Z. Hence there are certain densely packed planes and directions within the crystal along which scattered protons are unable to proceed. This phenomenon is referred to as 'blocking', and a typical blocking pattern is shown in fig. 8.12. The dark lines and points correspond to regions along which the scattered protons are unable to travel. In a sense they represent a 'shadow' cast by these regions. In this case the crystal orientation was such that a four-fold axis of symmetry lay normal to the screen, and hence the proton blocking pattern accurately reflects this symmetry, and it is possible to identify and index each of the points and lines making up the pattern.

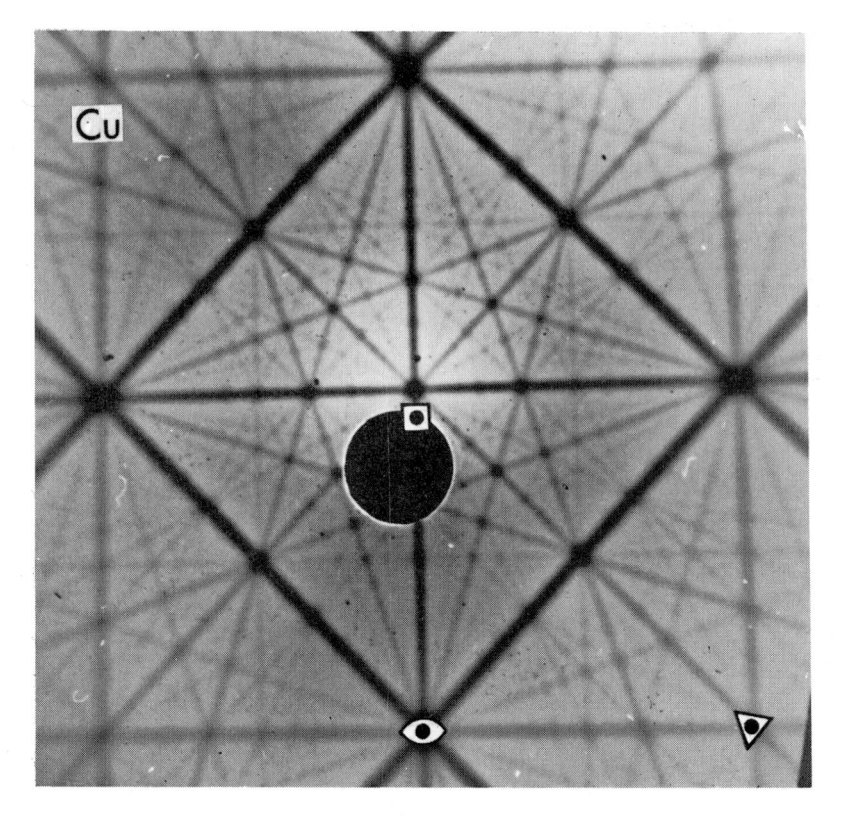

Fig. 8.12. Proton blocking pattern from a single crystal of copper. *W. White.*

To a large extent this technique has remained unexploited, despite the fact that it contains, in a very simple form, direct crystallographic information about the specimen. One drawback is that the theory of proton scattering is insufficiently understood for the spot and line *intensities* to be usefully related to the actual crystal structure. One possible application, however, could be as a quick and simple method for determining the orientation of single crystals, rather as in the Laue X-ray method (page 172). Further applications could lie in the study of thin films, since X-rays suffer from the disadvantage of penetrating too far into the specimen, hence being less surface sensitive, while electrons err the other way in requiring the specimen to be in the form of a very thin foil, and hence if thin films are to be studied they must first be removed from the substrate on which they were formed. Here they could be studied *in situ*.

A commercial version of the technique has been produced, under the name of the ' proton scattering microscope '. This is a singularly misleading choice of name since it certainly is not acting as a microscope. In a microscope there must always be a one-to-one correlation between the spatial orientation of points in the image and points on the specimen. The proton scattering technique, on the other hand, is more akin to a diffraction technique, in that different points in the pattern correspond to different crystallographic *directions* within the specimen.

Other, more sophisticated, techniques exist in which both the energy and the distribution of back-scattered ions, commonly of the noble gases, are measured. These are highly specialized in operation and the information that they yield is far removed from either microscopy or diffraction. However these techniques are extremely sensitive to surface chemical composition, and in this sense are complementary to the technique of Auger electron spectroscopy which was discussed on page 182.

Secondary ion emission

A further effect that can occur when solids undergo ion bombardment is that the surface of the solid is itself eroded away. This phenomenon is known as ' sputtering ' and has already been encountered in connection with Auger electron spectroscopy where it was used both to clean off surface contamination, and to enable the variation of composition with depth below the surface to be determined. Additionally, fig. 6.16 demonstrated the alteration in the surface structure caused by this erosion process.

In secondary ion emission analysis, however, we are concerned, not with the surface left behind, but with the atoms which are removed, since they can tell us what the surface composition had been.

Several versions of the technique exist, referred to variously as SIMS (Secondary Ion Mass Spectrometry), IMMA (Ion Microprobe Mass Analyser) and IMS (Imaging Mass Spectrometry), but basically they all employ a several kV primary ion beam which produces secondary ion emission, or ion sputtering, when it is brought to bear on the specimen surface. These secondary ions are then detected and analysed by means of a mass spectrometer. Material is also removed in the form of neutral atoms, but these of course escape detection. The technique is, therefore, destructive, but this does carry the advantage that fresh surfaces are continually being exposed, and hence that depth composition profiles may be obtained automatically.

Several different modes of analysis may be employed depending on the kind of information required:
(a) the mass spectrum from a particular area may be scanned in order to identify the various elements which are present.
(b) depth distributions for one or more elements may be obtained by measuring the variation with time of a selected emission over the whole surface, or of all the emission from a single point.
(c) a particular secondary ion may be selected to produce a near-instantaneous *image* of its distribution within the bombarded area.

The principal disadvantage of the technique is that, while detection sensitivities are in general extremely high, relative sensitivities are very variable, and it is virtually impossible to relate the intensity of the emitted ions to their concentration in the original specimen. Yields may vary widely according to the chemical state of the element, the presence of other species and the nature of the bombarding ions. The technique does have the advantage over the electron probe microanalyser that its sensitivity to elements of low atomic number is extremely high, even hydrogen being detected, while the fact that mass spectrometric analysis is used means that different isotopes can also be distinguished. It is however much more expensive than the electron probe technique.

The field-ion atom probe

Finally we return to the field-ion microscope, which was discussed on page 156. A recent development of this very powerful technique also makes use of mass spectrometric analysis of the ions which are removed from the specimen surface, this time by the highly controllable process of field evaporation. In the new development of this technique a form of mass spectrometer is coupled on to the image screen, into which a hole or aperture of a selected size has been introduced. The specimen is manipulated until the aperture covers the image of a selected group of atoms, and these are then field evaporated by means of a high voltage pulse. After leaving the specimen surface the atoms (or rather ions) follow the same trajectories as the imaging gas ions, and hence pass through the screen aperture, into the mass spectrometer, where they may be identified. In the limit the aperture could be made sufficiently small that it covers the image of only one atom. In this way it is possible to determine the chemical identity of single atoms, whose original location in the microstructure is uniquely defined—surely the ultimate in combined microscopy, structural and chemical analysis.

8.5. *Summary*

In this book we have covered a wide range of techniques and variations upon them. To a large extent these are mainly complementary to one another in the level of information that they provide, which is itself a tribute both to the ingenuity of man in devising such a variety of techniques, and to the ingenuity of nature in devising such a variety of information to be gathered. As a guide, Table 5 lists some of the parameters which define the performance of the more important conventional microscopical techniques. The list is not exhaustive, and more detailed information can be obtained by consulting the extensive reading list which follows.

Table 5. Operating parameters of the principal microscopical techniques

Technique	Magnification	Optimum resolution (nm)	Depth of field
Optical microscopy	×20 to ×1000	200	0·4–10 μm
Transmission electron microscopy	×200 to ×300,000	0·2	0·2 μm
Scanning electron microscopy	×10 to ×200,000	10	1 cm–1 μm
Thermionic emission microscopy	×10 to ×6000	20	2 μm
Field emission microscopy	×10^5 to ×10^6	2	—
Field-ion microscopy	×10^6 to ×10^7	0·2	—

FURTHER READING

R. BARER. *Lecture Notes on the Use of the Microscope.* Blackwell 1968.
A. L. E. BARRON. *Using the Microscope.* Chapman and Hall 1965.
A. H. BENNETT, H. OSTERBERG, H. JUPNIK and O. W. RICHARDS. *Phase Microscopy.* Wiley 1951.
D. BIRCHON. *Optical Microscope Technique.* George Newnes Ltd. 1961.
K. M. BOWKETT and D. A. SMITH. *Field-ion Microscopy.* North-Holland 1970.
D. G. BRANDON. *Modern Techniques in Metallography.* Butterworths 1966.
V. E. COSSLETT. *Modern Microscopy.* G. Bell & Sons Ltd. 1966.
V. E. COSSLETT and W. C. NIXON. *X-ray Microscopy.* Cambridge University Press 1970.
B. D. CULLITY. *Elements of X-ray Diffraction.* Addison-Wesley 1967.
R. W. DITCHBURN. *Light.* Blackie & Son 1963.
M. FRANÇON. *Progress in Microscopy.* Pergamon 1961.
R. F. GIFKINS. *Optical Microscopy of Metals.* Pitman 1970.
A. V. GRIMSTONE. *The Electron Microscope in Biology.* Arnold 1968.
P. W. HAWKES. *Electron Optics and Electron Microscopy.* Taylor & Francis Ltd. 1972.
P. B. HIRSCH, A. HOWIE, R. B. NICHOLSON, D. W. PASHLEY and M. J. WHELAN. *Electron Microscopy of Thin Crystals.* Butterworths 1967.
H. S. LIPSON. *Crystals and X-rays.* Wykeham Publications 1970.
T. D. MCKINLEY, F. F. J. HEINRICH and D. B. WITTRY. *The Electron Microprobe.* Wiley 1966.
E. W. MÜLLER and T. T. TSONG. *Field ion Microscopy.* American Elsevier Publishing Co. Inc. 1969.
V. A. PHILLIPS. *Modern Metallographic Techniques and their Applications.* Wiley-Interscience 1971.
R. E. SMALLMAN and K. H. ASHBEE. *Modern Metallography.* Pergamon 1966.
G. W. WHITE. *Introduction to Microscopy.* Butterworths 1966.

INDEX

Abbe resolution limit 21–3, 93, 100, 122, 131, 169, 175
Absorption 123, 128, 132, 137
Accommodation 3
Achromatic lenses 11, 40
Airy disc 24–6
Amplitude contrast 57, 59, 61–4, 65
Angular magnification 5
Anisotropy 82
Apertures 10, 34, 37, 66, 70, 91, 97, 101, 102
Aplanatic points 42
Apochromat 41
Artefacts 55
Astigmatism 12, 92
Atomic resolution 146, 157, 159, 194, 206, 212
Atomic scattering factor 170
Atom probe field-ion microscope 164, 211–12
Auger electrons 96, 127, 183, 201, 206
Auger electron spectroscopy 180, 182–5, 210
Autoradiography 132–4

Back-scattering 96, 115
Berg–Barrett technique 138
Binocular microscope 35
Blocking pattern 209
Bragg diffraction equation 19–21, 102, 108, 129, 140, 170, 173, 195
Bright field image 59, 97, 192

Carbon replica 111
Carbon extraction replica 112
Cathodoluminescence 97, 117
Characteristic energy losses 199, 206
Characteristic radiation 117, 127, 140, 182–3
Chemical analysis 140, 143, 164, 169, 198–201, 206
Chromatic aberration 10, 11, 40, 92, 96, 199, 205
Circle of confusion 9, 21, 27
Cockcroft–Walton generator 203
Coherent elastic scattering (see Diffraction)

Colour contrast 58, 60
Compensating eyepiece 47
Compound microscope 7–9, 33–6
Computer simulation 198
Condenser lens 34, 36–8, 39, 89
Contact microradiography 130, 181
Contrast 4, 28–9, 57–64, 88, 94, 97–101, 109, 110–11, 114–18, 123, 132, 148, 159, 192, 194
Critical illumination 37
Crystal structure 19, 168–9
Curvature of field 40

Dark field image 29, 63, 64–70, 75, 99, 137, 192
De Broglie 86, 87
Debye–Scherrer technique (see X-ray powder photography)
Depth of field 27, 37, 40, 55, 94, 109, 113, 132, 212
Depth of focus 27, 50, 94
Diaphragm 37, 66, 70
Diffraction 15–26, 59, 65, 70, 95, 97, 101–8
Diffraction contrast 97–100, 195–7
Diffraction grating 17–19, 21
Diffraction patterns 102–8, 168, 171–81
Direct (crystal) resolution 100–1, 194
Dislocations 30, 97–99, 101, 107, 138, 166, 195–7
Dispersion 10
Dyson's long working distance objective 43

Elastic scattering 95, 183, 206
Electron diffraction 177 (see also Selected area diffraction)
Electron gun 88, 89, 204–5
Electron lenses 88, 90
Electron microscopy 86–121, 193
Electron probe microanalyser 96, 117, 140–5, 146, 182, 198
Electron spectroscopy 182–6
Electron wavelength 87, 89, 121
Emission microscopy 146–67
EMMA 198–9, 200

215

Empty magnification 45
Energy-analysing microscope 200
Energy-selecting microscope 201
Environmental cell 44, 203, 207
Etching 51
Exit pupil 8, 45
Eye 2–3, 11, 44
Eyepiece 8, 44–7

Fermi energy 148
Field emission 148, 150–1, 205
Field emission microscope 150–6, 158, 179
Field evaporation 162–3
Field ionization 156
Field-ion atom probe 211–12
Field-ion microscope 146, 156–67, 168, 179, 187, 194
Field lens **45–6**
Filters 37, 55
Fluorescence 60, 84
Fluorescence microscopy 84–5
Fluorites 41
Focal length 2
Fourier techniques 170, 198
Fraunhofer diffraction 17, 21, 22, 23, 102
Fresnel diffraction 16

Gauss image plane 9
Geiger counter 129
Grain boundary 30, 51, 97, 133, 166
Graticule 46, 48

High energy electron diffraction 177
High voltage electron microscopy 202–4, 207
Holography 188, 190–3
Hooke 7, 34
Huyghens eyepiece 46
Huyghens principle 14, 16, 22

Illumination 36–8
Image analysing computer 48, 188, 189–90
Image contrast (see Contrast)
Image formation 1
Image shearing 48
Immersion objective (see Oil immersion objective)
Incoherent elastic scattering 95
Inelastic scattering 96, 181, 183, 199, 206
Interference 14–19, 21–3, 61–4, 78, 95, 191–2

Interference contrast 74–9, 192
Interference microscope 77
Interferometry 78–80
Ion back-scattering 207–10
Ion beam techniques 187, 207–12
Ion bombardment 166, 184, 210

Kerr magneto-optic effect 84
Kikuchi lines 108, 120
Köhler illumination 38
Kossel camera 144

Lang topography 139–40
Laue technique 171, 210
LEED (see Low energy electron diffraction)
Leeuwenhoek 6
Lens equation 2
Limit of resolution 3, 23, 26, 29, 39, 74, 87–8, 93, 113, 131, 135, 136, 148, 159, 193, 200, 205, 212
Linear magnification 2, 5
Long working distance objective 43
Low energy electron diffraction 178–81, 183

Magnification 2, 4, 5, 9, 32, 35, 39, 45, 56, 88, 113, 135, 147, 152, 159, 212
Magnifying glass 6
Mass spectrometer 181, 211
McArthur microscope 36
Mechanical stage 33, 91
Metallurgical microscope 35
Micrometry 47–8 (see also Image analysing computer)
Microstructure 30–2
Microtome 49, 92
Multiple beam interferometry 80

Near point 3
Necessary magnification 44–5
Numerical aperture 23, 26, 28, 39, 45, 49, 54, 64, 87–8
Neutron diffraction 181

Objective lens 8, 26, 38–44
Oblique illumination 64
Oil immersion objective 27, 40, 41–3
Opaque stop microscopy 66
Optical microscopy 33–56, 188–93

Pearlite 54
Phase contrast 58, 60–4, 70–4, 76–7, 192

Photoelectron spectroscopy 185-6
Photoemission 147
Photography 47
Polarized light 36, 58, 81
Polarized light microscopy 81-4
Powder photography (see X-ray powder photography)
Preferred orientation (see Texture photograph)
Projection eyepiece 47
Proportional counter 129
Proton scattering 207-10

Ramsden eyepiece 46
Rayleigh criterion 23-6, 28
Refractive index 10, 23, 42, 59
Replica (see Surface replica)
Resolution 3, 21-7, 37, 54, 92, 109 (see also Limit of resolution)
Resolving power 3, 93
Retina 2-4
Rotating crystal X-ray method 172-3

Scanning electron microscope 96, 109, 112-21, 141, 146, 182, 183, 185
Scanning transmission electron microscope 204-7
Schlieren illumination 70
Scintillation counter 129-30
Secondary electron emission 96, 114, 181, 183
Secondary ion emission 210-11
Secondary ion mass spectrometry 211
Selected area diffraction 102-5, 168, 199
Semi-apochromats (see Fluorites)
Simple microscope 4-7
SIMS (see Secondary ion mass spectrometry)
Specimen preparation 48-54, 91-2
Spectroscopy 31, 168-9
Spherical aberration 9, 11, 41, 42, 43, 92

Staining 29, 49, 64, 101, 144, 194
Stereomicroscopy 35-6
Stereoscopic pairs 91, 114, 145
Surface replicas 109, 110-12
Surface studies 31, 54, 109, 118, 155, 165, 179, 184, 210

Texture photograph 104, 176
Thermionic emission microscope 146-50
Thin lens 1
Transmission electron microscope 87, 89-92 (see also Electron microscopy)
Two-beam conditions 105-9
Tyndall scattering 29

Ultramicroscope 29, 66
Ultraviolet radiation 55, 84
Ultraviolet microscopy 84
Uncertainty principle 151

Wave optics 12-19
Weak beam technique 195-7
Work function 148, 150, 154

X-ray diffraction 168, 169-77, 181
X-ray diffraction microscopy 137
X-ray emission 96, 117, 122, 123
X-ray fluorescence 182
X-ray microscopy 122, 130-140
X-ray powder photography 173-6
X-ray projection microscope 134-5, 152
X-ray reflection microscope 135
X-ray spectrometer 129, 141, 174, 199
X-ray spectroscopy 181-6
X-ray spectrum 124
X-ray topography (see Lang topography)

Zernike 70
Zoom lens 35

THE WYKEHAM SCIENCE SERIES

1	†*Elementary Science of Metals*	J. W. MARTIN and R. A. HULL
2	*Neutron Physics*	G. E. BACON and G. R. NOAKES
3	†*Essentials of Meteorology*	D. H. MCINTOSH, A. S. THOM and V. T. SAUNDERS
4	*Nuclear Fusion*	H. R. HULME and A. McB. COLLIEU
5	*Water Waves*	N. F. BARBER and G. GHEY
6	*Gravity and the Earth*	A. H. COOK and V. T. SAUNDERS
7	*Relativity and High Energy Physics*	W. G. V. ROSSER and R. K. MCCULLOCH
8	*The Method of Science*	R. HARRÉ and D. G. F. EASTWOOD
9	†*Introduction to Polymer Science*	L. R. G. TRELOAR and W. F. ARCHENHOLD
10	†*The Stars; their structure and evolution*	R. J. TAYLER and A. S. EVEREST
11	*Superconductivity*	A. W. B. TAYLOR and G. R. NOAKES
12	*Neutrinos*	G. M. LEWIS and G. A. WHEATLEY
13	*Crystals and X-rays*	H. S. LIPSON and R. M. LEE
14	†*Biological Effects of Radiation*	J. E. COGGLE and G. R. NOAKES
15	*Units and Standards for Electromagnetism*	P. VIGOUREUX and R. A. R. TRICKER
16	*The Inert Gases: Model Systems for Science*	B. L. SMITH and J. P. WEBB
17	*Thin Films*	K. D. LEAVER, B. N. CHAPMAN and H. T. RICHARDS
18	*Elementary Experiments with Lasers*	G. WRIGHT and G. FOXCROFT
19	†*Production, Pollution, Protection*	W. B. YAPP and M. I. SMITH
20	*Solid State Electronic Devices*	D. V. MORGAN, M. J. HOWES and J. SUTCLIFFE
21	*Strong Materials*	J. W. MARTIN and R. A. HULL
22	†*Elementary Quantum Mechanics*	SIR NEVILL MOTT and M. BERRY
23	*The Origin of the Chemical Elements*	R. J. TAYLER and A. S. EVEREST
24	*The Physical Properties of Glass*	D. G. HOLLOWAY and D. A. TAWNEY
25	*Amphibians*	J. F. D. FRAZER and O. H. FRAZER
26	*The Senses of Animals*	E. T. BURTT and A. PRINGLE
27	†*Temperature Regulation*	S. A. RICHARDS and P. S. FIELDEN
28	†*Chemical Engineering in Practice*	G. NONHEBEL and M. BERRY
29	†*An Introduction to Electrochemical Science*	J. O'M. BOCKRIS, N. BONCIOCAT, F. GUTMANN and M. BERRY
30	*Vertebrate Hard Tissues*	L. B. HALSTEAD and R. HILL
31	†*The Astronomical Telescope*	B. V. BARLOW and A. S. EVEREST
32	*Computers in Biology*	J. A. NELDER and R. D. KIME
33	*Electron Microscopy and Analysis*	P. J. GOODHEW and L. E. CARTWRIGHT
34	*Introduction to Modern Microscopy*	H. N. SOUTHWORTH and R. A. HULL
35	*Real Solids and Radiation*	A. E. HUGHES, D. POOLEY and B. WOOLNOUGH
36	*The Aerospace Environment*	T. BEER and M. D. KUCHERAWY
37	*The Liquid Phase*	D. H. TREVENA and R. J. COOKE
38	*From Single Cells to Plants*	E. THOMAS, M. R. DAVEY and J. I. WILLIAMS
39	*The Control of Technology*	D. ELLIOT and R. ELLIOT

THE WYKEHAM TECHNOLOGY SERIES

1	*Frequency Conversion*	J. THOMSON, W. E. TURK and M. J. BEESLEY
2	*Electrical Measuring Instruments*	E. HANDSCOMBE
3	*Industrial Radiology Techniques*	R. HALMSHAW
4	*Understanding and Measuring Vibrations*	R. H. WALLACE
5	*Introduction to Tribology*	J. HALLING and W. E. W. SMITH

All orders and requests for inspection copies should be sent to the appropriate agents. A list of agents and their territories is given on the verso of the title page of this book.

† (*Paper and Cloth Editions available.*)